The sudden silence is loud single pair of eyes in the b disbelief; others are narrow are clenching tight with h close ring – humans, lizard-l winged Banasthaurs – gun- from all across the galaxy. A

Or, more particularly, at the .... your belt, which you accidentally revealed when your coat fell open. Your lightsabre.

It has been only a year since you discovered the secret; the secret which your mother had kept from you since birth; the secret behind your grand-father's death, and your father's murder. Since then, you have run from that secret, knowing that, someday, it would come back to haunt you like this.

A section of the crowd parts, allowing a menacing figure to pass through their ranks. He carries his blaster rifle almost carelessly at his side, yet you know that he could drop you dead where you stand in less time that it takes to snap your fingers. His strange armour bristles with defences; wrist lasers, rocket launcher, flame projector. He is the most feared bounty hunter in the galaxy, and you have just made him your personal nemesis.

Though you cannot see his eyes under that antiquated helmet, you know that he too is staring at the lightsabre you wear at your side. It feels like enough time has passed already for night and day to have passed several times over, but Boba Fett takes his own sweet time to consider the meaning of what he can see.

"The boy's a Jedi," he whispers, loud in the cramped silence of the compact bar.

"Kill him."

LOST JEDI ADVENTURE GAME BOOKS

JEDI DAWN

PAUL COCKBURN

BXTREE

Published in the UK in 1995
by BOXTREE LIMITED, Broadwall House,
21 Broadwall, London SE1 9PL

JEDI DAWN and THE BOUNTY HUNTER titles first
published in the UK in 1993 by Boxtree Limited.

10 9 8 7 6 5 4 3 2 1

Cover illustration by Paul Campion
Designed by Design 23
Printed and bound by Cox & Wyman, Reading, Berks.

ISBN: 0 7522 0135 2

A CIP catalogue record for this book is available from
the British Library

CONTENTS

HOW TO PLAY YOUR LOST JEDI ADVENTURE GAMEBOOK

If you have never read a book like this before, you may find it a little strange. Unlike a traditional story, there is not just one tale winding its way through the book, but hundreds.

After you have finished reading these rules and the Introduction, you will start your adventure with paragraph 1. Each paragraph has its number in large bold type at the top; you can find different paragraphs using the index numbers at the top of each page.

At the end of a paragraph, you are given a number of choices, and the one you pick determines which part of the story you read next. For example, if you were to read paragraph 1 now, you would see that it describes your arrival on the planet of Toprawa. At the end of the paragraph, you are asked if you want to walk through the security checkpoint, or to wait for some other passengers to walk through first. Each choice has a different paragraph number attached to it. So, if you choose to go through the checkpoint, you read paragraph 16 next, or if you choose to wait, you read paragraph 31. Keep going through the book like this, reading a paragraph, answering the questions at the end, and going on to the paragraph number shown.

We call these separate sections of the book "paragraphs", but they can vary in length from just a few lines of text to almost a page. Most of the choices at the end of each paragraph allow you a free choice of where to go next. However, in some places your choice is limited because of something special about your character, or something he has done already in the adventure. In some cases your adventure ends, because you have gone wrong somewhere, and your hero has been caught or killed. Don't worry; start again at paragraph 1, and try some different choices.

Before the game starts, however, you must get to know the hero of your adventure – Havet Storm, the Lost Jedi. You must also do the following jobs:

• Fill out a **Character Sheet**. This gives you the chance to decide if he is strong, fast, technically skilled or good with weapons, or maybe just very strong in the Force.

• Choose your **Equipment**.

The Character Sheet

On the opposite page you can see a blank Character Sheet. Another copy can be found at the back of the book. You might want to make some photocopies of this page, in case you want to change your character's scores after your first attempt.

On the right, you can see a picture of Havet Storm, and a few facts about him. On the left there are six headings – Strength, Speed, Blaster, Lightsabre, Technical Skill and Jedi Power Points. These are Havet's *Attributes*. Beside each heading is a box. This is where you record Havet's score in each Attribute. You need to do this before the game starts.

You may spend 20 "points" to fill in these boxes. Start with the first five Attributes. You might want Havet to be strong and good with a blaster, and give each of these attributes three or four points each, and just two to Lightsabre, Speed and Technical Skills. Or you could give him a very high rating in one Attribute, such as Technical Skills, and twos and threes in the others. **You must spend at least 1 point on each Attribute. However, don't spend more than six points on any Attribute**.

Whatever points you save from these first four Attributes, you keep as Jedi Power Points. These are very important. Your Jedi Power can make the difference between success and failure on many occasions. Don't start with less than 6 – it's best to have too many than too few.

So, spend your Attribute points now, and fill in the boxes. Remember, they should total 20.

Using Attributes

During your adventure, some paragraphs may ask what Havet's score is in a particular Attribute. For example, Havet might need to lift a heavy weight, so the paragraph reads:

If you want to try lifting the weight, add your Strength Rating (from your Character Sheet) to the number 700. That is the number of the next paragraph you should read (so, if your Strength is 2, go to paragraph 702). Go to that paragraph now.

Look up Havet's score in the Attribute, and follow the instructions. If Havet is strong enough (or fast enough, or skilled enough) to overcome the challenge, he'll succeed; if not, he'll not be able to manage, and you'll have to look for another solution to your problem.

Havet Storm

Strength 4

Speed 4 3

Blaster 4 3

Lightsabre 4 3

Tech Skills 4

Jedi Power Points _____ 0 _____

Don't spend more than 6 points on any Attribute or increase any Attribute past 6 when using JPPs

Equipment

Arf 528

Lightsabre [belt] 505

DL25 Blaster [holster] 507

ID 520

[Arf] 529

[bag] 532

_____ ☐ _____ ☐

_____ ☐ _____ ☐

_____ ☐ _____ ☐

_____ ☐ _____ ☐

Data Bank

503	504	509	510	511	513	514	515	516	517	518
521	525	526	527	530	533	541	542	544	550	551
552	553	554	555	556	557	560	562	563	565	568
569	572	574	580	584	586	589	590	599	603	604
605	606	608	614	618	551					

Time track ☐ ☐ ☐ ☐ ☐ Read 595 ☐ ☐ Read 56

Using Jedi Power Points

There are five main ways you can use your Jedi Power Points.

• To temporarily increase an Attribute score (spending one Jedi Power Point increases your Ability by one).

• To mind-influence someone.

• To provide basic healing to someone injured (including yourself).

• To move small objects.

• To change a dice roll in combat (see Combat, below).

Increasing an Attribute: At any time when you are asked to look up your score in an Attribute, you may spend Jedi Power Points to provide a temporary increase to your score. For instance, in the example we have just looked at, you might decide that it is absolutely vital that Havet lift the heavy weight, and that a Strength of 2 might not be enough. So, you could spend 2 Jedi Power Points, and instead of reading paragraph 702, you could read paragraph 704 instead.

Jedi Power Points are a "reserve"; by calling on the Force, Havet can push himself harder than normal. Use the space beside the box to keep a record of how many Jedi Power Points you have left each time after you spend any (so, in our example above, if Havet had 8 Jedi Power Points before he lifted the weight, he'd have 6 after).

Don't increase any Attribute to more than 6 unless you are told to.

Mind Influence: In certain circumstances, you can reach out with the Force to influence someone, much like Obi-Wan Kenobi does near the beginning of the original Star Wars film, when he and Luke drive into the town, and are stopped at a check-point. You can't "brainwash" someone with this power, but you can "nudge" them in the direction you prefer.

When you have an opportunity to use your powers, you will read an instruction like this:

If you use your Jedi Mind-Influence power to make the guard look the other way, first choose how many Jedi Power Points you will spend. Tick them off on your Character Sheet. Now add the number to 300, and that is the number of the next paragraph you should read (so, if you spend 3 Power Points, you would go to paragraph 303). Go to that paragraph now.

Healing: If you are injured, you may spend Jedi Power Points to recover. You can also use this power on others. The book provides instructions at the right time.

Telekinesis: You may be able to reach out with the Force to move small objects. In particular, Havet can reach out towards his lightsabre, and may be able to make it return to his hand if he drops it.

You'll spend Jedi Power Points in many different situations, but there are places in the adventure where you can recover them. Keep your Character Sheet up-to-date, recording the number of Jedi Power Points you have left. This is your *current* total. The score in the box is your *starting* score – this is the most your current score can ever be.

Combat

Combat works in a slightly different way. You need a six-sided dice or a pack of cards (just the Ace-Six from each suit). When required, roll the dice or draw the next card (shuffle them often!).

When you get into a fight, keep a note on a piece of scrap paper, or use a bookmark to record the paragraph where the fight started.

The paragraph you were reading when the fight begins tells you where to find out how tough the opposition is. You are told to read a paragraph in the Data bank. This tells you something like:

There are 4 Security Guards for you to deal with. Each has Skill Level 1 with a Blaster. The Combat begins At Range.

Combat starts either **At Range** (at least 10 metres away), in which case you use your blaster in order to fight back, or **Up Close**, in which case you can use your blaster or your lightsabre. Check your equipment (see below). To fight At Range, you must have a blaster or some other weapon like that, and you must have it Ready (if your blaster is hidden in your bag, you have to get it out, which takes one Turn). Up Close, you use your lightsabre. The same rule applies; if you don't have it Ready, then you must spend one Turn getting it out of Arf's secret compartment.

If you want to change from At Range to Up Close during a fight, you must spend one round without fighting back, while you run up to the enemy. The same is true if you want to change from Up Close to At Range.

Combat takes place in Turns. Each Turn, everyone gets the chance to use their weapon. Starting with Havet, take each person's Combat Skill (you use either your Blaster score or your Lightsabre score, depending on which weapon you use; if you don't have a weapon at all, you can only fight Up Close, and your Combat Skill is 1). Roll a dice (or draw a card). The target is normally a score of 7 or more – that's a hit. So, if you gave Havet a Blaster score of 3, you'd have to roll a 4 or better to hit the target. Each of the Security Guards in the example above only gets to hit if they roll a 6 (Combat Skill 1 + 6 equals 7). After you have checked each fighter in the Combat once, start a new round.

Some targets are harder to hit. Stormtroopers, for example, wear armour, so you have to score 9 or better to hit one of them! On the other hand, you might find a weapon which is more powerful. Your lightsabre is one of these – you always add 1 to any dice roll. So, if you have a Lightsabre skill of 3, and you roll a 3, you would hit a normal target (Combat Skill 3 + 1 for the lightsabre + 3 on the dice equals 7).

One hit is all it takes to disable an opponent. Unfortunately, the same is true for you. The first time you are hit, the battle is over, and you have lost.

Fortunately, you can spend Jedi Power Points to change the result of a dice roll. Each Jedi Power Point increases or decreases the die roll or the card by 1. So, if Havet has a skill of 3 and is firing at a guard and he rolls a 3, you could spend a Jedi Power Point to increase that to 4 – and that would be a hit. And if one of the security guards got lucky and rolled a 6, you could spend a Point to reduce that to 5. The Force would have protected you from harm.

As you can imagine, if you get into too many fights, you spend Jedi Power Points like they were going out of fashion. Sooner or later, however, either Havet is going to get hit, or you will succeed in defeating the enemy. The paragraph you were reading when you started the combat tells you what happens next.

Keep some scrap paper handy (or use pencil in the margins of the book) to keep track of how many opponents you have to defeat, and scratch them off one by one if you succeed. In some situations, you might also have to keep a record of how many rounds it takes to win the battle. The enemy might have sounded the alarm, for example, and you'll have to hurry to complete the fight before more enemy forces arrive.

In some battles, you can surrender even after the fighting has started. The instructions tell you which paragraph to read next. If you've run out of Jedi Power Points, this might be a sensible thing to do. One hit, remember, and it's all over.

If you win a battle, you can take any weapon you capture. Normally this is just a standard blaster, so you would check **508**. However, you might find something more interesting, in which case you should record the paragraph number of whatever it is you find. So, if you find an X-wing starfighter, write X-wing in the space on the left, and write **999** beside the first box. Sadly, you can't actually find an X-wing in this adventure.

If you lose a battle, don't despair – all might not be lost. And even if it is, you can start again!

Remember:

• Read the instructions in the paragraph where the fight breaks out carefully to see what you have to do to win the fight.

• Find out who your opponents are, and if there are any special factors (like a time limit).

• Find out if you start At Range or Up Close. You need your a blaster or your lightsabre to fight Up Close, and a blaster to fight At Range. If you don't have a weapon, you must get Up Close; your Combat Skill is then 1.

• You must have your weapon Ready; it takes one round to bring a weapon out of hiding.

• It takes one round to change from being At Range to being Up Close and vice versa.

• Fight one round at a time; Havet goes first. Add a dice roll to your weapon skill to see if you hit. Normally, you need a total of 7 or more

• Add 1 to all rolls when you use your lightsabre.

Example of Combat

This example should help you understand how Combat works. Havet (with a Combat Skill of 3 and 5 Jedi Power Points) confronts 4 security guards (with a Skill of 1). The Combat starts At Range. Unfortunately, Havet's blaster is in his flight bag.

In round 1, you decide Havet must get his blaster out. So, you don't roll to see if he hits anyone, just for the Guards. There are four of them, so you roll the dice four times – and get a 5 and three 1s. Ha! Missed! Now Havet is ready to fire back.

In the second round, you roll a 6 for Havet – so he nails one of the Guards with his first shot (3+6=9 – more than enough) One of the remaining three Troopers rolls a 6, so Havet spends a Jedi Power Point to reduce that to a 5.

Round three. Havet gets a 2 – which would require 2 Jedi Power Points to convert into a hit, so you decide not to alter the score. Again, one of the security guards rolls a 6, and Havet spends a Jedi Power Point to convert that into a miss. He has 3 left.

In the fourth round, Havet gets a 5, and another Trooper is taken out. The other two both miss.

In round five, Havet gets a 3, and spends a Point to convert that into a hit. The last Trooper misses.

In the sixth round, you decide Havet will close in and finish the fight off with his lightsabre. So, Havet doesn't roll this round, but the Guard does (getting a 2 – missed again). Now Havet is close enough to use his lightsabre in round seven, and he rolls a 5 to finish off the Combat.

Equipment

During the game, Havet has access to various bits of equipment. You will keep a record of these in the Equipment box.

Havet actually starts the game with some gear. He has his small droid, "Arf". He has his lightsabre. He can, if you choose, have a blaster.

You keep track of the equipment Havet has by ticking boxes. This not only shows what he has, but where he has it. Look at the Equipment Box now. "Arf"'s name is followed by a small tick box – which we have ticked for you already – and a paragraph number, number **528**. If you were to read that paragraph now, you would see the following:

One of your most treasured possessions is "Arf", the small K9-series droid your grand-father left for you. "Arf" runs on batteries, and moves smoothly on small repulsorlifts. He's about 40 centimetres long, and has a box-like body. His head is filled with micro-processors allowing him to "think". He is voice-activated, obeying only your commands. He has a sound recorder in his ears, and can play-back at your command. He has a short video record function, using his eye-cameras, which you can play-back onto a blank surface (like a wall).

His body is hollow, with a small access hatch hidden cunningly in the belly. A small panel on his back contains a DNA-sample reader, so that if you press your finger to it, the hatch pops open. This is how you first discovered your lightsabre, which grand-father had hidden in the droid's body. The droid's structure is cunningly formulated so that – in place – the lightsabre looks like part of its internal workings, which defeats all sensor scans or inspections.

You carry "Arf" round in the large pocket of your coat. He is light, and you wouldn't go anywhere without him.

That tells you everything you need to know about Arf. The droid is with you throughout the adventure, so if the chance comes to use him, you can. You can re-read a ticked Equipment box' paragraph any time you wish. Just make a note of where you are in the adventure, so you don't lose your place. So, if you want to remember what "Arf" can do, re-read **528**.

Now look at the next line. This shows your lightsabre, and is followed by two boxes and two paragraph numbers. One describes your lightsabre as being **Ready**, the other describes it as **In Arf**. At the start of the game, you must pick one of these two boxes and tick it – will you carry your lightsabre on your belt, where you can get at it quickly, but where it might be seen by someone, or do you keep it stored in Arf's belly?

Depending on which one you choose, tick one of the boxes. Now read the paragraph number given beside it – **508** if you keep it ready, **529** if you hide the lightsabre in Arf.

You can swap between the two locations at any time – but not halfway through reading a paragraph! Just swap the box you had ticked for the other one.

Of course, if you lose your lightsabre (shame on you!), then you remove the tick altogether.

Finally, you need to decide if you will carry a blaster or not. You can choose to arrive on Toprawa without a blaster – and hope to pick one up later. Or, you can tick one of the two boxes on the third line, choosing to have a blaster **Ready** or **In Bag**.

So, make your choice now. Blaster or no blaster? If you decide to carry one, tick one of the boxes. Now read the paragraph number given beside it – **507** if you keep it ready, **531** if you hide the blaster in your flight bag.

Obviously, if you pick up any equipment later, add it to this Box. Put the name of the item on the left, and then the paragraph number which describes it in the small box alongside. All the information you need is given to you when you find the item...

The Data Bank

During the game, you will pick up various pieces of information. Some of this you have to remember for yourself. Other pieces are remembered for you in the **Data Bank**.

At several points in your adventure, you may read an instruction like this:

Check 533.

If you are ever told to "check" a paragraph, put a tick in the correct box number in the Data Bank, then read the paragraph. **Make sure you don't lose your place in the adventure in the meantime!**. Keep a finger or a bookmark in the page you leave, or write the number of the paragraph down on some scrap paper.

The Data Bank gives you information, and it may allow you to do some special stuff. If it tells you to continue with your adventure, come back to the paragraph number you started from.

If you want a practice, check **533** now.

You can always re-read a "checked" paragraph to remind yourself of something. Just keep a note of your place.

At some point in the adventure, you might read an instruction like this:

If you have checked 599, go to 786.

If you haven't checked 599, go to 801.

This means you don't have a choice as to which paragraph you go to next. Look at your Data Bank. If you have ticked 599, your next paragraph is 786. If you haven't, go to 801.

The Clock

Finally, during one part of the adventure, you will have to race against the "clock". All will become clear as you play. When told to, tick off the boxes on your clock display. When the clock reaches the final box, read paragraph **56**.

OK, that's all there is to it! Read the introduction. Havet is on his way to begin his adventure.

INTRODUCTION

It isn't until the battered old passenger transport is finally rising up on its repulsorlifts, pushing up and away from the landing area and up through the atmosphere, that you start to relax.

That was close. Very close. And you've been close before, so you know what you're talking about.

Your name is Havet Storm. You come from a well-populated planet on the outer edge of Imperial space. You are sixteen standard years old. Your mother and father are dead – as far as you know you have no close living relatives anywhere in the universe.

For the last year of your life you have been on the run, skipping away from dangers real and imagined. It seems hard to believe that you ever had an ordinary life, but there must have been a time before when you weren't a renegade, an outcast. When you were just a boy living with his mother on a well-populated planet on the outer edge of Imperial space. You know there must have been a time like that, because you can remember the day it all changed.

It was the day your mother was taken into hospital, illness and exhaustion having finally caught up with her. She never recovered. Alone in the house on that first night, looking for some things to take into the hospital for her, you found a box. It was locked, but you found the key hidden in your mother's purse. There were a few letters, souvenirs from family holidays, that kind of thing. No still-slides, no tapes of the family – no visual records at all, in fact – but, otherwise, the kind of junk you collect as a family.

Except… there was also a toy dog, a K9-series droid, the kind of thing fond parents used to give their children as a companion. And, when you touched a small panel on its back, the droid came to life, and a voice spoke through its mouth, a deep, resonant and vaguely familiar voice.

"Havet, you don't know me, but this is your grandfather speaking – Morvet Storm. I don't know how much your parents have told you about me, but I am a Jedi Knight, one of the last of our breed. I am old and I am tired, and my enemies are closing in around me. I may never get the chance to speak to you again, but I am sending you this small toy, so that you will remember me, and what I stood for. Who knows, one day you may come to stand for the same things.

"I have a gift for you, Havet. When your father was born, I hoped I would one day pass this gift to him, but he was unlucky, and so I never had the opportunity. So, instead, I pass it to you."

18

As the voice faded, a small, hidden hatch in the droid's belly popped open, and a cylinder popped out. It had a small control at the base, and a continuous energy lens guarded by a flared disk. That aside, the cylinder was almost featureless – until you activated the control.

At once, a blade of pure energy, glowing orange-white, sprang from the lens. It slashed through pieces of metal furniture as if they were cloth. The shock made you drop the cylinder, at which point the energy beam shut off. As if on cue, your grand-father's recorded voice continued.

"This is a lightsabre, Havet, the weapon of a Jedi. It is powerful enough to cut through any material yet known in the universe. Properly trained, a Jedi can wield his lightsabre to block blaster fire! Sadly, unless I am very much mistaken, that training will be denied you.

"Havet, the Jedi are not like ordinary beings. Each has a special power, an ability to tap the mysterious power-source known as the Force. Like a beacon, the Force exists to provide a light for our journey through life. However, some Jedi turn aside from the light –"

At this point, with a harsh crackle, the recording broke up, as if the storage medium had been corrupted. You looked for control filters on Arf to counter the noise, but found none. Then you realised, what you had thought was static was in fact blaster fire! The battle – of whatever it was that you were listening to – ended very quickly.

There were snatches of your grand-father's voice then, challenging his attackers. Finally, you heard him cry "Vader! Has it come to this?" and there was an abrupt silence. The recording was still running, and you waited, breathless, for the end. Your grand-father's voice came again, spluttering, agonised.

"Havet... the dark side... the death of all Jedi. Never reveal... never..."

That was the last of the recording, though you listened to the silence for some while. Arf offered a few whimpering noises, picking up on your sorrow. The air around you felt as solid as glass.

That night, you listened to the words of another on her death-bed. Your mother confirmed the story; amplified it. Your grand-father had been hunted down, executed as a traitor to the Empire, as were all Jedi. You father, who might have followed in Morvet's footsteps, suffered a debilitating accident as a child, and never underwent Jedi training. Even so, the same agents who caused your grand-father's death, arranged an accident for your father. His freighter's navigational computer sent him spinning into a star's raging heart.

Your mother apologised for never having spoken of this before. "Havet – I always feared it would be you next." She moved you from planet to planet, hiding, running, always fleeing in front of the unseen shadow of grand-father's killers.

You stayed with your mother all the next day. At dusk, she passed on, and you were alone.

All through that night, as you sat alone in an unfamiliar house, you put the pieces together. Your grand-father, a Jedi Knight, killed because of what he was; your father, a humble man, crippled in his youth, but still carrying the Jedi inheritance inside him, also slain; your mother, who had constantly kept you on the move from planet to planet, never settling in any one place for more than a few months, sheltering you from the people who would have done the same to you.

Come morning, you packed your few possessions, including your new found companion, Arf, and the powerful lightsabre. Within the hour, you were leaving that world behind you, moving on. You have always known that you must keep moving, to stay ahead of the mysterious power which murdered your family. Inside, you felt the power of the Force, the curse your grand-father had warned you of. You learned how to use it, experimenting during the many lonely hours you spent in hiding. You learned that many people throughout the Empire feared the Jedi, feared the unseen power of the Force. On some worlds, where you slipped up, they found you out, and you had to escape yet again.

On the last world you visited, Korphir, you were starving before you joined a circus side-show, acting as a mind-reader. No-one could fathom your secret. They grew jealous, frightened. Then, one night, some of the other performers came looking for the "boy-freak", murder in their hearts. So you ran. And you swore you would never use the Force again.

So, here you are, on a low-speed passenger ferry, entering orbit around a new world, ready to start a new life. You've got it all worked out in your mind; get a job, keep a low-profile, and never *never* allow anyone a glimpse of what you truly are. That means keeping out of trouble. It also means you don't dare use your personal comlink, in case the Imperial authorities can trace you. That will make it harder to find work – you'll have to visit any opportunities in person.

Your past and future seem pretty clearly mapped out. Which leaves just one mystery. You couldn't fathom it out on the day you found

Arf, and you haven't figured it out to this day. Your grandfather was dead before you were born – so how did he know that he could leave you the lightsabre, how did he know your name?

NOW BEGIN YOUR ADVENTURE...

1

The repulsorlifts whine, and the ancient transport shudders as it descends towards the landing pit. You glance nervously out of the port, wondering if the pilot knows just how fast you're falling. At the last moment, with a lurching kick from the antigravs, he proves that he must have flown this junk-flyer a thousand times. You land, and hardly bounce off the pit floor at all. OK, not a classic landing. Still, what can you expect? This was the only ticket you could afford when you left Korphir, and it didn't entitle you to comfort. Just be glad you made it here.

And where's here? Another planet. Another new start. Wonder how long it'll be before you have to jump another fast freighter out into the void... Don't be negative, Havet. This could be a great world to hide out on. No-one here knows anything about you, and – with luck – that need never change. All you have to remember is to keep your Jedi powers hidden and your mouth shut. It means never being able to have a comlink (you dare not register yourself with the Communications Bureau), which might make life a bit awkward, but you've coped before.

Stepping down the ramp from the transport, you find yourself in the main spaceport of Toprawa, an important Imperial military base and trading centre. The Empire is supposed to have it in for Jedi, right? So, this is the last place they'd expect to find one.

The spaceport is busy, bustling with activity. Along with your dozen or so fellow passengers, you walk across the landing pad to a small shuttle. Seconds later, and you're at the main terminal building, and stepping into a spartan lounge filled with bored passengers waiting for their flight. A tedious song plays over the speakers. How come these places always look and sound the same?

You try to look casual, shrugging your flight bag firmly onto your shoulder. No-one seems to be paying much attention to your group. The rest head towards the Luggage Claim area, but you have everything you own in one bag. You decide to head for the Arrivals Checkpoint.

As you round the corner, your stomach jolts with fear. Four port security guards armed with blasters are standing at the gate! What if they start checking your ID documents? Will they stand up to examination?

You hesitate, wondering if they'll pick on you as you walk through alone, ahead of the other arrivals. Should you keep going, and hope they'll pick on someone else? Or wait, and try to go through the checkpoint with the others?

If you go on, go to 16

If you wait, go to 31

2

The alley lies ahead of you, dark and dirty. A chill settles in your bones. The Force is screaming in your mind that this is a place of evil. How come?

If you have checked 569 in your Data Bank, go to 41

If you haven't checked 569, go to 39

3

You muscle a little space for yourself at the counter. At your side, a man in a turban and a white jacket is holding a data pad loaded with a local news card. He doesn't seem to be concentrating on it, though; his eyes are straying across the room, to where an attractive blonde girl is sitting at a table, looking at her watch. Perhaps you could borrow the pad, and see if there's any work to be found.

After a few moments, the girl gets up to go. The man watches, and finishes his drink quickly. It looks like he's going to follow her...

If you ask to borrow his data pad, go to 13

If you sit still and finish your meal, go to 29

If you leave the cafe, go to 44

If you have checked 503, you may want to read paragraph 504 before you make up your mind. If you have not checked 503, check 509.

4

No-one seems interested in you. The corporal has disappeared, and you can hear other guards being ordered back into position. Perhaps this would be a good time to leave.

As you slip from the office, you glance through the open doorway of another room, and see your Flight Bag on a desk. A few items have been pulled out onto the table – including your lightsabre (looks like they haven't realised what it is yet!). Perhaps you could recover your stuff?

If you enter the room, go to 10

If you try to recover your lightsabre, go to 18

If you want to leave the Terminal, read 512 again first, then go to 46

5

Reading the guy's data pad serves two functions. First, it allows you to make sure he doesn't shake off your influence and follow the girl; second, it lets you search through the local news pages for any work that might be going.

Hmmm. Not much doing on the jobs front at all. Some jobs at a big agri-complex are being advertised, but they don't start for a month, and you'll have starved to death by then... Office jobs, which you don't qualify for, banking, insurance – no, nothing at all.

In fact, the only organisation which seems to be hiring anyone is the Imperial Research Station, which seems to need everything from computer programmers to skiff drivers. Well, you could manage some of those jobs. It says "subject to security status" after most of the jobs, however, which is a real obstacle. The last thing you want is someone rummaging around in your past.

Surely, though, they're not going to check with the Imperial Central Database for some of these jobs. How sensitive can the work they're doing be? It might be worth going to the Station at some point, just to see what they have on offer.

Oh, oh. The guy in the turban is beginning to shake off your control. Time you were gone!

You pass him back his pad, thanking him graciously, then – throwing a few credits across the counter (maybe they won't notice you didn't leave a tip!) – you head for the exit.

If you head for the Shuttle back to the spaceport district, go to 199

If you go back into the Commercial District, go to 169

6

You manage to hitch a ride into the City with a haulier delivering produce near the spaceport. Of course, he expects you to pay for the ride by unpacking deliveries at the stop-off point. Needless to say, he doesn't own an antigrav sled, so it's pretty thirsty work.

By the time you finish, you're ready for a drink. There's a cantina on the other side of the street, and you can feel a few credits in your pocket crying out to be spent on a Star Racer (assuming they have your favourite drink on this planet). Of course, you're not exactly loaded at the moment, and you do need to find a job…

If you enter the cantina, go to 150

If you save your money and go looking for work, go to 169

7

You decide you have to see if your instincts are playing you truthfully or not. Once outside the cafe, you trot across the street to stand in the shadow of one of the massive columns which support the Rapid Transit Monorail. From that vantage point, you have a clear view of the cafe entrance. Taking a quick look around, you catch sight of the girl, her long blonde hair making her extremely visible, even over quite a distance. She's at the foot of the escalator leading up to the station – too far away to catch, even if you wanted to.

Looking back, you see the cafe door open, and the man in the turban steps outside into the street, shaking his head as if to clear some vestiges of sleep from his mind. He looks across the street, and catches sight of the girl ascending into the station. You see his mouth clench, as if he is suppressing a curse, and he takes a hard look around. Is he looking to see if you're anywhere around? Well, you don't take the chance, ducking back out of sight. When you next take a peek, the man is running along the street towards the stairs which lead up into the station. From close by, you hear a train hissing towards you.

There doesn't seem to be any doubt about it. The man is stalking the blonde girl, following her into the station. As she disappears from view, he swings open the stairway door. The escalator is too far – if you're going to do anything about this guy, you'll have to follow him up the stairs.

If you follow the man up the stairs, go to 64

If you decide it's none of your business and head back into the Commercial District, go to 169

8

Can you afford afford to have someone to run a check on your ID right now? Maybe not, so you get up from your seat, walk to the rear of the Shuttle, and hit the Emergency Door release. Your fellow passengers gasp in alarm as the door bursts outwards on a rush of compressed gas, and you feel the driver hit the brakes as you launch yourself through the exit.

You hit the ground hard, roll, and come up running. The security guards at the checkpoint are about 50 metres away, close enough to cause you real trouble if you aren't fast on your feet. About another 30-40 metres away, there's a small building, which would give you some cover, and there are more buildings – warehouses and suchlike – a little further on, where you might be able to shake off pursuit.

First things first – get out of range!

Add your Speed Rating (from your Character Sheet) to the number 130. That is the number of the next paragraph you should read (so, if your Speed is 4, go to paragraph 134). Go to that paragraph now.

9

Al the Alchemist's cantina is just as you remember it, more's the pity. As you come through the door, you catch the same disgusting odours, and the heavy, oppressive air makes you feel almost physically sick.

Of course, it could just be that you're a tad nervous about running into Boba Fett again. You try to peer into the corner from the doorway, but you can't see the end of the bar counter, much less work out if Fett is there or not. A few other regulars are, though. The big Wookiee is growling at a humanoid with green eyes (nothing unusual in that, except he has ten of them) who seems to be trying to persuade him of something in a loud argument at a nearby table. The octopoid is unconscious on the floor, three of his limbs clutching desperately to the legs of a fixed table, as if he is frightened of being carted away while he sleeps.

You walk a little further in. There's a small alcove on the other side of the room which isn't occupied. You start making your way over when, suddenly, you see him, almost in the exact spot you were heading for. Boba Fett is sitting on a stool, negotiating with a Nalroni trader. He is facing almost directly towards you, concentrating on his discussion with the golden-furred humanoid. Fett's blaster rifle is propped behind him, against a side door which he appears to have bolted shut. The alcove is just to his right.

It's a miracle he didn't see you come in, but he has to notice you soon. Just how are you going to keep out of his way?

If you go over to the Wookie's table, go to 35

If you leave the cantina, go to 51

If you walk towards the alcove, go to 63

10

Seeing your flight bag just sitting there, you can't resist the temptation to try and grab it. You sneak towards the open door. The passageway is empty, and so you duck into the room – and blunder straight into the back of a security guard who was out of sight before...

The guy howls for help before you can stop him, and help arrives before you can make your escape. This second distraction doesn't improve their temper any. The corporal arrives.

"You again! Well, you can congratulate yourself, smart-guy! Vermilion's disappeared. Diamond will have my head for this, but – as a leaving present – I'll give her yours as well!"

It looks like your adventure is over. Perhaps you should start again.

11

No-one raises a hand to stop the turbanned man as he drags you from the cafe and out into the street. He has an extremely strong grip on your collar, so you don't even try to resist. A few passers-by look your way, and you consider calling out for help, but there's no sign that any of them are willing to get involved. Maybe it's best that you just go with the flow here.

He takes you off the main street into a darkened alley between two buildings, and pushes you roughly back against a wall. "OK," he says, smiling in a way that doesn't resemble any genuine smile you've ever known, "who are you?"

"Havet Storm," you reply. "Listen, I'm sorry if she's a girl-friend or something. I'll just mind my own business in future, right?" He looks you over, trying to decide what to do about you. "Ask anyone on the streets, kid, and they'll tell you – don't fool with Vermilion." He points at his chest. "That's me." You'd figured that out for yourself, but you nod just to prove you were listening. "I have some business with the lady, boy. Grown-up business. Keep out of the way. Or…" He pulls back his coat, to show off a blaster on his hip, which means that it was an "or…" as in "or else". That's OK. You've been threatened before, on dozens of different worlds. Threats are easy. In fact, the sight of his Merr-Sonn Quick 6 blaster nearly causes you to say – "That's not much, man; look, I prefer a BlasTech DL-44!" You resist the temptation. Just because you can't take his threats seriously, doesn't mean he has to know that.

Vermilion gives you one last long look, then drops his coat so that the flap closes. "We understand each other, then?" he asks. "Yes sir," you reply.

He walks away, leaving you in the alley. You give him some time to get clear, and then follow him back onto the street. By the time you emerge from the alley, the coast is clear. There's a woman using her comlink on the corner, and you wonder if you should ask her if you could borrow it, and call someone about what just happened. Whoever the guy was, he had a real problem over you seeing Facet. Are you going to let him bully you around, or what?

If you have checked 525, you may wish to read that paragraph again before you make your next choice.

If you have checked 530, you may wish to read that paragraph again before you make your next choice. Make a note of this paragraph so you can find your way back here.

If you have checked 541, you may wish to read that paragraph again before you make your next choice. Make a note of this paragraph so you can find your way back here.

Otherwise, if you return to the Commercial District, go to 169

If go in search of a Shuttle back to the Spaceport District, go to 199

12

As you turn from the counter to find a place to sit, you hear a cheerful voice call "Hello!" Sitting at one of the tables, there is a blonde girl – and her face is instantly familiar. "Don't I know you?" she asks. You juggle your food and drink, and walk over towards her, hand out-stretched. She giggles as you spill a little of the fruit juice. "Come and sit down," she says. "Born-trar is from Kli'aar, and I've never known anyone more fussy about cleanliness and order in all my life. If he sees you spilling stuff all over his cafe, you'll be outside in the bins with the garbage!" The Kli'aari cafe owner arrives even as she finishes speaking, throwing two of his four arms up in the air, and mopping up your spillage furiously with the other two.

You put your meal down on the table, and sit down. The girl is trying to remember where she knows you from, so you tell her. "Of course!" she laughs brightly. She orders herself a mineral water, making it look like she's going to stay for a while. Good.

You're reminded again just how pretty the girl is as you sit opposite her. "My name's Facet," she says brightly after a while. She says she has been waiting for someone from work, but that they haven't arrived. "I work in Personnel at the Imperial Research Station – over by the spaceport. Have you seen it?" You tell her you haven't been on Toprawa long. "Really? Have you come here to work?" she asks. "What do you do?"

If you tell her you are looking for work, go to 327

If you tell her a lie, go to 338

If you change the subject, go to 350

13

Before the man in the turban can rise to follow the girl, you place your hand on his arm. "Excuse me," you smile, "mind if I borrow your data pad? Need to find a job – you know how it is."

The man wavers for a moment.

If you use your Jedi Mind-Influence to convince him to stay, pick how many Power Points you wish to spend. Tick them off on your Character Sheet. Now add the number to 20, and that is the number of the next paragraph you should read (so, if you spend 3 Power Points, you would go to paragraph 23). Go to

that paragraph now.

If you don't use your Jedi skill, go to 38

14

How embarrassing. You must have blushed all the way through to the inside. The girl's voice was just loud enough to make sure that most of the people in the carriage heard her. A few military types close by glower at you, wondering if they should intervene.

Facet's eyes are flashing. You can see that she finds it quite amusing, as well as irritating, that you have tailed her here, and then had nothing to say. The train slows, braking to halt at the next station. You try to avoid those deep, rich blue eyes, and notice that her ID card is peeking out of the top of her suit pocket. You see her name – Facet Anamor – and a very unflattering holo slide. The card shows that she works at the Imperial Research Station.

Well, that was very illuminating. You look up once more into those eyes. The train pulls gradually to a halt. "Well," she asks, challenging you to reply. You fumble for the door release, and step off the train. "Well," you reply, feeling more comfortable with a little more space around you. "Catch you later, Facet." She smiles, and it looks like a fairly genuine smile. "I hope the Army gets you soon," sneers one of the soldiers from behind her, "it'll make a man out of you."

"How come it didn't work for you?" you ask as the doors close.

Moments later the train is slicing out of the station, and you find yourself – where exactly? Broadwall, according to the station board. It looks like a run-down version of something out of an old vid; slum housing, cheap shopping malls and empty factories. You really don't want to stay here.

If you wait for the next train in the same direction and go to the Imperial Research Station, go to 160

If you go back the way you came to the Commercial District, go to 169

15

You make a big show of going through your pockets, looking for your ID. "Sheesh!," you mutter, trying hard to sound embarrassed and stupid, "I changed my coat this morning – and I guess I left my ID in my other jacket." Which is just about the lamest excuse you could have offered, of course. It doesn't impress the security guard, or his two buddies, who have finished with the other passengers. "Off the bus, kid," he snarls. You obey. After all, it's not as if you have a lot of choice.

The guard takes you to meet the Captain, who seems to be in charge here at the check-point. He looks you over. "What do we have here, Sergeant?" he asks. "The boy says he left his ID in his other clothing, sir!" the guard replies, sneering with disbelief. "That could be an expensive mistake, son," offers the Captain. "You know the penalty for not carrying your ID?" You do, only too well.

If you use your Jedi Mind-Influence to convince the Captain that you're just a stupid so-and-so who forgot his ID, select how many Power Points you wish to spend. Mark them off on your Character Sheet. Now add the number to 320, and that is the number of the next paragraph you should read (so, if you spend 1 Power Point, you would go to paragraph 321). Go to that paragraph now.

If you don't use your Jedi skill, go to 36

16

You keep walking towards the checkpoint. A couple of the security guards look you over, but it's not you they're interested in today. With a very slight sigh of relief, you pass through the gate, and towards the main doors of the terminal building.

Don't be so paranoid, Havet! There's no way they could be looking for you! You're just a planet-hopper, going about his business. Stay calm!

Go to 46

17

Boba Fett waits for you to reply. This gives you a moment longer to study the vast range of weaponry on his person, the blaster rifle propped on the floor and the Wookiee pelts strung about his waist. This doesn't look good. Perhaps fake ignorance would work? Trying hard to look even younger than you are, you smile sheepishly. "Boba

Fett? Um – the name is familiar, sir, but I never…"

You never saw him move, but you find yourself at that instant staring at the business end of his blaster rifle. "Are you trying to say you never heard of me, boy?" The idea doesn't seem as brilliant as it did a few moments ago. Fett snarls beneath the helmet. "You'd better pray you never hear of me again."

For a moment, you wonder if you are going to be allowed to leave. Then, with the same impossible speed, Fett swings the butt of the rifle blaster up and into your middle. You collapse, all the air driven from you body. Fett flips you over with his boot. "This isn't a place for children. You'd better leave."

If you draw your lightsabre, go to 170 – you must have checked 508 to select this option.

If you draw your blaster, go to 177 – you must have checked 507 to select this option.

If you leave Al's cantina, go to 34

18

Concentrating hard, you lock onto your lightsabre with your mind. This is a trick you learned some time ago, in another tricky situation like this. As the Force reaches out from inside you, you see the lightsabre twist slightly on the table. You concentrate harder, and the grip spins to face you. One last pull, and the lightsabre flies from the desk, through the open door, and lands in your palm with a satisfying slap.

You'll have to forget the rest of your gear – you can hear someone moving about in the room. It's time you were gone!

Recovering your lightsabre cost you 2 Jedi Power Points. Amend your Character Sheet.

Go to 46

19

About a nanosecond after you recognise the Blas-Tech EE-3 pointed right between your eyes, you recognise who is holding it. Worse yet, he recognises…

Go to 223

20

You realise there is no chance of escape. There are four security guards close at hand – including the guy you knocked over – and who knows how many more could come running at a moment's notice? You decide to put your hands up and be a good boy. "Sorry, officer!" you stammer. "You spooked me… that is, I was miles away and I didn't know you were a guard."

"Yeah, yeah…" the guy snarls, clambering to his feet. "Over here, stupid. Put your bag on the counter. Now, up against the wall."

The guard gives you a quick frisking, taking your ID card from your jacket. He doesn't find much else, but then he wouldn't, would he? He starts on your flight bag, and you know only too well what's in there. You wonder if you should make a run for it. Your friend is delving into the bag, while the other three security guards from the checkpoint seem much more interested in keeping an eye on one of your travelling companions, a tall man in a turban and white coat, who has just collected his luggage from the carousel.

"He's coming, Corporal," one of the guards whispers. The guy with his hands in your bag looks up (it's a miracle he hasn't found your blaster already!). He throws the bag back at you, then swipes your ID card through a machine at the desk.

"You'll keep, kid," he snarls, handing you back your card. "Next time you show up on the computer, you'll be hearing from me. Now get out of here."

He doesn't need to tell you twice! Which way's the exit?

Check 503 and 510

Go to 46

21

Reaching out with your Jedi Mind-Power, you try to influence the man to stay in his seat for a moment longer. For a moment, you feel him start to relax, but then his willpower stiffens, and you lose control. Whew! He's strong! You should have used more power on him.

Go to 38

Reaching out with your Jedi Mind-Power, you try to influence the man to stay in his seat for a moment longer. You trying to sooth him with calm words. "You'd like to help me, wouldn't you?" He listens. His eyes take on a slightly glassy aspect, and his shoulders relax visibly. He turns back to face the counter, pushing his data pad towards you.

"Sure," he says. "Take your time. I know what it's like to need work. Things have grown pretty tough here on Toprawa of late."

He leans against the counter rail, and you take a moment to glance at the door. The girl has gone, the door closing behind her as she steps into the street.

Turning back, you see that the man is staring at his empty cup, as if trying to remember why he is still sitting there, and what he is supposed to be doing. It'll take him a few moments yet to shake off your influence.

If you want to read the data pad, go to 5

If you want to leave the cafe immediately, go to 42

Reaching deep into his mind, you feel the man sag under your influence. "You'd like to help me find a job, wouldn't you?" you ask, your voice calm and soothing. The man nods, and pushes his data pad towards you, his eyes glassy, his movements stiff. You've got hi–.

"Nie, yeen don't!" The cafe owner, a white-skinned humanoid with a large pair of eyes, four arms and an accent you couldn't cut with a vibro-shiv, leans over the counter, his huge paw-like upper right hand descending on the data pad like a joint of meat dropped from twenty metres up. "Yeen boy useen kinda fluence on yeen. Make yeen do what he says!"

Your friend in the turban has gone almost as red as his turban, shaking off your influence. His hand flicks towards his hip, but he stops. You'd be prepared to put your last few credits on there being a blaster under that long, white coat, but he clearly isn't going to start a fight in here. Instead, he grabs the lapel of your coat, and hauls you out of your seat. "Outside," he hisses.

"I haven't finished my meal!" you protest, but Four-Arms has already cleared your plate away, so maybe you have. The man drags you towards the door. The rest of the people in the cafe look 100% solid on his side. No-one likes a mind-bender. Think how much worse things could get if they suspected you were a Jedi?

Moments later, you're outside on the street. Your captor hasn't released the strong grip he has on your lapels. He takes a long look around – probably seeing if he can see where the girl went. She's safely out of sight. Good for her, bad for you. "I'm not very pleased with you, boy!" he hisses. "Let's go some place and discuss it."

If you want to try and break free, add your Strength Rating (from your Character Sheet) to the number 110. That is the number of the next paragraph you should read (so, if your Strength is 2, go to paragraph 112). Go to that paragraph now.

If you allow him to take you wherever he wants, go to 11

27

You hand over your ID. The security guard runs it through his portable reader. Moments later, his eyes widen, and you realise the trouble you had at the spaceport has come back to haunt you.

"Step off the Shuttle," the guard orders, briefly showing the screen on his data reader to his colleagues. They keep their hands by their blasters. You step off the Shuttle with guards flanking you on both sides.

They escort you to the officer in charge of the check-point, a captain. He looks as though he has had a busy day. "What have you got here, sergeant," he asks, tiredly. "This boy's ID has a Code 510 tag on it, sir. A Security Infringement at the spaceport. The reporting officer was Corporal Kiell, Port Security Detachment." The captain takes a look at the guard's data reader. "No details. Looks like Kiell didn't file a report before he was transferred to the penal colony."

"You know, I could easily pick up where Kiell left off, kid," the Captain announces. "A 510 is a major infringement of Imperial Security Regulations."

If you use your Jedi Mind-Influence to convince the Captain that you're not worth bothering with, pick how many Power Points you wish to spend. Mark them off on your Character Sheet. Now add the number to 320, and that is the number of the next

paragraph you should read (so, if you spend 1 Power Point, you would go to paragraph 321). Go to that paragraph now.

If you don't use your Jedi skill, go to 36

28

Something in the urgency of the bearded man's plea makes you realise you had better do as he says. After all, there is an unconscious guard in a closet to explain otherwise. You jab the down button, and return to the foyer. At the first gate you come to, you hand in your metallic green pass, and go through. You hear an argument at one of the other gates; you keep your eyes to your front and ignore it.

As you go towards the door, you brush into an elderly woman. "Go into the city," she hisses. "Find some new ID! We can't keep rescuing you like this?" Is that what this is, a rescue? From what? And why do you need new ID? And who are "we"?

Ever get the feeling you're the only one who doesn't know what's going on? As you leave the IRS, you get the strong impression you're falling deeper and deeper into something you may not get out of.

If look for a hostel in which to spend the night, go to 50

If you take the Shuttle into Toprawa City, go to 169

29

You stay seated, grateful for a few minutes rest. The man in the turban picks up his data pad, throws a few credits onto the counter, and stands up. You look over your shoulder to see that the blonde girl has gone. The man follows. Something about the situation worries you but – in the end – it isn't any of your business. Unless you want to make it your business.

If you finish your meal and then go looking for work in the City, go to 169

If you decide to follow the man and the girl, go to 44

The odds look hopeless. Port Security Guards may not rank very highly in the Imperial hierarchy, but there are plenty of them, and you end up just as dead if you get shot by one of them as you do if a Stormtrooper takes you down.

Your relax your stance, dropping your bag and your weapon. "OK, OK!" you call. "Big mistake! Let's all just keep calm here, OK?" Seconds later you're at the business end of three or four blasters, and a corporal is searching you roughly. Both your ID and your flight bag disappear somewhere. If they search it thoroughly…

The corporal puts his face up tight to yours. "You're mine, boy! You'll get ten-to-fifteen for this little stunt. What were you afraid of? Something in the bag you don't want us to find?" You keep quiet. The corporal looks like the kind of guy who treats answers as further provocation. "What's a brat like you doing with a blaster, huh?" Definitely no answer, you don't have a clever excuse to cover that one anyway.

The corporal drags you to an office beside the Checkpoint, throwing you into a chair. He punches keys on a desk console. The screen fills with the face of a harshly beautiful woman. Her eyes flash, eyes which – you notice – have irises which are almost colourless, like glass…

"Report." Her voice spits from the speaker. "Commander… ma'am… I've captured a boy…" On the screen, you see the woman lean forward, her face bright with anger. "What about Vermilion?" "He – he – that is, I –" the corporal stammers. "I thought the boy might be a decoy!"

"In which case, Kiell" remarks the woman, "he's doing his job admirably. More likely, this kid is just a courier who got spooked at the checkpoint. You have his luggage and ID?" The corporal nods, unable to speak. "Then throw him away – we're after bigger fish right now. I want Vermilion, and I want the codes he's carrying. Get back out there and catch him!" The corporal races out like he's on fire. Which leaves just you and the communications console. And the woman with the sparkling, colourless eyes.

"As for you," she whispers, "I expect we'll meet again. Without ID, you can't so much as breath on Toprawa. Sooner or later, a patrol will pick you up, and you'll be mine. Save yourself the worry, and surrender. My offices are in the Security Wing of the Imperial Research Station, just a mile from the port. When you get there, ask to be taken to see me. My name is Diamond. I'm in charge of security here. I expect we have a lot to talk about."

The screen goes blank.

Check 511 & 512

Go to 4

31

You turn towards a small data centre, pretending to be interested in the local news and weather. Your hands feel clammy, and there's sweat on your brow. What a great start this is!

You wait for some sign of the other passengers making their way to the gate, but they're all still waiting at the Luggage Claim area. What's the delay? Suddenly, there's a tap on your shoulder, making you jump half out of your skin. Turning, you come face to face with a member of the Port Security Detachment.

"Excuse me," he asks, with a sneering grin, "did you just arrive on the transport from Feena? Mind if I ask you some questions?"

If you wait to hear what he has to say, go to 80

If you use your Jedi Mind-Influence to convince him to leave you alone, pick how many Power Points you wish to spend. Tick them off on your Character Sheet. Now add the number to 300, and that is the number of the next paragraph you should read (so, if you spend 3 Power Points, you would go to paragraph 303). Go to that paragraph now.

If you try to escape, go to 174

32

You continue to walk away from the Imperial Research Station, the bearded man in the suit close behind you. After a while, when you are confident you are no longer in range of the surveillance cameras at the station, you slow your pace. The bearded man comes a little closer, and introduces himself as Scarlett. You try to make it obvious that you're not trying to make friends.

"What help could you offer me?" you ask, abruptly. "A new ID, perhaps…" he replies. "Or a way of striking back at the Empire. It depends…" He continues walking, while you come to a stop. "Depends on what?" you ask. "On what you have to offer in exchange," he answers. "But let's go somewhere more private to discuss it."

If you go with the bearded man, go to 49

If you ignore him, and look for a place to eat instead, go to 141

33

Facet looks genuinely surprised when you ask if you can see her after work. "You're a fast worker!" she laughs, thinking the prospect through. "OK – you're on!" She offers you a data card carrying her address, then realises you don't have a personal pad. She finds a sheet of paper instead, and writes quickly on it. "Don't lose this, Havet!" she says as she hands the sheet over. "Oh, and Havet… see if you can arrange to have a bath first!"

Cheek! Still, she may have a point. It has been rather longer than usual since you hit the showers. As for your coat, it could probably walk to Facet's apartment even without you in it.

"Come on," she says, "I'll show you out."

Check 525

Go to 47

34

You make your way to the front entrance of the cantina. From this side, you see that there is a narrow staircase leading to the upper floor. A sign says 'Staff Only'.

If you go up the stairs, go to 58

If you leave the cantina and you have checked 568, go to 69

If you leave the cantina but you haven't checked 568, go to 97

35

You make your way quickly to the table where the Wookiee is seated, but you realise Fett has seen you. He is on his feet in an instant, and you arrive at the table at the same time. The Wookiee and his companion look up, vaguely surprised to see a young human stranger and an infamous Bounty Hunter coming eyeball-to-facemask right in the middle of their own argument. Ten-eyes scampers off, but the Wookiee settles in his seat, with a relaxed grin on his hairy face.

"I really didn't expect to ever see you again," Fett says briskly. His fingers flex on his blaster rifle. "Didn't I tell you I'd kill you if I did?" You try to act cool. Fett, on the other hand, is growling. Or is it him? You check the Wookiee; he isn't smiling any more, his face is distorted with fury. He is staring at a number of scalps of Fett's belt. Wookiee scalps.

"I couldn't remember," you reply, "if you said you'd kill me, or if I said I'd kill you." Fett starts; he can't believe his ears. All the same, his blaster rifle starts to swing up in your direction – until with a wild swing of his paw, the Wookiee smashes it to the floor. It looks like you have an ally!

You must fight Fett. Read 578, then use the combat rules from the beginning of the book. Remember this paragraph number so you can find your way back.

If you win, go to 91

If you lose, go to 104

If both you and Fett are still alive after two rounds of combat, go to 117

36

"What's your name, boy; where are you from?" The Captain looks hard into your eyes, trying to make up his mind if you're worth bothering with. You answer, respectfully. For a moment, it looks as if the Captain is going to let you go, but then he stiffens. "Run a visual ID check, Sergeant, see if his face rings any more bells than his ID card." He turns back to you. "Something about you makes me unhappy, Havet Storm."

If you fight a combat, read 523. Use the combat rules from the beginning of the book. Remember this paragraph number so you can find your way back here.

If you win the combat, go to 81

If you lose the battle, go to 92

If you surrender after the combat has begun, go to 84

If you don't want to fight, but you have checked 513, go to 48

If you don't want to fight and you have not checked 513, go to 60

37

There is a slight delay, and then an enormous explosion – with you right at the centre of it. Now how did that happen?

If you want to start again so you can find out, go to 1

38

The man gives you an impatient look, and throws a few more credits on the counter. "Why don't you use your own?" he snaps. "Broken!" you shrug. He sneers "Better get it fixed, then, huh?" and with that turns away and heads for the door.

If you follow him, go to 44

If you take the extra money (you could use it!) and go job-hunting once you have finished your meal, go to 169

39

Hey, this is a broad daylight in an Imperial City, how dangerous can it be? You decide to cut through the alley. If you're right, the part of town where all the hostels and cheap rental apartments are should be just a few blocks to the west.

The alley turns a few times, twisting between the backs of run-down apartments. It's getting pretty dark along here – just the kind of place you'd expect to get ambushed... Fortunately, after a few more turns, you're almost through the worst of it, and you see a man come round the corner ahead of you, walking in your direction. He looks harmless, enough – a small, middle-aged man, thirty or forty kilos overweight. You really shouldn't be so –

Suddenly, the guys looks up, startled. He isn't looking at you, but rather at somebody, or something in the shadow of a fire escape ahead of you. He looks terrified! What can he have seen to make him so afraid?

If you stay to find out, go to 185

If you turn back, and leave the alley the way you came, go to 83

40

You hand over your ID, and the security guard runs it through his portable reader. Moments later, his eyes are virtually standing out on stalks. He pulls his blaster in one smooth movement. Seconds later, his stunned colleagues have done the same. "Off the Shuttle," the guard barks, the tension in his voice almost making it crack. Your fellow passengers gawk through the windows as you are lead off, wondering what kind of criminal desperado you are.

The guards escort you to the Officer in charge. He looks as though he has had a busy day, but he perks up when he sees his men pushing a prisoner ahead of them. "What have you got here, Sergeant?" he asks. "This boy's ID flagged a Code 511, sir. All sightings to be reported to Commander Diamond at the IRS immediately." The captain frowns. "There must be some mistake. This is just a kid, not the leader of the Rebel Alliance!"

"No mistake, sir! The Commander wants this kid." The Captain sighs. "Then we'd better send him to her, Sergeant. Gift-wrapped." The Sergeant salutes, and goes to fetch some binders from the checkpoint. The captain gives you a lingering once-over. "I don't know what you've done, kid, but frankly, I wouldn't be in your shoes for anything."

Frankly, you feel much the same way.

If you choose to fight a combat, read 523, then use the combat rules from the beginning of the book. Keep a note of this paragraph number so you can find your way back here.

If you win the combat, go to 81

If you lose the battle, go to 92

If you surrender after the battle has started, go to 84

If you accept that the odds are too great to fight your way out, and surrender before things start, go to 54

41

You realise quickly just why it is your instincts are shouting such loud warnings. This is the very same alley in which you watched that Pierc guy get murdered. The place seems haunted by evil. You could leave and take the long way round, y'know.

Instead, you steel yourself to walk between the run-down apartment buildings. It's quiet (too quiet?). After several turns, you reach the point at which you saw Pierc killed. There is no evidence left to show that it ever happened, but the memory will stay with you always.

Reaching the far end of the alley, you feel a lot better. Or, at least you would if you weren't so certain that you and Pierc's killer will meet again before much longer.

If you head towards one of the nearby hostels, go to 50

If you take the Shuttle into Toprawa City, go to 72

42

You wait a few moments, watching the man in the turban wrestle with his confused mind. He stares at his cup, knowing he's supposed to be doing something, but unable to remember…

Of course, the effect can only last so long, so you pay up and leave. Outside the cafe, you stop to wonder just why he was so interested in the blonde girl. Perhaps you should have warned her? Well, it's too late now. There's no sign of her anywhere, and too many routes she could have taken. You strongly doubt if you'd even recognise her again.

So, you've done your good deed for the day (even if you're not quite sure what it was). You could get back to finding some work, or you could satisfy your curiosity about the man in the turban. Something about him is preying on your mind, like an itch you can't reach.

If you get back to looking for a job, go to 169

If you wait for the man in the turban to leave the cafe, go to 7

43

The grey-skinned waiter grudgingly takes your order – you decide to try the special. "Good choice," he says automatically, heading off for the kitchen. You look around. The place is largely empty, except for a very attractive blonde girl, a shade older than you, and someone sitting in a booth near the back of the cafe. All you can see of the mystery customer is a pair of light-coloured leggings worn over short red boots.

One good thing of arriving at this hour is that your meal comes quickly. The flip side is that it is very over-cooked – it's probably been sitting in a warmer since lunch-time. You consider complaining, but there's not much point making a fuss. It tastes OK, and it's filling. You gulp it down, and lean back. The blonde girl catches you looking at her, and smiles, nervously checking her chrono a moment later.

Read 538. Remember to come back here after.

If you go across to speak to the girl, go to 57

If you finish your drink, go to 70

44

You wolf down the last few mouthfuls of your meal, and head for the exit. You're not sure why, but something doesn't feel right, and you can't just let it go.

The young girl is ahead of you, walking under the Rapid Transit Mono. Seconds later, you catch sight of the blood-red turban of the man. He is keeping to the side of the street, hugging the doorways. The girl doesn't look back.

She steps on an escalator up to the Mono-Rail. The man waits a moment, then runs through the door leading to the stairs. You've come this far, what are you going to do next?

Read 539. Remember to come back here after.

If you take the escalator, go to 53

If you take the stairs, go to 64

45

Shortly afterwards, you're back out on the street outside the IRS. You have a lot to think about, and you could do with somewhere quiet you could nurse an ice-cold Star Racer while you work everything out. Didn't you notice a place back towards the spaceport? It's worth a look.

You notice a tall bearded man wearing a suit and a hideous red belt. As you walk away from the IRS, he follows, crossing the street to drop in just behind you. "If you've got problems with our friends in the Empire," he says, his voice no louder than a murmur, "I may be able to help you."

If you have checked 557, go to 416

If you haven't checked 557, and you listen to what he has to say, go to 32

If you ignore him and go back towards the spaceport area, go to 99

46

Outside the terminal, shuttles queue for business, taking tired businessmen and Imperial servants into the city. What are your plans? A decent meal would be a good start, or maybe a place to stay.

If you look for a place to stay, go to 50

If you look for something to eat, go to 141

If you take the shuttle into the city, go to 72

47

One of Facet's aides takes you down to the reception area. The visitor's security pass on your coat is removed, and your belongings are returned.

If you have a Blaster amongst your equipment, read 617

Go to 45

48

Under guard, you are taken into the checkpoint, where the Sergeant trains a camera on you. The image comes up on a console screen. Through the keyboard, he then orders the central computer to compare it to the visual records in its data banks. Moments later, a chime rings from the console's speaker. The sergeant turns back to the console screen, his eyes widening. You can guess what he has seen there; instead of a record of juvenile offences, he has seen your image matched perfectly with that of the gunman who caused such mayhem at the spaceport. "Captain!" he calls, reaching for his blaster at the same time.

If you choose to fight, read 523, then use the combat rules at the front of the book. Remember this paragraph number so you can find your way back here.

If you win the combat, go to 81

If you lose the battle, go to 92

If you feel the odds are too great to fight your way out, go to 84

49

Scarlett leads you to an apartment block, close to the main road, but sheltered behind a few discount warehouses and closed down factories. In one of the upper floor rooms, he sits you down on an old packing case. You noticed that he just walked in – there were no locks on the door. You guess no-one actually lives in this building. You don't blame them.

He walks over to a rusting metal container. "Drink?" Hmmm. Good idea – it's too much to expect that he has a Star Racer in there though, isn't it? Too true it is; he brings open a carton of some Toprawan milk. What creature this stuff came from you wouldn't want to know.

"OK, Havet, here's the pitch. Toprawa has had a raw deal. The Empire has stifled trade, closing the factories and forcing people out of work. They want to make Toprawa unattractive to outsiders, and to depress the local economy so much that the people who stay have to work for them or starve. You with me so far?" You grin sarcastically to show that you're not a complete idiot. You hadn't realised you were going to sit through a current affairs lecture, though.

"So, my people want to make changes. They want the Imperial Research Station closed down. What we think is that they're doing some top secret research in there, and that if we blow the lid on it, they'll move somewhere else, and things can get back to normal round here."

This doesn't quite ring true, but Scarlett is on a roll and you don't interrupt him. "The best way to find out what is going on inside the Station is to get to someone on the inside, and as far as we can see the best person to get to is Facet Anamor." Oh, oh! "You see, there are three types of people who work at the IRS. Military fanatics; forget them, they wouldn't tell you the time of day. Toprawan workers, who are kept from all the really secure stuff. Imperial scientists and engineers, who work in the most sensitive areas, but who don't mix much with people outside the Station. And there's Facet..." Doesn't that make four? Or doesn't she count as a type?

"Facet isn't an Imperial die-hard. But her father is Druth Anamor, the head of the Research Department, the guy working on all the really sensitive stuff. He got her the job; pulled strings. I mean, she isn't old enough to blow bubbles – know what I mean? No offence intended, Havet."

"None taken." You sip more of the strange drink. "Who are 'your people', and why should I help you?" He grins, a little nervously. "We're people like you, Havet. People who don't fit in. Outsiders. That's why a few of us have banded together to join the Rebel Alliance."

"A rebellion?" you scoff. "Against the Emperor? That's kind of a long shot, isn't it?" Scarlett nods in agreement. "Only if we can't attract people like you, Havet." Oh, really? Why are you so important – except for the fact that you know Facet Anamor, that is? "The Empire has all the good cards, but we have the right cause. And we only recruit people we can trust." Oh, sure.

"And you think I can get the information you want from Facet?" He nods again. "We have people on the inside, Havet, but no-one high enough to find out what is going on. Facet is close enough to the top to know everything. So, if someone gets close to Facet, we might hear what she hears from daddy. She seems to have taken a shine to you, Havet." You splutter a mouthful of the milk across the floor. "She has?" you choke. "Why, what do you know?"

Check 557

If you have already checked 525, go to 73

If you have already checked 553 or 554, go to 62

(If you have checked both 525 and 553/4, you may pick either 62 or 73)

Otherwise, go to 93

50

A sign attracts you towards a cheap hostel close by the port, but off the main through routes. There are several in this district, catering for through passengers laying over on Toprawa on their way somewhere more interesting. You check the place out; it looks OK. Only one main exit, a service access at the rear, and lots of passages and corridors where you could lose anyone who came looking for you.

If you have checked 569, go to 59

Otherwise, if you want to rest up for the night, go to 139

Or if you look for something to eat, go to 141

Or if you go into the city to look for work, go to 6

51

You try to leave before Fett sees you, but too late. The other customers in the cantina dive for cover as he offers no warning, but opens fire immediately as you dive for the door.

You must fight Fett. Read 579, then use the combat rules from the beginning of the book. Remember this paragraph number so you can find your way back.

If you win, go to 91

If you lose, go to 104

If both you and Fett are still alive after two rounds of combat, go to 117

52

You hand over your ID, and the security guard runs it through his portable reader. Moments later, he hands it back to you, moving onto the next passenger. Your new ID passed! The guards finish their job, then step off the Shuttle. The check-point barrier is raised, and the Shuttle passes through. You're not the only one breathing a sigh of relief.

Go to 86

53

As you make up your mind to follow the girl, you hear the approaching whine of a Mono-Rail train, humming along on its repulsor cushion. You run for the foot of the escalator, and run up the steps three at a time. A set of automatic gates bars your way, and you fumble for the correct credits, finally dropping them into the slot as the train enters the station. Hitting the platform at a rush, you look round, trying to find her on the crowded platform. Catching sight of a flash of blonde hair just along from the entrance, you dive towards the doors of the nearest carriage.

Walking along the train as it moves out of the station, you meet up with the girl in the front carriage. She is sitting on one side, reading the notices on the walls, but she looks up as you enter the carriage. She seems almost irritated to see you.

Not so sure of what you're doing here, you take up position by the doors. Moments later, she rises, and walks boldly over to where you are standing.

"Are you following me?" she asks, in a low voice. "Because if you are, at the next station I shall call Security. And if you aren't, then I'd like to know what you are doing."

Check 515 if you haven't already done so

If you have already checked 541, you may choose to go to 89

If you haven't already checked 525, and you ask her for a date, go to 74

Otherwise, if you tell her about the man in the turban, go to 68

If you get off at the next stop, go to 14

The guys at the check-point have become very excitable, now they think they have a major criminal on their hands. You are restrained by binders fastened over your wrists, and kept under close watch while they arrange for transportation to a detention centre. After a while, a security skiff arrives, and you are locked securely in one of its cells for the short journey to Toprawa's Imperial Research Station, at which there is a top-security detention centre.

The journey takes but a little while. At the end of it, the cell door opens, and you step out into bright sunlight. Blinking the pain from your eyes, you look around. The skiff has entered a high-security compound, surrounded by active response fencing, guarded by Imperial military personnel and perimeter defence droids, and watched over by high towers with more guards and clusters of sensitive sensor arrays. Six stormtroopers are posted to watch your every move.

Two of them step aside at the approach of a figure wearing the uniform of an Imperial Commander. Tall, with short-cut black hair, a fierce and determined expression, and a lean, powerful-looking body, the woman steps gracefully towards you, so close that you catch a slight whiff of her perfume, and the heat of her breath on your face.

"Hello, Havet," she says softly, for your benefit alone. "Remember me?" Um – yes, you do. This would be Commander Diamond, head of security, and a woman who seems to have developed an uncommon degree of hatred for you. Not good news.

"Take the boy up to my office. I'll be along shortly."

Go to 330

55

Your first shot causes mayhem, as passengers dive for cover, and the four security guards react to the sudden appearance of drama and death. They react slowly, clumsily, as you squeeze off your shots. For a moment, you have an edge. Then you hear a scraping noise off to your left, and you realise that the odds were always just that little bit too long.

Another guard appears from a ready room nearby. In the second it takes you to locate him, he levels his blaster at you. You try to turn, but there is no time, no time at all! In stop-frame motion, you watch him squeeze the trigger, and the terrible energy of his blaster discharges directly at you...

And then you wake. You shiver, finding yourself bathed in sweat, and chilled by the air circulator above you. Instead of a pointless death in a spaceport arrivals lounge, you find you are still on the cramped ship from Feena, several hours from docking. A dream!

Or was it just a dream? The Force has often given you premonitions before, but never anything as clear and direct as this! If this is a warning, then you have learned your lesson. Fear is a warrior's greatest enemy, as well as his closest ally. You must not over-react; Toprawa is just another world where no-one has ever heard of Havet Storm, where no-one knows his secret. So take it easy, Havet. When you need to draw your blaster, you'll know.

Forewarned is forearmed. Now you begin your adventure for real. Go to 1

56

In the distance, you hear a dull rumbling sound, and then a closer explosion shakes the building. You stumble. Another massive explosion kicks in the windows, and fills the room with dust and debris. The Rebels have started their attack on the Station, and you have run out of time.

So close. What could you have done to improve your chances? Why not try playing Jedi Dawn again?

57

You're normally not as pushy as this, but something about the way the girl smiled at you gives you a bit of extra courage. Either that, or the Force has some very peculiar ways of showing itself. Whatever, you walk over to the girl's table.

"Mind if I join you?" you ask. "No!" she replies, and she looks genuinely pleased to see you. She is really very attractive. Her eyes are the deepest blue you've ever seen. "I'm supposed to be meeting someone, but it looks like I've been stood up." You tell her that the guy must be flying his ship without a hyperdrive, and she laughs.

"My name's Facet," she says brightly after you have chatted for a while. The moron who has stood her up works with her. "I work in

Personnel at the Imperial Research Station – over by the spaceport. Have you seen it?" You tell her you haven't been on Toprawa long. "Really? Have you come here to work?" she asks. "What do you do?"

If you tell her you are looking for work, go to 327

If you tell her a lie, go to 338

If you change the subject, go to 350

58

You slip upstairs, curiosity having got the better of you. The upper floor above the cantina is locked – probably Al's living quarters. You could break in, but you'd easily be caught. Forget it.

The stairs continue, leading up to the roof. You have a reasonable view from up here – many of the surrounding buildings are single-floor. Looking out over the street, you can see into an alley opposite the cantina. At once, you are gripped by a strong sensation of apprehension, as if the Force is trying to warn you…

If you have checked 569, go to 71

If not, go to 98

59

Just as you get ready to enter the Hostel, you notice a security guard in the lobby. You hold back. Then you see another guard in a ground car along the street, and another talking to the owner of a grocery store. The area is crawling with cops! An old man sitting on the porch of an apartment block watches you watching them. "They're lookin' for someone!" he says. Of course they are, you soppy old fool. "Witness to an incident near Al's cantina. Must be big. Half the cops on Toprawa are looking for him."

You start to turn away. The old man coughs. "Young fellow, apparently. Long coat. Asked me if I'd seen him." He looks you dead in the eye. "I still haven't, have I?" You take it back; the old boy is a lot smarter than you thought.

If you head back the way you came, go to 99

If you leave the spaceport area and head into the City, go to 72

Under guard, you are taken into the checkpoint, where the Sergeant trains a camera on you. Through the keyboard, he orders the central computer to compare your image with its visual records. Your heart pounds, even though you don't expect it to come up with anything. After all, they're only going to be comparing it to the database here on Toprawa, right? And even if they go into the Imperial net, surely they aren't going to dredge up anything from your past so easily!

Moments later, a chime rings from the console's speaker, and the Sergeant checks the report. "Nothing." The Officer takes another long look at you, and – fortunately – decides he can't be bothered processing the datawork on some stupid juvenile who can't remember to carry his ID. "Let him go, Sergeant," he orders. "And you, when you get home, find your ID and a tube of adhesive, and stick it to some part of yourself where you won't forget it next time!" Choking back a retort about where you'd like to stick his ID, you follow the Sergeant back to the Shuttle.

The other passengers give you the eye as you get back on board. Half of them had you down as a runaway, the rest figured the security team would roust you just to meet their quota. Frankly, you don't care what they think. The check-point barrier is raised, and the Shuttle passes through. Moments later, you're back on the highway.

Go to 86

61

Better safe than sorry. You take the fire escape, which brings you down into a small yard at the back of the cantina. Slipping out through the gate, you jog as inconspicuously as you can up the street. No-one follows you. For now, all is quiet.

So, where do you go from here, Havet?

Go to 99

62

"Well," says Scarlett, "we know about the job she offered you. Don't be surprised, that's how she works. She has dozens of people spying against each other." Surely all Scarlett wants is the same thing in reverse. What's so different about his offer?

If you have checked 556 and you want to tell Scarlett about it, go to 95. Keep a note of this paragraph number so you can find your way back

Otherwise, go to 88

63

The Force must be looking after you, or something, because you manage to walk the length of the room and into the alcove without Boba Fett looking up at you once. Has he forgotten you? Never mind that now. The alcove shelters you from sight, but you can still overhear Fett's conversation with the Nalroni trader perfectly.

"So, you can't actually be certain where the Millennium Falcon is?" asks Fett. "Not certain, no," replies the Nalroni, in his falsetto, whining voice. "Solo isn't working for us, or for any of his other contacts. It seems most likely that he and his ship are holed up somewhere, waiting for a cargo. If Jabba the Hut doesn't know where that is, I don't think we're likely to find out."

You pity this Solo character if Fett is after him. Wonder what he's done?

"Very well, Karaff," Fett says after a few moments. "I shall have to try and pick up his trail elsewhere. I shall leave Toprawa just as soon as I have killed the brat hiding in the alcove above us. Thank you for your assistance."

You hear the Nalroni laughing while you digest what you have just heard. Fett must have seen you from the first moment you entered the cantina, and he hasn't exactly forgiven you! You're in deep trouble now, Havet!

If you use your lightsabre to hack through the wall behind you, go to 75

If you draw your blaster, go to 90

If you use Arf to set up a decoy, go to 103

64

Something about the man in the turban disturbs you. You're not quite sure if he is following the girl or not, but he's acting so furtively, he must be up to something. From somewhere close behind, you hear the approaching whine of a Monorail train, humming along on its repulsor cushion. There's no time to reach the escalator, so you race instead towards the nearby stairwell.

As you burst through the door, you enter complete blackness, and you almost stumble as you bring yourself to a halt. The lights must be fused or something. Hands out-stretched, you grope for the stairs, knowing that the train is almost in the station above. You grit your teeth, determined to get there in time, but it's your single-minded determination which lets you down. As you bang your foot against the first step, an arm snakes round your throat, and the business end of a blaster grazes your temple. A hoarse whisper rasps in your ear. "I don't know what your game is, boy, but you shouldn't get involved with things which don't concern you."

"Hey – I just wanted to catch the train!" you argue, but your attacker just grips you tighter. "I bet you don't even know where it's headed! Now listen, off-worlder. This is your one and only friendly warning. Stay away from Facet Anamor. Walk out of here now, and don't look back. If I see you again, I'll kill you."

Overhead, you hear the rumble as the train closes its doors and leaves the station. Your assailant removes the gun from your head, and pushes you towards the street level exit.

If you go quietly out into the street, go to 87

If you still have your lightsabre and wish to draw it, go to 96

If you have a blaster, and you wish to draw that, go to 100

65

You hand over your ID, and the security guard runs it through his portable reader. Moments later, he hands it back, moving onto the next passenger without another word. Relax, Havet – they're not after you. They finish their job, then step off the Shuttle. The checkpoint barrier is raised, and the Shuttle passes through. You're not the only one breathing a sigh of relief.

Go to 86

66

It doesn't look good. There are four of them – including the guard sprawled on the ground – and who knows how many more can come running at a moment's notice? It's too late to back out now, though – you've pulled your blaster. The guards hesitate for a moment, allowing you a free shot, but they're drawing their weapons, and at this range they're not likely to miss very often. Havet, you're in it up to your neck! It's time to swim or get out of the water!

If you surrender immediately, go to 30

If you choose to fight, read 505, then use the combat rules from the beginning of the book. Remember this paragraph number so you can find your way back

If you blast two of the guards, go to 82

If you lose the battle, go to 55

67

Then it hits you. The blonde girl walking away from the alley is none other than Facet Anamor! The woman from the Imperial Research Station who seems to attract so much attention, walking past – or away from – the alley where a man was just murdered! Coincidence? Maybe. You watch carefully, making sure the dark-haired killer doesn't appear. Facet continues up the street, until she reaches the distant Research Station with its high fences and heavy security. Only when she is safe inside do you run back down the stairs to the exit from the cantina.

Go to 34

68

"I'm not your problem," you say quickly, before anyone else in the carriage gets involved (it's crawling with soldiers, all listening to your conversation). "You were being followed!" Her face clouds over. A young officer leans forward, his brittle stare directed straight at you. "Are you OK, Facet?" he asks. "Yes," she replies. "I just had some news I wasn't expecting, that's all."

She motions for you to join her on a seat away from the door. "What did you see?" You tell her about the man in the turban. With a few simple questions, she gets all of the details. "Vermilion," she whispers. "He must be planning to kidnap me." She thinks it through. "I'll have to live out at the Station for a few weeks. What a pity; I quite like my little apartment in the City."

You're on the point of offering to house-sit for her (hey, it'd be cheaper than renting!) when she says. "I'm really very grateful. Can I do something for you? Could you use some work?"

It's the best offer you've had all day (because it's the only offer you've had all day). "Good," she smiles. "We're almost at the Station now. Take this –" she presses her card into your hand "– and if anyone asks, tell them you have an appointment to see me." She gets up from her seat. "I'll see you in an hour. I just need to take care of a few things first."

The train pulls into another stop. Facet shakes your hand and moves quickly to the door, leaving you to go onto the end of the line. The other passengers look at you as if you had just won the lottery. They really seem to dislike you – it's great!

Check 541 & 551

Go to 160

69

You can't just stay here. Even though you're worried about the murder in the alley, you have to go back out on the street sometime. So, you pull back the door, and –

You hear a dull thump, and a blow crashes against your chest. Your eyes are misting over, but you catch a glimpse of the killer, smoking blaster in hand, retreating back into the alley in which she has been waiting for you since you entered the cantina...

Your adventure is over. Start again

70

You nurse your drink, thinking about what comes next. The grey-skinned waiter drops some heavy hints about closing. Moments later, you watch the blonde girl sweep past, heading for the door. You feel a momentary regret that you didn't have the courage to talk to her. A friend or two here on Toprawa wouldn't go amiss.

Moments later, the other customer leaves too. You catch a glance of a tall man, in a white coat and a red turban. He pauses in the doorway, looking up the street in the direction the girl took. Something tugs at your senses – something about the way he was hiding in the shadows until now. It doesn't quite feel right somehow.

There have been times when your instincts have kept you alive. Your grand-father told you should always listen to the Force. But then, your grand-father died for being a Jedi, didn't he?

Read 540. Remember to come back here after.

If you follow them, go to 44

If you stay and finish your drink, then head for the Shuttle, go to 199

71

Of course, it's obvious why your instincts were jangling so loudly. That alley across the street was where you saw that guy murdered. You have an excellent view of the very spot from up here, but there is no body, no sign at all that anything ever happened.

And no sign of the killer. You could leave the cantina now in perfect safety, it seems. Of course, the fire escape down into the yard might be safer still…

If you take the fire escape, go to 61

If you go back downstairs, go to 34

72

Prices on Toprawa are pretty steep. Even the Shuttle into the City seems to dig deep into your meagre reserves. You need a way to make some credits, and fast.

You step off the Shuttle in the main business district of the City. It's busy, noisy and very unfamiliar. In fact, you could get lost very easily here. It might be an idea to find a base of operations you can work from while you explore.

Across the way, there's a small cafe which doesn't look too expensive. Perhaps if you buy something to eat, the owner will steer you towards some lodgings and a job?

If you go into the cafe, go to 150

If you continue to explore, go to 169

73

"Don't be bashful," says Scarlett, "we know she has asked you to go to her apartment. All we want is for you to keep that appointment, and perhaps to see her again on some other night. That's not so bad, is it?"

"You don't want me to help kidnap her?" you ask. "No," says Scarlett slowly. "We just want to find out what she knows, and to have you in a position to influence her."

If you have checked 556 and you want to tell Scarlett about it, go to 95. Keep a note of this paragraph number if you want to go off and read 556 first.

Otherwise, go to 88.

74

Her voice was just loud enough to attract the attention of every other passenger in the carriage. Several of them are large soldiers;. you feel very exposed. "Um –" you say, unhelpfully.

One soldier, a really unpleasant individual with a scar from a knife cut across his nose, leans forward. "Is everything OK, Miss Facet?" he asks. Sure, she's fine, look at her she's smiling. "I think so, Gierret," she replies. "I'm just waiting to see why this boy was following me." Well, it can't get any worse, can it? So, you might as well be hung for a sneatta as a loomis.

"I saw you in the cafe," you start. "Yes," she replies, "and I saw you." Good start. "Well, I just wondered if – I'm new on Toprawa, you see, and I haven't met anyone else – not that you're just anyone, but – um – well, anyway, I wondered if, perhaps, you'd – um – show me around?"

The silence that follows is like a chill wind on a hot day; it gets right through to the marrow of your bones. Facet thinks about what you have said for a long time. Then she leans to one side, and takes a napkin away from a young soldier who is eating his lunch (well, actually, he's been watching you for the last two minutes, like everyone else). She scribbles on it in lipstick.

"You're on," she says, and hands you the napkin. Everyone in the carriage sucks in a long breath, and you find that you are even more the centre of attention than you were before. Only now the suspicion has been replaced by envy. The train pulls into the next-to-last station on the line. "I'll see you later." says Facet. You take the hint, and step onto the platform. A few seconds later, you're alone with your napkin, as the train pulls out. Every eye in the carriage is on you.

So, what next? You're at a stop called Broadwall, according to the station board. Looking over the platform wall and down into the streets below, you see what a delightful part of town it is. It looks like a run-down version of something out of an old vid; slum housing, cheap shopping malls and empty factories. Freight ships lumber overhead, their engines howling as they lift away from the spaceport. You really don't want to stay here.

Check 525

If you wait for the next train in the same direction and go to the Imperial Research Station, go to 160

If you go back the way you came to the Commercial District, go to 169

75

Knowing that your life expectancy can be measured in seconds, you quickly pull out your lightsabre, and activate its blade. Heads are just starting to turn in the direction of the gloomy alcove as you slash through the wall. Shutting off the beam, you dive out into the street. With luck, Al's customers will assume you had some kind of industrial cutter, not a Jedi lightsabre!

You've gained a few precious seconds on Fett. There's nowhere you can run to that he can't find you, but you might be able to get an edge before he comes through the side door.

Decide now if you want to begin the fight At Range or Close-Up. Now read 558, and use the combat rules from the beginning of the book. Keep a note of this paragraph number so you can find your way back here.

If you win the combat, go to 91

If you lose the battle, go to 104

If you are both alive after three round of combat, go to 117

76

You decide you have to get rid of Facet's transmitter, and so you follow Scarlett's directions to an electronics repair shop on a back street somewhere well back from the main highway. A sign names the business as Vattali's Repairs. The shop is open, but there are no customers. A small, blue-skinned humanoid with delicate, long fingers comes to the counter. You show him the bracelet.

"You want to get this off?" he asks, in a high, piping voice. "You'll be lucky! I've seen these Imperial locks before – you need two pairs of hands and all kinds of specialised equipment." He shakes his head. "Don't think I can help you."

"Can't you give it a try?" you ask. "Scarlett said it was important I got rid of this thing." The shop-owner laughs (you think it was a laugh, anyway). "I suppose we could try. You'll have to help. I'll get my tools."

So, just a few moments later, you're holding a needle-thin probe against a tiny electronic contact in the lock of the bracelet. The blue-skinned alien holds a cutter in his delicate fingers. "I'm going to cut the main bolt," he twitters. "Keep perfectly still. If you don't keep that contact closed, you'll fuse the lock permanently." You hold your breath, and call on the Force to help steady your hand as Vattali goes to work.

You must use your Tech Skill and your Jedi power to do your share of the work. Decide how many Jedi Power Points you will spend, and add that number to your Tech Skill (from your Character Sheet). Add the total to 250. That is the number of the next paragraph you should go to. So, if your Tech Skill is 3, and you spend 3 Jedi Power Points, you would go to 256

77

Up close, you can see the damage that was done to Al's cantina during the battle (not to mention the damage you and Boba Fett dished out!). The place has been gutted by fire. It looks like Al the Alchemist will be out of business for some time. From where you stand, the place has actually been improved.

There's no sign of Al; just a bearded guy in a suit and a red belt picking through the debris.

If you have checked 557, go to 105

If you havn't checked 557, but you have checked 616, go to 415

If you haven't checked either of these, go to 78

78

At a guess, you'd say the man must be some kind of insurance assessor. You wonder if Al was covered for being crushed by a space shuttle?

You turn away. What are your plans now, Havet?

Go to 99

79

It takes a moment for the credit to drop. The blonde girl in the street is the same girl you saw in the cafe in Toprawa City. Coincidence? Maybe, but something's tingling in the back of your mind. Perhaps you could pay another visit to that cafe soon.

Meanwhile, you watch the girl continue up the street, until she reaches the distant Research Station with its high fences and heavy security. There's no sign of the dark-haired killer. You think long and hard about what you have seen, then finally make you way to the stairs.

Go to 34

80

You draw on all your strength in an effort to stay calm. The guard looks you over, then speaks in a low voice. "You boarded the flight on Korphir, right? See anything suspicious? Anyone carrying anything unusual?"

Even though your mouth is dry, you manage to answer. There isn't anything you can tell him, after all. "Hmmm," he snorts, looking at the other passengers. "See the guy there, wearing the turban and the white jacket?" You look across at the luggage carousel. You hadn't noticed the man before. "I can see you're not going to be much use, kid. Get out of here, and carry on keeping your mouth shut, OK?"

Whew! They weren't looking for you after all! The guard waves at his comrades, to ensure they let you straight through. Time to make tracks, Havet!

Check 503

Go to 46

81

Despite the odds, you emerge unscathed from the battle. You take a moment to check that the coast is clear, then race towards a SoroSuub XP-38 two-seat landspeeder near the head of the queue at the checkpoint. A portly man and his wife, a red-head with vast amounts of jewellry, cower in their seats as you approach, blaster still in hand.

"I'm looking for somewhere I can hire a car," you say.

The man stares at your blaster like he expects that to talk. The red-head jabs him in the ribs. "Borrow mine!" he chokes. Naturally, you can't turn down such a generous offer. "Thanks," you reply. "There might be a few people along here in a minute who I'd prefer not to see." The portly man lifts his head just enough to see where a security guard lies sprawled close by, and this seems to provide him with the final burst of energy he needs to open the door and get out. His wife is already stepping from the landspeeder. Moments later, you're behind the controls, powering the repulsorlift to max and turning the XP-38 out of the queue.

"One thing," says the man as you get ready to leave. "When – um – if your friends catch up with you, don't let them shoot up my car, OK?" You gun the engine. In seconds, you're hitting 270 kph along the highway, and praying that the police give you long enough to get back close to the spaceport, so you can ditch his landspeeder without a scratch on it, or on you.

Go to 86

82

It's bad enough ending up in a gun-battle with four policemen. It's all the worse knowing that none of it was necessary. Much too late to avoid the carnage, your mind becomes clear and your aim focussed. Your aim your blaster, and the first guard falls. The others react slowly, and you keep the advantage you gained. They return a few shots, but one-by-one you take them down, while making a dash for the exit. You reach the Terminal doors, taking one last look back.

The realisation of what you have done sends you reeling, and you clutch the door to regain your balance. The Troopers, panicked by your action, responded wildly. Not one shot came anywhere close to you. But some passengers and people working at the port weren't so lucky.

Worse, you also realise it has all been in vain. A security camera has it lens pointed right at you. By tonight, every policeman and informant on Toprawa will know your face. By morning, they'll have pulled your ID off the passenger records, and they'll know everything about you. Is this your Jedi curse come to haunt you? Why did grand-father make it sound like this power would be so good? Perhaps the people on Korphir were right – the only good Jedi is a dead Jedi.

Whatever. For now, you've got a more important fish to fry. Like staying alive.

Check 513

If you want to look for somewhere to stay near the spaceport, go to 50

If you decide to keep to the streets and look around, go to 99

83

It's not the bravest thing you've ever done, but you decide to make a quick turn-around, and leave the alley the way you came. Before you can take more than a few steps, however, you hear a woman's voice shout "Ta'al Pierc – you traitor!", followed by the dull whine of a laser pistol, and a short scream. Ducking around the corner and looking back, you see the man has fallen to the ground. He's lying very still.

A figure steps out from the shadows under the fire-escape. It steps towards the body, a laser-pistol in its fist, ready-light winking threateningly. It hits you at once – you've just witnessed a cold-blooded murder!

The assassin turns, and you look into the eyes of death. Cold eyes; a dark, thin mouth; close-cropped black hair. A face you'll never forget. And, what's more, the killer is a woman! Her eyes seem to find yours, even though you'd swear she couldn't know you were there! The muzzle of the pistol tracks towards you. Time you were gone!

If you have already checked 511, check 514

If not, check 569

Go to 102

84

The odds have become too much. You take a minute to bury your lightsabre under a pile of loose stones (no point getting into any worse trouble than you can afford), then throw the blaster off into the distance. "OK, I'm done! Don't shoot!" you call. The guards rush up, their blasters aimed squarely in your direction. "Rebel scum," they hiss.

Rebel? You? You protest that you were just trying to stay alive, and one jump ahead of the authorities, but no-one's interested. They search you, then haul you off to a detention centre. After a few hours in there, experiencing Imperial Justice from the sharp end, you start wishing you had been a member of the Rebel Alliance. Boy, if only you had your time over again…

You've failed in your adventure this time round. However, Havet can have his wish. If you want to start again, go to 1

85

Leaving the man in the turban sitting in his place, completely confused by your Jedi power, you grab the remains of your meal and head for the door. You're not quite sure why you're following the girl, but that's what you're doing. Perhaps you're curiou , perhaps you want to warn her.

Outside on the street, it almost becomes academic – you can't see her. You're not even that sure you'd recognise her – after all, all you saw was a back view. She's blonde, tall, and wears a baggy jumpsuit. Just like any one of hundreds of others… Wait – there – walking along under the Rapid Transit Mono-Rail, heading for the station escalator. That must be her. Are you going to finish what you have started?

If you follow the girl up the escalator, go to 53

If you want to see what the man in the turban gets up to instead, go to 7

If you want to get back to looking for a job, go to 169

86

The day is ebbing away by the time you get back to the area by the spaceport. The streets are quiet away from the highway, and the convenience stores and malls are almost empty. There's a brief shower of rain, and you huddle under an awning outside a low-rent hostel, wondering what you should be doing next. Just what have you achieved since you arrived here? One thing's for sure, the last few credits in your possession aren't going to be there for long at this rate.

A short distance down the street, you can see a faded sign announcing Al the Alchemist's cantina; "All you can eat for 10 credits!" A broken neon light announces that it sells Star Racer. Man, you could really use one! Opposite that, an alley disappears between jaded apartment buildings, heading roughly in the direction of some hostels and low-rent hotels. Sleep or food – they both sound good from here!

If you have checked 526, check 527

If you head for Al's place, go to 216

If you take the alleyway towards the hostels, go to 2

If you keep to the main streets, go to 50

87

You're not sure what you've run headlong into, but it's obvious your assailant has the drop on you. As he pushes you through the stairwell exit, you try to catch a glimpse of his face in the light from outside, but he's too clever for you, and drops out of sight behind the stairs, only the cruel muzzle of his blaster and the dark red of his turban showing. Point taken.

You walk over to a shop front, hoping to catch a glimpse of the blonde girl – Facet Anamor, did he say her name was? – or your mystery opponent, but you see no-one fitting either description. Maybe it was none of your business anyway.

If you want to get back to looking for a job, go to 169

If you want to head back towards the port district, go to 199

88

Scarlett clears away all trace of your time in the room. "We want you to join us, Havet. We have to know what is going on at the IRS. The Alliance needs the information, and you need us." Oh, really? "Why's that," you ask. "Because in a situation like the one you're in, there aren't too many easy ways to stay neutral. The Empire knows that. So, if they aren't convinced that you're working for them, they'll assume you're working for us."

"You have to take sides. Maybe not right now, not right here, but soon." Sure. "Don't try to frighten me with your nonsense," you shout, leaping to your feet. "I've survived on other worlds without getting onto the wrong side of the Empire; why should things be different here?"

Scarlett looks quite sad for a moment, then he gestures for you to follow him to the door. "I understand," he says. "If you change your mind, you can always find us. Try hanging around at Al's cantina." You sweep past him, heading quickly down the stairs. Moments later, you're back out on the street on your own."

Go to 99

89

Other passengers on the train are looking at you very closely. Facet spoke just loud enough to attract everyone's attention, without actually inviting the many soldiers on the train to come over and tear you apart. Sheepishly, you pull the card she gave you from your pocket. "It's not what you think," you insist. "I just thought I'd come and see about that job right away!"

Facet relaxes, and her laugh takes the ice out of the atmosphere. "You shouldn't be so quick off the mark, Havet. I might start thinking you're desperate." She takes a long look at your grimy clothes. "And don't you think you ought to go and change into your best clothes?" These are your best clothes. Still, she has a point. A bath wouldn't go amiss.

"You're right of course," you agree. "I just had some free time today, so I thought – y'know – strike while the iron is hot." Facet nods, though it's clear she doesn't believe you. "Fair enough. Go to main reception, show them that card, and tell them to send you to my office." The train slows at another station. Facet moves to the door, and you start to follow her. "No, go onto the next stop. I'm have some private business." Facet steps from the train, and gives you a little wave. Moments later, she's out of sight, and you're moving onto the end of the line.

Go to 160

90

Knowing that your life expectancy can be measured in seconds, you quickly pull out your blaster. There's nowhere you can run to from the alcove that Fett can't cover from where he was sitting. All you can do is keep low, and wait. Surely he won't just open fire in a crowded room!

An ear-splitting crack dispels that idea. Fett fires once into the ceiling, and the cantina's patrons are reduced to panic. Some dive to the floor, others flee towards the exits. "Everyone out!" yells Fett, encouraging their departure. Screaming and howling, they do just that. The barman takes a brief look over in your direction, and decides that he would sooner have the place shot up than argue with the deadliest bounty hunter in the galaxy. In just a few moments, there's just you and Fett left. It seems off to think that just a small wall shields you from him. You try to work out how his first attack will begin. After all, it's as easy for you to cover the area just inside the doorway in which he was sitting as it is for him to cover the rest of the cantina. Surely this is stalemate.

Fett doesn't see things the same way. The small rail separating the alcove from the main body of the room suddenly splinters under the impact of a direct blaster rifle hit. Fett is by the main door! He must have ducked out of the side door and made his way round!

You're hopelessly pinned down. Just how you're supposed to get out of this, Havet, the Force only knows!

You must fight a combat against Boba Fett. Read 559, and use the combat rules from the beginning of the book. Keep a note of this paragraph number so you can find your way back here.

If you win the combat, go to 91

If you lose the battle, go to 104

If you are both alive after five round of combat, go to 117

91

You almost can't believe it! Despite all his advantages in weapons, experience and murderous intent, it is Boba Fett who lies in the dust once the fighting stops, not you. With one fortunate hit, you have defeated one of the most feared men in the Galaxy!

Fett isn't dead, though he lies almost motionless on the ground, clutching at his leg wound, almost unconscious with shock and pain. The fight spilled out onto the street early on, and took place in full view of several dozen people. Fett tries to raise his arm as you approach, but he doesn't have the strength. Nor can his fingers quite reach the fallen blaster rifle nearby. His breath comes in pain-filled gasps as he searches for some other method with which to strike back at you. Even in the midst of this, he manages to grit his teeth (well, you assume he does, the helmet makes it difficult to tell exactly what he's doing in the face department) and to face you defiantly as you approach.

"You'd better finish me, boy," he sobs, the pain lancing through him. "If you don't... I shall hunt you until the last... day of my life."

You're sure he means it. You step over him, weapon extended, and reach down with your free hand. Touching his throat lightly, you allow the Force to flow into him, and he passes swiftly into a healing, motionless sleep. Your hand lingers for a moment longer. The temptation to remove his helmet, and to look at the features of the man who has swore to kill you is a big one. You wonder what he looks like...

As you reach forward, there is a crashing roar from above. The sky above the spaceport is lit as if by lightning. You realise instantly that, somewhere above you, a titanic battle is being fought.

Check 563

Go to 203

92

The battle goes against you from the start. Your opponents keep you pinned down, and you can't get a decent shot off at any of them. The end comes quickly. Trying to get an angle for a better shot, you raise your yourself a little too high... something powerful and brutal kicks into your body, lifting you off the ground. You can smell burning and pain.

Your head is swimming with exploding lights as you fight to control the pain. Somewhere through the mist you see the guards approach, kicking your weapon away. Rough hands pull at you clothing, and you know they've found your lightsabre when you hear a voice say "Look here – he was a Jedi!"

Somehow you know that those were always going to be the last words you'd ever hear. Everything fades into darkness.

Your adventure is over. If you wish to start again, go to 1

93

Scarlett seems a little flustered by your question. "Well, it's obvious from what has happened that she must like you. I mean, you're a stranger and everything, but she has taken the time to –" He halts in mid-sentence, seeming to change his mind.

"I think it might be an idea if we forget this conversation for now, Havet." he says, rapidly clearing up the evidence of your stay. I'd like to think we could be allies sometime in the future. Remember, if you ever need to find us, we'll find you. Of course, if you spend some time around Al's cantina, near the spaceport, I'm sure we'll bump into each other again sometime."

"What does *that* mean?" you challenge him to stop fooling around. Scarlett ushers you through the door. "The Alliance needs people like you, Havet. One day, you'll realise you need us."

Scarlett takes you to the exit out into the street. He has become very agitated, and clearly wants to be out of here quickly. "Follow that road; it'll take you back towards the are near the spaceport. We'll be in touch." He slams the door shut.

Perhaps the guy is off his rocker. Never mind, you need never see him again.

Go to 99

94

You turn to the guy in the corner. Up close, you see he is some kind of soldier, a mercenary, maybe. He wears antiquated armour, and a helmet with a T-shaped viewplate, completely hiding his face. Some kind of sensor array is poking from the top. He has a heavy-looking pack on his shoulders, and a BlasTech EE-3 rifle is propped at his feet, virtually out of sight, but easily within reach. Al the Alchemist obviously doesn't require a dress code from his customers.

Still, guys like this usually know the score on a planet. You decide to make conversation.

"What is this stuff?" You sniff the drink experimentally – it has the same odour as Tigersnake venom, only not so pleasant. "It looks like the stuff the Wookiee is combing out of his fur."

The mercenary doesn't speak. He doesn't even move. It suddenly occurs to you that it must be extraordinarily difficult for him to drink anything wearing that helmet. What a loser. The guy is probably a ship-spotter at week-ends. Still, maybe you can make him loosen up. "No wonder they give this stuff away free. What kind of moron would drink it by choice?"

The helmet shifts marginally towards you.

"I would." With exaggerated calm, he takes a straw from the counter dispenser, and pops it into his glass. He raises it to his chin, and the straw disappears. You hear him take a long pull. For some reason, it doesn't seem anything like as funny as it would have done a few moments ago.

Check 516

If you apologise to the man, go to 101

If you wait to see what he does next, go to 119

If you decide to find less hazardous standing-room in another part of the cantina, go to 126

95

Something about Scarlett makes you decide you have to trust him. And so you roll back your sleeve to show him the transmitter Facet gave you. Scarlett whistles softly. "She said that if I ever met up with Vermilion again, I was to press this white stud, and help would come." You show Scarlett that the bracelet does not come off.

"Well," says he says, with an exhausted grin. "That makes things a little more difficult. I can't bring you into the Rebel Alliance while you're walking round with a location detector strapped to your arm." You grimace. "Does that mean you don't want my help?" you ask. "Well," Scarlett answers, "I hope you can still work on getting close to Facet, and find out what she can tell you, but this thing makes it difficult for me to contact you again. It needs thinking about."

He thinks it over for quite a while. Eventually he comes up with an answer. "There's a guy I know, has an electronics repair shop. Maybe he can help you get that thing off." He tells you the address. "If you get rid of it, try hanging around Al's place. We'll make contact with you there."

He stands up, and clears away all trace of your time in the room. He gestures for you to follow him. Moments later, you're back out on the street on your own.

If you go immediately to the repair shop, go to 76

If you decide not to, go to 99

96

Despite the risks – if you keep using your lightsabre, you'll alert everyone to the fact that you're a Jedi – you draw your weapon, thumbing the control so that the energy blade springs into life. Your opponent is immediately revealed, dazzled by the blinding orange-white light from your weapon. It's the guy with the blood-red turban and the white coat. He has his hands up in front of his eyes, and grunts with pain. He's holding a Merr-Sonn Quick 6 blaster.

You call on him to drop his weapon, and he slowly eases his grip, letting it fall to the floor. His hands lower, so that you can see his face. The surprise has passed now, but he still looks unable to believe what sees. You've seen that look before. Lightsabre equals Jedi; Jedi equals death!

"Is that what I think it is?" he gasps. "A lightsabre! Then, you must be – but how is that possible? All the Jedi were killed years ago!" You're in no mood to answer questions. "What's your business with the girl?!" you snap, trying to sound threatening, even though your heart is pounding. "Are you her protector?" he asks, mockingly. "Could be," you answer. He laughs.

"I don't think so. You see, I was on the same flight that you arrived on. You boarded at Korphir, right? I got on at Feena – I saw you argue with the flight attendant about your bag."

"I don't know how come you know Facet Anamor, but she's bad news. You know who her father is? He's Druth Anamor, senior weapons designer at the Imperial Research Station."

"What's that to you?" you demand, shifting your stance so that any plans he's preparing are disrupted. He considers this for a moment, biting his lip, then seems to resign himself to telling you more. Of course, this could all be a big act. "My name is Vermilion. I lead the people on this planet who are –" he hesitates for a moment "– part of a Rebellion against the Empire."

If he thought that was supposed to impress you, he quickly realises his mistake. "What rebellion," you ask. His mouth flaps for a moment, like a stranded sand-fish, then he regains his composure. "I don't think this is a conversation we should be having in the stairwell of a Monorail station on an Imperial military base-world, do you?" He has a point, but you're not comfortable with trying to walk the streets with him as your prisoner either. He seems to come to the same conclusion.

"Let me say just three things. One, if you are a Jedi, then you have no business siding with the Empire. The Emperor and Darth Vader have hunted your people into extinction – I haven't heard of a single Jedi in years. Second, the Empire has become a dark and sinister threat to all of us, every living soul within the galaxy. Third, Facet's father is engaged in the development of something in that Research Station, something powerful. We have to know what it is. We thought Facet might be the key to finding out just what it is – she's never struck us as a particularly evil girl; if she has a spark of decency within her, perhaps she can tell us just what is going on, and help us defeat it.

"So, we mean her no harm, believe me. I can see you're not ready to join us; fair enough, I don't blame you. If you ever change your mind, we can help you. But for now, keep away from Facet Anamor and the IRS!"

Vermilion leans back against the wall, his plea finished. The ball is in your court.

If you want to make certain Vermilion doesn't reveal your Jedi secret, go to 195

If you let him go free, go to 109

97

You step out of the gloomy cantina and into the light outside. The fresh air is very comforting after all the smoke and cooking smells inside the cantina.

The street is fairly empty, with just a few people going about their business. Now it's time to work out your next move. There's the alley opposite, which would be a good short cut back towards the hostels. A hot bath and eight hours sleep would be very welcome. Or you could walk back towards the highway, and catch the Shuttle into Toprawa City. Then there's the big complex along the street – perhaps they are looking for new workers.

If you enter the alley, go to 2

If you look for a Shuttle into the City, go to 72

If you investigate the Imperial Research Station, go to 160

98

From your vantage point on the roof of Al's cantina, you have an excellent view of the street, including the alley opposite. A small, rotund man is walking towards you, looking around nervously. He goes out of sight behind an outbuilding, then you see him again, much closer, turning a sharp corner. He freezes, and a look of stark terror passes over his face. He seems to be staring at a shadowy figure under a fire escape. A voice calls out: "Ta'al Pierc! You traitor!"

Then you hear a heavily-silenced blaster cough, and the man slumps to the ground. The shadowy figure steps out, inspects the body from a distance, then disappears, heading through the dark alley towards the street. You caught a glimpse of short, black hair and a dark jumpsuit.

Stars and black holes – you've just witnessed a murder! Should you call the police or something? You look around wildly, trying to see if there's anyone who can help.

While you try to gather your thoughts, you see two security guards enter the alley from the far end. You catch your breath – will they see the killer? No, they run straight to the body. One searches the dead man's pockets, the other keeps watch. Then they pick the corpse up, and hurry back the way they came. You realise at once that they are going to cover up the deed.

Which means only you can possibly find the answers. First, you need to see whoever it was who fired that shot. You check the street. There's no-one there who matches the brief glimpse you had of the killer, just a couple slowly walking arm-in-arm, a blonde girl and an old man with a stick. Could one of them have slipped out of the alley while you were looking for help?

Check 569

If you have already checked 525 or 541, go to 67

If you haven't checked either of those, but you have checked 515, go to 79

If you haven't checked any of those three numbers, go to 110

99

You are in the area just outside the spaceport. It would be a smart move to explore this area; it can't do any harm to get to know the back alleys and cut-throughs round here, in case you ever need to leave Toprawa in a hurry.

The main highway leaves the port through its entrance tunnel, and cuts across a steep hill in the direction of Toprawa City. Another broad highway follows the port perimeter to the north. Up ahead, there is a research complex. There are factories and works along the highway and off the side roads, many of them closed and derelict. No-one is offering any work. People blame the high planetary taxes, the huge influx of off-worlders at the Imperial Research Station and the collapse of trade because of "rebel activity". The word is you need a high security clearance permit to work at the port or the IRS.

Taking a breather, you check your bearings. The alley behind you leads to the area where all the hostels and cheap rented accommodation can be found. A rest would do you good. Alternatively, there's a cantina over the street. This might be the right time to get a drink and a bite to eat. Or, if you need to make a call, there's a guy working on a broken speeder bike who would probably let you borrow his comlink.

After all this tramping around, you've developed tired legs and a healthy appetite. So, what next?

If you have checked 525, you may wish to read that paragraph again before you make your next choice

If you have checked 530, you may wish to read that paragraph again before you make your next choice. Make a note of this paragraph so you can find your way back

If you have checked 541, you may wish to read that paragraph again and then borrow a comlink. Make a note of this paragraph

so you can find your way back

If you use the alley as a short-cut and go to find a hostel to rest up in, go to 2

If you go into the cantina, go to 216

If you catch the Shuttle into Toprawa City, go to 169

If you check out the Imperial Research Station, go to 160

100

Drawing on a desperate strength you didn't know you had – perhaps the Force lends it to you – you push back against your assailant, crushing him against the wall. He expected you to try and pull free of his grip, and your sudden move takes him by surprise.

You hit the floor, and roll away, putting the stairway's bulk between yourself and your assailant. In an instant, your blaster is in your hand. The stairwell is pitch black, and you can't see your target, but you can hear him scuffing the floor with his boots as he spins towards you. In your mind's eye, you can see the blaster in his hand...

If you open fire, go to 120

If you wait, go to 130

101

All of a sudden, your brain is back in control of your mouth, and it's telling you this would be a good time to apologise. At a speed you wouldn't believe if you watched it on a slow-motion replay, he has pulled the blaster rifle up to his shoulder, giving you a fine view of the muzzle.

"Listen, sir…" you begin, but you never get the apology out. "Do you know who I am?" His voice sounds like a brush fire.

"You're Boba Fett," shrills a voice from your left, "the most feared Bounty Hunter in the galaxy!" Fett manages to look even more perturbed (even through the helmet!), and he swings the rifle round, aiming fractionally past the back of your head. There is a thunderous roar, and you hear the same shrill voice shriek in agony, then go silent.

"One of the reasons I'm the most feared Bounty Hunter in the galaxy is that I don't like to be disturbed. Not by squeaky-voiced B'trillans, and certainly not by snivelling little boys."

The hairs on the back of your neck would be standing on end, if they hadn't been burned away by the flash from Fett's rifle. At a pinch, you'd guess that the next words you speak could have a direct relationship with your life expectancy. What will those words be?

If you choose "Yes sir, sorry sir", go to 123

If you choose "You can't be Boba Fett, everyone know's he's uglier than you", go to 129

If you choose "I'm sorry, I've never heard of you, but I'll certainly remember you from now on", go to 17

102

You head back out to the street as quickly as you can. Whatever that woman is selling, you don't want any! If she comes after you, to make certain that there is no witness to her crime, it'll be easy for her to find you on the street. The only place you can head for is that cantina on the other corner. You could slip in the side door and – if she follows you – back out again.

Then again, do you really want to be trapped in an enclosed space with a killer? Perhaps you could out-run her?

If you run across into the cantina, go to 125

If you run up the street, go to 142

103

Your biggest problem, of course, is the fact that you are trapped in the alcove. Boba Fett can cover the whole room from the side door, so that if you stick your head out, he'll blow it off. You, on the other hand, would have to vault over the rail to get out of the alcove, and you'd land a metre from where Fett is standing. What you need is something to distract Fett's attention.

Lying flat on the floor, weapon extended, you pull Arf from your coat pocket. It's a struggle, but you make it eventually. Setting the mechanical dog on the floor, you aim him at the steps leading down into the main room, then press your fingers against the DNA reader to activate him. As his batteries stir into life, you press the voice control, so that Arf doesn't start yapping.

You can't give him any clever verbal orders, seeing as Boba Fett is about six metres away behind the wall, and would hear everything. Instead, you program the toy through its cursor keys and number pad. You hit the RUN key, and send Arf on his way. As you programed him to do, Arf swishes out into the centre of the main room, and then flips on his voice channel. His first bark sounds very loud, until it is drowned in the report of a blaster rifle, which rips through the air. Arf is picked up bodily, and thrown across the floor, sparking furiously.

But the sacrifice wasn't in vain. As Fett tracked the wrong target, you leapt from the alcove, vaulting the balustrade furthest from Fett's reach, then crashing into a table. As it gave way under the impact, you were already rolling away, and another blast of energy from the blaster rifle missed you by a hair's breadth. You fetched up by the small stage, in clear view of Fett's position. The big difference is that you are now ready to fight back.

Check 560

You must fight Boba Fett. Read 561, and use the combat rules from the Introduction. Remember this paragraph number so you can find your way back

If you win the combat, go to 91

If you lose the battle, go to 104

If you are both alive after five rounds of combat, go to 117

104

You gave it your best shot, but Boba Fett was just too good for you. You collapse, injured by a hit you never saw coming. Moments later, you realise that Fett is standing over you, blaster rifle ready to finish you off. A wave of black night washes over you…

Bad luck this time, Havet. Perhaps you could try again?

105

You realise that it is Scarlett who is exploring the destruction wrought on Al's cantina. You push through the door; he looks up as you enter. He looks irritable, as if annoyed that he could have been sneaked up on so easily. He has a very concentrated air about him.

"Havet," he says, grumpily. "Do you have any good news for me?"

If you have checked 525, 553 or 554, go to 140

If not, go to 118

106

You are taken to the cellar of an old school. Armed guards watch the doors, and the interior is crawling with people running this way and that, moving stores and carrying messages. You are taken directly to meet the leader of the Toprawan rebels – Vermilion. He strokes his brow under the blood red turban he wears, and leans across the desk to speak. "You're very privileged, Havet. We don't normally allow anyone to see our HQ. However, since we have an important job for you, we thought it only fair. We're going to strike a major blow against the Empire, and we want your help.

"Remember Ta'al Pierc? He told us that the Imperial Research Station was designing some control systems for a new laser weapon – a huge device which could destroy a planet. Then Alliance supporters on Ralltiir heard that Bevel Lemelisk, a top Imperial scientist, was building a battle-station the size of a large moon. We put the two together, and realised they were building the space-station to house the super laser. They call it the Death Star.

"Grand Moff Tarkin, who is in charge of the project, is openly boasting that it will crush the Rebellion. But we had one important stroke of luck. The Emperor wanted copies of the Death Star plans brought to the Imperial capital. The convoy carrying them was ordered to stop off at Toprawa, to pick up the separate plans for the super laser control systems from the IRS. We heard about this in advance and intercepted the Imperial convoy. It cost us a great deal."

"The battle over the spaceport..." you say, putting two and two together yourself. Vermilion nods. "We crippled the Imperial convoy, and captured the plans. Now all have to do is get those plans into the hands of the Alliance, so they can work out how to defeat the Death Star. Three things are working against us. One, we can't fly the information out – the Empire has thrown a tight blockade around Toprawa. Two, we don't have the equipment to transmit the the rest of the Alliance. And three, we can't wait – Dart fleet will be here any day.

"We have just one chance. Princess Leia Organa of Alderaan is close by in the *Tantive IV*. If we get the information to her..." Vermilion rubs his forehead again, looking close to nervous exhaustion. "We're going to attack the Imperial Research Station. It has the best communications on Toprawa, with a burst transmission system which can handle tightly compressed data. We aim to get the whole message off before the Empire can jam the transmission."

Wow! These guys are crazy? What part are you supposed to play in this madness? "We have the plans for the battle-station, but not the plans for the super laser. We need both. So, we want you to go inside the IRS. When we attack, you take advantage of the confusion, find the super laser plans, and get them to the communications centre. We transmit the whole lot to Princess Leia, blow up the Station to cover our tracks, and that's that." That's the plan? Vermilion waits to hear your reply. The scheme smacks of suicidal desperation. Only a head-case would be a part of it.

"I'm in," you reply.

If you have checked 556 or 552, read that entry before you make your next choice. Remember this paragraph number so you can find your way back

If you have checked 547, read 619

If you want to go to the Rebel armoury, go to 107

If you want to go to their Electronics Lab, go to 108

If you want to get some sleep, go to 124

If you want to visit the sick bay, go to 128

If you are ready for your mission, go to 121

107

You visit the Rebel armoury. The senior armourer hands you a BlasTech DL44. "This is a real weapon," he says. "No mucking around with one of these. Want to take it?"

If you take the weapon, add it to your Equipment box and check 581. You must remove all your other blasters (you're going to leave your bag with the Alliance for "safe-keeping").

Go to 122

108

A wild-haired young man is in charge of the Electronics Section. "Can I help you?" he asks.

If you have checked 556 or 552, you may choose to show him – go to 143

If you have checked 560, you may choose to go to 145

If you have checked 575, you may choose to go to 147

If you're ready to leave the Electronics Section, go to 122

109

You take your time deciding. After all, whatever this guy says about Rebellions and Darth Vader and everything, he's still the only one who can finger you to the authorities. But what are you supposed to do, kill him? Wouldn't that make you as bad as everyone says the Jedi are?

Everyone except Vermilion.

You thumb the control and the lightsabre beam shuts off, plunging the stairwell into darkness. "I'll think about what you've said," you whisper, then you duck out of the stairwell, and back onto the street. Moments later, in the partial shelter of a backstreet shop which sells old animated vids, you finally stop shaking, and start thinking about where you go from here. Life on Toprawa isn't proving to be easy!

Check 542

If you return to the Commercial District, go to 169

If go in search of a Shuttle back to the Spaceport District, go to 199

110

No-one comes out of the alley. The couple stroll off to a nearby park, the blonde girl walks briskly to the distant research centre, and the old man hobbles into an apartment building. Could one of them have been the killer? You don't see it…

Eventually, you accept that the killer has gone. What was it all about? Who was the dark-haired assassin? Too many questions, too few answers. You take the stairs back down to the cantina.

Check 515

Go to 34

111-113

The man in the turban has an extremely strong grip on your collar, and he drags you along the street, ignoring the astonished stares of passers-by. You consider yelling for help, but you're not sure you wouldn't get into worse trouble. He's still looking to see if he can see where the girl went, stretching up to peer over the heads of the people in the street. While he's off-balance, you make an attempt to twist out of his grip, but his free hand clamps on your arm like a vice.

"You're not going anywhere!" he hisses. "I haven't finished with you yet!"

He gives up trying to find the girl, and hauls you into a darkened alley between two buildings instead. A blaster has appeared in his hand. He rams it into your spine, and drives you against the wall, frisking you thoroughly. "Havet Storm," he says, reading your ID or something. He takes your blaster. He finds Arf in the other pocket, and you hear him curse as he tries to wrestle it out. After a moment, he gives up. Thank goodness, he hasn't found your lightsabre.

"How long have you been on Toprawa?" You consider lying, but realise there's nothing to be gained from not playing things straight. "I thought I recognised you. I flew in on the same flight. You came here from Korphir?" That's right; how come he remembers? Is he just pretending he noticed you on the flight?

"So," he continues, "what's your interest in Facet Anamor?" That's a good question. You stall for time. "You mean the girl in the cafe?" He isn't amused. "You know who I mean! You're too much of a wimp to be her bodyguard, so what are you? A friend?"

You tell him as much as you know. He isn't impressed. "OK," he hisses, pressing you even more closely against the wall. "Here's the deal. If you work with the IRS, you already know who I am. Just pass on a message to Diamond, and let her know that if she wants to catch Vermilion, she needs to send men after me, not boys. On the other hand, if you are just some innocent off-world fly-by-night, take some advice. Stay away from Facet Anamor, stay away from me, and get off Toprawa as soon as you can. Get it?"

You got it. You maybe didn't understand it all, but you got it. The man throws you into a pile of rubbish. Lying still, you let him disappear before you move.

Dusting yourself down, you head back out to the street. No sign of Vermilion, just a few ordinary people going about their business. You think about borrowing a comlink to call someone about what just happened. But who? And what are you supposed to say? After all, do you honestly know what it was all about? Whoever the guy was, he had a real problem over you seeing Facet. Are you going to let him bully you around, or what?

You have lost your Blaster – remove it from your Equipment Box

If you have checked 525, you may wish to read that paragraph again before you make your next move

If you have checked 530, you may wish to read that paragraph again before you make you next move

If you have checked 541, you may wish to read that paragraph again before you make you next move

Remember this paragraph number so you can find your way back

Otherwise, if you return to the Commercial District, go to 169

If go in search of a Shuttle back to the Spaceport District, go to 199

114

The man in the turban has an extremely strong grip on your collar. He keeps looking to see if he can see where the girl went, stretching up to peer over the heads of the people in the street. While he's off-balance, you sweep forward with your leg, and smash one arm out straight. The man goes over your thigh, crashing heavily to the ground. In an instant, you reach into his coat, where you detected a blaster nestling in hip holster. Passers-by scream in fear and scatter in all directions as you level it at his head. He glowers at you as you frisk him, coming up with an ID.

"Vermilion," you read. "Merchant. Are you buying or selling today, Mr Vermilion?" He tries to shake you off, but he knows he has to be careful with the blaster aimed right between his eyes.

"So," you continue. "Why are you so interested in that girl in the cafe?" He snorts. "Your girl-friend is Facet Anamor. She works for the Imperial Research Station; her father is in charge." None of that sounds much like an excuse, unless... You step back, slipping his blaster into a pocket of your coat. "I don't know what your problem is, but I don't need any hassle from you. Keep out of my way, man, or I'll have to get rough next time."

You back away, heading for a nearby junction so that you can start putting some distance between yourself and this incident. "We'll meet again," he growls, getting to his feet. A siren sounds in the distance, and he jerks his head away. With a last defiant glance, he sets off along the street, heading in the opposite direction. That's fine by you.

Well, it's been fun, but you don't think you should hang around here any more. Time to find some different entertainment.

Check 547

If you return to the Commercial District, go to 169

If go in search of a Shuttle back to the Spaceport District, go to 199

115-116

The man in the turban has an extremely strong grip on your collar, so you allow him to pull you along, trying to look like you have given up resistance. He looks to see if he can see where the girl went, stretching up to peer over the heads of the people in the street. While he's off-balance, you draw on all your strength and twist out of his grip. Before the startled man can react, you hit him hard, across the back of the neck, and he drops to the floor, completely out cold.

In an instant, you reach into his coat, where you detected a blaster nestling in hip holster. There's some ID, which says his name is Vermilion. He also has a small purse, with a few high denomination credits and charge cards. A passers-by close at hand yells out, and you realise that he thinks you're robbing Vermilion. Actually, that might not be such a bad idea. The police are less likely to be interested in a simple street crime. After all, is Vermilion going to report it? You think not.

Moments later, you are on your feet, running up the street to put distance between yourself and the fallen man. Up above, you hear a train rumbling into the station of the Rapid Transit Monorail. That would be a good way to get away from the scene of the "crime". Alternatively, you could lose yourself in the Commercial District.

Check 547

If you return to the Commercial District, go to 169

If go up the elevator to the Monorail, go to 53

117

The battle rages. Fett fires blast after blast in your direction, looking to overcome you with sheer firepower. The fight spills along the street, as you try to find some cover. Staying alive is hard enough, you never manage to get Fett in your sights. What you need, Havet, is a miracle...

Fett takes aim again. The blast that flashes past seems impossibly bright, and the roar of its impact greater than anything you have ever heard before. Another massive shock wave follows. What in the galaxy is he firing at you now? You raise your head to take a look – and see that Fett is no longer firing, but is staring up into the sky.

Some kind of massive battle is taking place in the sky overhead! Alarms ring; people flee for cover. It looks like you just gained your miracle, Havet; will you live long enough to enjoy it?

Go to 203

118

Scarlett listens as you tell him what you have been doing. "None of that is any use, Havet." He steers you back towards the door. "Let me make it clear to you, Havet. If you want us to help you, you have to give us something in return. We want you to get inside the IRS. Manage that, and then we'll talk." He pushes you out of the ruined cantina. You brush dust and ash from your coat. What a nerd. Perhaps you'd do better without him anyway.

Go to 99

119

It takes a while before you realise what the man said. His helmet shields his eyes, making it impossible for you to gauge his reactions. Finally, he puts down his glass. "Who are you, boy?" His voice, muffled by his helmet, is harsh. Behind you, there is a discreet shuffling as the other patrons of the cantina put some distance between them and the confrontation you have a starring role in. They seem unduly frightened - after all, it's just one man and a blaster rifle...

The tension is becoming oppressive. Perhaps you should say something; perhaps you should move away. Perhaps you shouldn't have got out of bed this morning.

If you back away, go to 159

If you reach out with the Force, go to 144

If you reach for your weapons, go to 168

120

This is no time to hesitate, Havet! You reach into your mind, trying to draw on your rough impression of the narrow stairwell, and aim at the sounds ahead of you.

You must fight your mysterious assailant. Read 543

If you win the combat, go to 137

If you lose, go to 148

121

"I'm ready," you announce. Vermilion hands you a small glass bottle. "Get Facet to drink this if you can; it'll put her to sleep for hours." He claps you on the back. "Good luck," he says. "We'll start our attack an hour after you go in. I reckon you'll have about another 30 minutes after that before we've completed the transmission. Then we blow the place to pieces."

"What happens if I'm still inside?" you ask. "Don't be," replies Vermilion, dryly. Enough said.

You step out into the street. The final chapter in your adventure starts right here.

Check 572 if you haven't already done so

Add the sleeping potion to your equipment. Check 590

If you have checked 525 and you want to visit that location, go to 230

If you have checked 553 or 554 and you want to go to the IRS, go to 163

122

You are in the HQ of the Rebel Alliance (Toprawan branch).

If you want to go to the Rebel armoury, go to 107

If you want to go to their Electronics Lab, go to 108

If you want to get some sleep, go to 124

If you want to visit the sick bay, go to 128

If you are ready for your mission, go to 121

123

Realising your mistake, you back away from Boba Fett, hands extended to show you are unarmed. "I'm sorry... I had no idea..." you fumble. The battered helmet turns fully in your direction. "I believe you," he says. "I accept that you made an honest mistake. You may go."

Hmmm. That all seems pretty reasonable. Perhaps Fett isn't the blood-thirsty maniac people say he is. "Just two things. First, if I ever see you again, I'll kill you. Second, take your blaster and leave it on the counter. You have no right to carry a weapon unless you're prepared to use it."

If you have no blaster, or if you hand over whatever blaster you are carrying, go to 138
If you want to use your blaster against Boba Fett, go to 177

124

Suddenly all the activity of the last few days catches up with you.

Man, you're tired. You find a bunk in a corner of the main room, and – ignoring everyone around you – fall instantly to sleep.

Read 502

When you wake up, go to 122

125

The sound of footsteps from the alley helps you reach a decision swiftly. You dive across the street, and into the side-door. Or, at least, that was the plan. It turns out that the side-door wasn't actually open – something on the inside has jammed it shut. Feeling just a little afraid, you glance back at the mouth of the alleyway, just in time to catch a glimpse of the dark-haired assassin pulling back. She's seen where you are and what you're doing. She's waiting for you to try to run, so she can have a clearer shot.

Then again, you can't stay in this doorway for ever…

If barge the door down, add your Strength Rating (from your Character Sheet) to the number 150. That is the number of the next paragraph you should read (so, if your Strength is 2, go to paragraph 152). Go to that paragraph now.

If you run up the street, go to 158

126

Something about the way the strangely-armoured man reacted spooks you, and you move steadily back from the counter. The man finishes his drink, seemingly ignoring you; the other patrons of Al the Alchemist's are also moving away, so that you find yourself moving in the middle of an expanding bubble of clear air in the otherwise crowded tavern.

His drink finished, the man at the counter turns round, sweeping his arm up, his finger pointed at your forehead. It suddenly occurs to you that he has an array of wrist lasers on his wrist. "No-one," he rumbles, his voice low through the helmet, "ever called Boba Fett a moron before."

This isn't a good time to be funny. So, why do you reply: "There's a first time for everything."

The Force screams a warning into your mind; even before Boba Fett himself knows what he is going to do, you *feel* his intentions. In barely half-a-second, he'll raise that blaster rifle up from the floor and cut you down. What will you do in the four-tenths of a second before that happens?

If you draw your lightsabre, go to 170 – you must have 508 checked to select this option

If you have checked 507 and choose to draw your blaster, go to 177

If you to make a run for the door, go to 181

127

You have this sneaking suspicion you've made a mistake. The guard on the ground is snarling angrily, and his colleagues are coming over, unfastening their holsters. You take to your heels without thinking. A warning klaxon sounds, and you hear more guards coming from all sides. You can either surrender, or pull your blaster and try to fight your way out.

If you surrender, go to 30

If you choose to fight, read 506, then use the combat rules from the beginning of this book. Remember this paragraph number so you can find your way back

If you blast all the guards, go to 157

If you lose the battle, go to 55

128

The Rebels have a fully-equipped medical unit in their HQ. The Doc checks you over. "You'll live," he announces, once he has put you to rights. "Want something for those spots?"

You resist the temptation to shoot him.

Read 582

Go to 122

The room goes chillingly quiet. Fett turns to face you. "Say that again," he whispers.

You take a deep breath. "I said, you can't be Boba Fett, because I heard he's even uglier than you are." Behind you, you hear the sound of feet carrying their owners to some distant place of safety. Other than Fett, the barman is the only person you can see, and he is breaking all kinds of records at removing breakables and still managing to back off to the furthest depths of his bar.

"Who are you, boy?" Fett asks. "Did Solo send you?" Solo? Who's he? "That's right," you reply, improvising quickly. Fett stiffens. "Is he here?" he murmurs tensely. "Close enough. He says he wants to talk. Outside, near the landspeeder repair shop, three blocks south." Fett puts down his drink and picks up his weapon in a single fluid movement. He prepares to leave, but pauses at your shoulder. "Next time I see you, messenger-boy, I'll kill you." You grin. "That's just what he said you'd say." Fett grips his blaster rifle even more tightly and leaves the room. The astonished sigh of relief from the other customers washes over you like a tidal wave.

Al (the Alchemist) looks both relieved and terrified. He pours another tankard of the slop and sets it in front of you. You eye it cautiously, and decide not to let it get any closer to your stomach than it is now. "Hey, Al. How long does it take to walk to that repair shop and back?" Al shrugs his shoulders. "Four minutes." You grab your belongings, and head for the door.

Go to 34

You face off with your mystery opponent. You try to reach out with your mind to gauge his intent, but by the time you receive anything, it's clear he isn't going to fire. The door opens suddenly, spilling light into the stairwell. Part-dazzled, you duck lower behind the protective cover of the stairs. By the time you realise what he intended, your assailant has gone.

You slip your blaster into its holster, in no hurry to go out through the door. A young couple come down from the Monorail. They glance apprehensively at you, then go out through the door. Neither of them gets shot, so you figure you're safe and step out into the daylight.

So, Havet, what was that all about? The girl and the man in the turban have gone, and you have no idea if she is safely away from him or not. In the meantime, you've survived a close call. And they call this a secure military base? How come you can never find a cop when you need one?

Check 544

If you go off to find the Shuttle back to the spaceport area, go to 199

If you go back into the Commercial District, go to 169

131

You start running, as hard as you can. You're not exactly a professional athlete, so it comes as no surprise that you are still several metres short of your goal when the first blaster shots ring out from behind you. You hit the dirt hard and try to find what cover you can. There isn't much.

If you fight this combat, read 523, then use the combat rules from the beginning of the book. Remember this paragraph number so you can find your way back

If you win the combat, go to 81

If you lose the battle, go to 92

If you don't want to fight, but you have checked 511, go to 54

If you don't want to fight, and you haven't checked 511, go to 84

132-133

You start running as hard as you can towards the small building. You're not the fastest thing on two legs, but the security guards at the check-point are slow off the mark, and you are almost at the first building before they fire their first shot. It looks as if you're going to make it!

Ooops! You spoke too soon. The whine of repulsorlift motors fills the air. Two Imperial Scouts mounted on Aratech 74-Z speeder bikes are racing after you!

If you want to duck into the building, go to 162

If you choose to fight, read 524, then use the combat rules in at the beginning of this book. Remember this paragraph number so you can find your way back

If you win the combat, go to 146

If you lose the battle, go to 92

If you surrender, and you have checked 511, go to 54

If you surrender, but you haven't checked 511, go to 84

134-136

You run as hard as you can towards the small building. It looks like some kind of small office building, with two floors. If you can reach it, you'll be out of sight.

The security guards are still trying to work out where you disappeared as you reach the building. Slipping round the back, you can see that there's a small patch of open ground, littered with lengths of wire and abandoned crates. Beyond, there are several warehouses. If you can reach them, perhaps you can lose your pursuers before they can call in reinforcements.

Ooops! You spoke too soon. The whine of repulsorlift motors fills the air. Two Imperial Scouts mounted on Aratech 74-Z speeder bikes are racing in your direction. They don't know where you are yet, but even at half throttle they can cover a lot of ground. What you need is an edge.

If you want to duck into the building, go to 162

If you try to get across the open ground, go to 171

If you search the junk, go to 175

137

You fire a single shot, the report roaring in the confined space, and ringing in your ears. You stay perfectly still, sheltering behind the stairs until your hearing clears, and your eyes adjust to the gloom. There is a huddled shape on the floor.

Conscious of the fact that someone is bound to come and investigate the loud noise soon, you cross to the side of the fallen man. Your eyes take in a long, white coat and a blood-red turban. He is injured, quite badly, in one arm, and has fainted with the shock. You allow the Force to flow out from your hands as you inspect his wounds. You can feel that the next few moments are critical; if you can stabilise his condition now, he will survive, and with conventional medical help, he should be up and around again in no time.

If you use your Jedi powers to help the man, go to 176

If you leave quickly, before anyone comes to investigate, go to 189

138

Moving extremely slowly, and with painful caution, you obey Boba Fett's instructions. You see the small sensor array attached to his helmet twitching as it runs a sweep over you for any concealed blasters. Finally, Fett pronounces himself satisfied.

"Now get out of here," he says, turning away from you. Someone far off in the bar issues a soft whistling noise. You walk towards the door, trying to keep your head high. It isn't easy. The Wookiee growls as you pass, and a grey-skinned, ape-like creature snorts mockingly.

You've never felt so humiliated in your life. But at least you're alive.

Go to 34

139

It's early, but you've had a long day, and you feel bushed. You decide to catch a few hours sleep in your room. The hostel is noisy, and the traffic outside keeps you from sleeping deeply, but you doze a little, and rest as much as you can. Come the morning, you awake early, ravenously hungry and ready to take whatever Toprawa throws at you.

So, what's it to be? You could get a ride into the City, or check out the neighbourhood around the Hostel and the Spaceport. Maybe you could find some work.

Read 502

If you want to catch the Shuttle into the City, go to 72

If you want to look for a free ride, go to 6

If you want to explore locally, go to 99

140

Scarlett listens, and his eyes open wide as he hears what you have been doing. He stops rooting around in the ashes of the cantina, and comes up close to whisper to you. "That's fantastic! You've done it! We can really make some progress now!"

He leads you back out into the street. "Let's go, Havet. There's someone you ought to meet!"

Go to 106

141

Your growling belly makes the decision for you. Yes, something to eat is the first priority. Seems like you're always hungry these days, Havet.

You walk a short distance until you reach a street with a few shops and apartment buildings. A cantina on the corner advertises cheap meals. Perfect. Of course, you're a stranger to this world, and this looks like a low-rent part of town. Should you take some precautions?

If you have a blaster in your pack and wish to retrieve it, go to 191

If your lightsabre is out of sight and you want to have it closer to hand, go to 202
If you everything where it is, go to 216

142

Something is coming towards you from the alley, and it isn't likely to be good news. You judge the distance across to the cantina to be too great, and so you turn along the street, in the hope that you can find somewhere to hide. There are a few people about, but not enough to confuse the issue. If you can find a shopping mall, or another alley, or just about anywhere other than this...

You run quickly along the sidewalk, not daring to look back. A few local citizens step from your path. Then you catch sight of a small indoor market, selling local produce. Lots of small stalls, people and noise. Maybe more than one way in and out too.

You leap through the entrance, cannoning off a stack of fruit-boxes, which fall to the ground, spilling their contents everywhere. Picking yourself off, and shrugging off the grasping hands of an angry stall-holder, you go deeper into the market, following its twist and turns in a wild race.

Great! There's a service entrance right at the back. The door is open, and the street outside looks clear. Just a few more strides…

A chilling, low voice stops you in your tracks. "Halt!" Your skin can almost feel the crosshairs from her blaster's sights. "Don't be stupid. Turn and face me… slowly."

If you try to fight your way out, go to 167

If you do as she says, and you have checked 511 or 514, go to 172

If you do as she says but you haven't checked 511 or 514, go to 173

143

You decide you had better be honest with these people, and you show the bracelet you were given to the Rebel electronics expert. He becomes very alarmed, and calls Vermilion. The Rebel leader looks very angry when he arrives. "You idiot!" he shouts. "You could have been tracked here!" You explain that you were told the device had to be activated. Vermilion isn't impressed.

"Can you get it off?" he asks. "Sure," says the wild-haired young technician, "but it will take two pairs of hands." Vermilion sighs. "Have you finished your other work?" The Technician says he has. "Fine. Take this stupid kid with you to your workshop. Let him help. I don't have time for this now." He rounds on you. "That was incredibly dumb, Havet. You could have compromised the whole operation. We'll have to launch the attack at once, just in case they have a tracer in that thing. Get it off in a hurry and get inside that Station!"

Go to 165

144

Tentatively, you reach out with the Force, trying to calm down the hatred you can feel seething inside Boba Fett's mind. You have never before encountered such hatred… such evil! Before you can weave your way through his mind, Fett reacts. With stinging speed, he slaps you hard across the face with the back of his hand. You fall to the floor. Fett turns away, dismissing you from his sight. The arrogance of the man! You'd really like to take him down a peg or nine!

If you have checked 508 and wish to draw your lightsabre, go to 170

If you have checked 507 and wish to draw your blaster, go to 177

If you leave without making any more fuss, go to 34

145

The Rebel Technician takes Arf and manages some simple running repairs. "That should keep him running for now. I'll do a better job after the attack."

Remove check 560

Go to 108

146

You defeat the two Scouts. There are shouts from the check-point, where they have just realised what has happened. However, you don't have to put up with any nonsense from them; you have the perfect means to get out of here – a fully-charged Aratech 74-Z Military speeder bike!

Dropping into the saddle, you power up the repulsorlift. You've ridden bikes before, but nothing this powerful! Just so they know you mean business, you pop off a couple of blasts from the laser cannon, then you ease the bike around and open the throttle. Moments later, the checkpoint is half-a-kilometre behind you, and disappearing fast!

Check 526

Go to 86

147

You show the transmitter you took from Diamond to the Rebel Technician. "Interesting," he says. "Looks like the kind of thing they use to control electronic binders, only this one has only one control, like a remote detonator. My guess is that it controls some kind of booby trap."

Go to 108

148

Everything happens terribly quickly. Your attacker seems to fire in the same instant that you pull the trigger on your own weapon, and the small space is filled with a thunderous, roaring noise. A microsecond later, you feel the impact as his blaster hits you hard, in the upper part of your arm – just about the only part of you which was visible. You scream out with the pain, falling back onto the cold, hard floor.

It takes a moment for you to recover your senses, and to reach deep into yourself with the Force to see what damage has been done. You are acutely aware that, at any moment, your assailant could be standing over you, blaster levelled to finish the job. Or that the police could arrive to investigate.

Waves of cold sweep over you as you try to soothe the pain with your Jedi powers. It isn't a severe wound, but you can feel the loss of blood and the shock eating at your strength. You have only a few moments, it seems, before you black out with the pain.

If you use your Jedi powers to heal your wound, go to 180

If you leave quickly, before anyone comes to investigate, go to 192

149

The smell of cooking overcomes your any doubts you might have had about entering the cantina. Quickly checking your weapons and your wallet, you head towards the door.

Go to 216

You walk into the cafe, a small, cramped sandwich bar selling local meats and cheeses and appetising dark bread. You walk up to the counter to order some food and a glass of some bitter fruit juice. The manager takes your order and tells you to sit down.

If you have checked 525, 541 or 618, go to 352

If you haven't checked 525, 541 or 618, but you have checked 515, go to 12

If you haven't checked either, go to 161

151-152

Summoning up all your strength, you hit the side door of the cantina with your shoulder. It moves fractionally, but whatever it was holding it closed stood up to your charge, and you wind up thrown to the floor. A few passers-by grin at your predicament. You can almost hear them thinking – "the poor boy's so desperate for a chocolate and banana milkshake, he's cracked his head against a locked door!" If only they knew…

You almost don't dare look back towards the alley, but you glance quickly over your shoulder. You can't see the dark-haired woman anywhere. Maybe that's good news, maybe she isn't after you at all. However, you can't shake the feeling that she is just watching you from somewhere, waiting for her chance to take you out in less public circumstances.

It still seems like a good idea to get off the street. However, the front door into the cantina is clearly visible from the valley, and it would be easy for the killer to finish you off with one shot. Perhaps you could consider another option?

If you run back to the front door, go to 187

If you blast open the side door, go to 193

If you take off down the street, go to 210

153-156

Summoning up all your strength, you hit the side door of the cantina with your shoulder, and in a thundering crash of shattered synthetic wood and pre-moulded plastic you break down the side door. The last few fragments of the door frame fall to the ground just after you do. By the time you clear your head and start trying to raise it off the floor, the interior of the cantina has gone very quiet.

The first thing you can focus on is a pair of heavy boots. Tracking up, you take in the legs of some antiquated armour. Your view of the owner's body and head is masked by the muzzle of a BlasTech EE-3 blaster rifle, which is pointed straight between your eyes.

If you have checked 516, go to 19

If you haven't checked 516, go to 200

157

You know, your grand-father would be dreadfully upset to find out you were cheating like this. Turn back from the dark side!

If things have been going that badly, you can always start again.

158

Everything seems to be stacked up against you. You've got a killer on your trail, the side-door into your chosen hiding place is locked, and the street is almost empty of traffic and pedestrians. If the black-haired woman wants you, she's going to find you.

One thing's for sure, you can't stay here – you're a sitting duck. You run away from the cantina, down the block towards an apartment building and a shoddy shopping precinct. A glance back doesn't show you anything; there's no sign of the killer anywhere. You slow down, take a good look around. If she's following you by taking par-allel streets and alleyways, you need to make a few sudden turns and reverses to throw her off. The apartment building is bound to have at least one additional exit from the side or back, and you'd be out of sight for a moment.

You duck in through the doorway, and bump into a man who was standing just inside. Was it your imagination, or did he make that happen deliberately?

If you have checked 504 or 509, go to 219

If you haven't checked either of these, go to 233

159

You step back from Boba Fett, who watches you intently. He is so sure that no stupid kid would just walk up and insult him, he has convinced himself you must be working for someone else. You see him snatch quick glances right and left, looking to see if there's a hidden gunman somewhere providing you with cover. The crowd behind you moves apart, opening a path to the door as they try to keep out of Fett's line of sight.

Finally, his patience snaps, and he snatches up the blaster rifle. You're still a few metres from the door. Can you make it?

If you run to the door, go to 181

If you reach for your blaster (you must have 507 checked), go to 177

160

The Imperial Research Station looks like the only happening place on the planet, workwise. The Rapid Transit Monorail runs to a terminus close by. Interesting that. No Monorail between the City and the Port, but one out here to the Station, ferrying workers and soldiers back and forth. Also, the road that runs around the outer perimeter of the spaceport and up to the main gates is heavy with traffic, which can't be said of many other roadways you've seen.

Something is happening here which is consuming just about all the energy Toprawa has left to offer; leaching off it so badly that the rest of the economy is dying, like it was a vampire drawing too much blood from its victim. Nice image that, Havet. Try not to mention it to anyone who works there.

As you get closer, you see that what looked from the distance like a single laboratory is in fact the street entrance to a whole complex of buildings behind a top security fence. The compound is vast, stretching right round to the edge of the space-port. The road you have walked along actually ends at a heavily-fortified gate. Armed guards and droids patrol the perimeter fence, and surveillance devices on high poles remorselessly scan the compound.

The sign over the door reads "Imperial Research Station". A small console facing out into the street displays a list of vacancies. You use the touch-screen, and find they have vacancies for drivers, pilots, droid engineers, programmers and data entry clerks, along with some heavyweight technical positions requiring qualifications in space engineering, lasers or guidance systems. These are way out of your league. Besides, the first division jobs are going to be for people with lengthy backgrounds in Imperial service, with a security rating to match. What you want is a job in some low-intensity field, where they might not be so rigorous in checking backgrounds.

No casual labour required. The Army supplies all the basic muscle and security. So, it looks like your best bet would be to ask for work as a driver or data entry clerk. You go back to those screens; the pay is OK, though they demand their pound of flesh for it – the hours are very long.

So, on balance, what are you going to decide, Havet? Working for the IRS is a bit like entering the lion's den, but you can't exist for more than another day or two on the few credits you have left in your coat pocket. How else are you going to earn a living?

If you enter the Imperial Research Station, go to 179

If you go back towards the main highway from the spaceport, go to 99

161

You take a look around the crowded cafe. "Take a seat!" the manager insists in a high, piping voice as he hands over your order. You wish. The cafe is crowded, and filled with the buzz of conversation and the clatter of cutlery and crockery. Most of the occupants seem to be either low-rank Fleet types, or office workers. Your clothes look a little out of place amongst all the smart uniforms and suits, and it leaves you feeling awkward. But, you've paid for your meal, so...

You look for someplace where you can eat, and you catch sight of an empty chair at a two-seat table, and a small piece of elbow room further along the counter.

If you choose to sit at the table, go to 224

If you choose the space at the counter, go to 3

162

You decide – wisely – that you are no match for the scouts on their armed and extremely fast speeder bikes. You duck into the doorway, breaking the flimsy lock. As you suspected, the place is deserted. A narrow metal staircase winds its way up from the reception area to the upper floor. Your boots ring loudly as you run up – at first the noise makes you wince, but then you realise that if you can't sneak up, neither can anyone else.

On the upper floor, there is a large open plan space, with just a few small rooms separated off. You find one which commands a clear view of the top of the stairs, and settle down to wait. The next few moments seem to last forever. You hear the bikes speed past outside. Moments later they're back, pulling up, and you can hear the two scouts passing questions and answers back and forth. Then silence. They must be looking round. Will they check upstairs?

Your answer comes as the sound of heavy boots on the stairs. Both of the scouts have followed you to the upper floor. Seconds later, you can see the helmet of the first appear in the stairwell, and you make ready to defend yourself.

If you want to wait to see if they find you, go to 178

If you choose to fight , read 534, then use the combat rules at the beginning of this book. Remember this paragraph number so you can find your way back

If you win the combat, go to 146

If you lose the battle, go to 92

If you surrender, and you have checked 511, go to 54

If you surrender, but you haven't checked 511, go to 84

163

You set off on your mission. Somehow, you have to gain access to the IRS building, and then to the top-secret research labs. It isn't going to be easy; at least you have your metallic pass.

You walk to the IRS from the main crossroads. About fifty metres from the building, your Jedi senses start tingling. Two men are talking, just along the street; you slip into a doorway to watch them. The nearer one, who had been blocking your view of the other, is a senior

Imperial officer. The other is Boba Fett. You listen in on the end of their conversation. "Where can I find this Facet Anamor?" asks Fett. "She was living quarters in the Station," says the Officer. Fett tells him that he has asked at the Station, but that Facet isn't there. "Well, she has an apartment on Market Street – 525, I think it is." Fett steps away, and into a landspeeder parked at the kerb. "I'll try there," he snarls, gunning the engine and pulling away.

What does Boba Fett want with Facet? You have to find out. The Officer has a landspeeder of his own parked close by – dare you risk taking it off him this close to the Station?

If you have checked 527, you may wish to read that paragraph again, and then go to 196

If not, you must fight the Officer. Read 583, then use the combat rules at the beginning of this book. Remember this paragraph number so you can find your way back

If you win the combat in the first two rounds, go to 209

If you fail to do this, go to 261

164

You and your assailant fire almost in the same instant, though – somehow! – neither of you hits the other in the darkness. You ears are ringing painfully with the thunder of the guns, but you hear the door open and slam, and your eyes are blinded briefly by the light from outside. You run quickly to the door, dropping your back against the wall. You pause, listening for the slightest sound outside. In fact, there is plenty of activity. People shouting and running, calling for the police. Sounds like your attacker is still close at hand.

You start as a small scrap of card is pushed under the door. You fight the temptation to go through the door at once; nor do you reach out and take the card for several moments. Finally, carefully, you drag the card back towards you with the sole of your boot. Opening the door a fraction, you see that your assailant has gone. In the light from the street you can read his hastily-scrawled message.

"Next time I'll kill you. Stay away from Facet. Vermilion."

Nice guy. Slipping your weapon into your holster, you get ready to go back out onto the street, and to slip away through the confused crowds before the police can arrive.

If you head back towards the spaceport, go to 199

If you find your way back towards the main Commercial District, go to 169

165

The Rebel Technician takes you along the street to a workshop, and pulls out his tools. "We'll have to hurry if you're going to get inside the IRS." He removes the metal cover from the bracelet, and places a probe on a small contact. "Hold that," he says. "Don't let it move; I've got to tackle the lock." He brings out a small laser cutter, and takes a moment to inspect the interior. "That's odd, there's a lot of extra packing in here – it's –" He jumps back; you almost lose your grip on the probe. "It's explosive! That thing's a bomb!"

Tick the first box on your Time Track.

If you want to continue trying to get it off, go to 263

If you abandon the attempt, go to 281

166

You interrupt the instructions, waving the address Facet gave you. "I've been invited to her apartment in town," you call. There's a brief pause, then the voice continues: "You've been busy," he comments, "and very clever. We didn't even know she had an apartment... If you're ready, the Alliance can use your help." You're more than ready! "You know Al's cantina, near the spaceport? Scarlett will meet you there." The speaker goes dead, and the house lights come on. You know a signal to leave when you see one. And now you know exactly where you should go next.

If you go directly to the cantina as instructed, go to 216

If you check out the area around the cantina first, go to 99

167

You spin quickly, trying to draw your weapon and throw the black-haired killer off the track. She is much too fast for you, however.

Before you can so much as reach inside your coat, she fires, and the searing energy pulse from her blaster throws you to the floor. Seconds later, you pass into blackness.

Your adventure is over. If you want to start again, turn to paragraph 1

168

Blazing with anger, you reach for a weapon. Boba Fett, though, has been around too long, and seen too many other attempts to kill him. With blinding speed, he jabs forward with his right hand. You don't have time to see anything, but you catch the buzzing sound of a vibro-shiv just as Fett strikes you down. Then all is still, except for the faint memory in your mind of the whirring blade, which slowly fades to leave a deathly silence.

Boba Fett has proved too much for you. Try again from the start

169

The main Commercial District of Toprawa City centres on a long street – Imperial Road. To the west, this street eventually becomes the highway leading back to the spaceport. To the east, it passes through some smart residential areas, and from there towards the coast. In the middle, for about three kilometres, it presents an unbroken facade of banks, insurance houses, shipping offices, commercial headquarters and the kinds of expensive shops that people working in the other places can frequent. Side streets play host to the support companies and the second-division players. You spend several hours trudging up and down Imperial Road, looking for someone who might offer you some casual work to tide you over the next couple of days. It's hopeless. The central area is too up-market, and they don't take off-worlders, or scruffy kids who look like they've stepped straight off a cheap passenger ship after a long flight.

Actually, it looks like jobs are at a premium in this town, except at the Imperial Research Station, which you're told is some kind of government/army establishment out by the main port. They've apparently quite a few vacancies; there's some kind of rush job they need to finish, and they don't have enough army people to do the work.

So, nothing much to show for all your effort so far. You take a moment to scan the Public Access Bulletins on a library screen, and find a small, dark-haired man in a long, grubby coat and a blood-red scarf standing in a dark doorway. He beckons to you.

If you have checked 521, read paragraph 522

If you have checked 521, or you want to catch the Shuttle back towards the spaceport, go to 199

If you haven't checked 521, and you want to talk to the man, go to 190

170

Fett clearly means you kill you. You step back, and pull back your coat, your fingertips reaching for the weapon on your belt. The crowd in the bar closes in, like water over a drowning man, all eager to see what Fett will do. You thumb the activator on the lightsabre, and the air is filled with its power. You shrug off the crowd, and rise to your feet, with the weapon extended.

Everyone is watching you intently, seemingly unable to believe their own eyes. Can this really be happening, here in this beat-up little cantina on a scrap-heap of a world? You feel like shouting at them – yes, it's true! This is a lightsabre – and I'm a Jedi!

The crowd parts, allowing a menacing figure to pass through their ranks. He carries his blaster rifle carelessly, yet you know he could drop you dead in less time than it takes to snap your fingers. His strange armour bristles with even more weapons. However, even though you cannot see his eyes under that antiquated helmet, you know that he too is staring at the lightsabre.

"The boy's a Jedi," he whispers, loud in the cramped silence of the compact bar. "Kill him." Fett steps back, beyond the reach of your weapon. Plenty of others to ready take his place…

If you want to talk your way out of this, go to 184

If you choose to fight, read 564, and use the combat rules from the beginning of this book. Remember this paragraph number so you can find your way back

If you win the combat, go to 194

If you lose, go to 206

171

Your plan to run across to the abandoned warehouses quickly goes astray. On the rubble-strewn ground, you step awkwardly on a loose piece of pipe, and turn over on your ankle. The pain is excruciating! Even before you hit the floor, however, you can hear an even greater problem coming your way – the scouts have tracked you down, and are closing the gap on their speeder bikes.

If you use the Force to combat your injury, go to 183

If you choose to fight, read 536, then use the combat rules from the beginning of this book. Remember this paragraph number so you can find your way back

If you win the combat, go to 146

If you lose the battle, go to 92

If you surrender, and you have checked 511, go to 54

If you surrender, but you haven't checked 511, go to 84

172

Slowly, hands spread wide, you turn to face your nemesis. As you guessed, the black-haired assassin is Diamond, the Head of Security at the Imperial Research Station. You have already earned her attention once. This time, it could be fatal.

"Havet Storm," she breathes. "You keep turning up like a bad credit." She is sitting at the foot of a pile of empty shipping cartons. She holds her blaster lightly in one hand. "If I didn't know better, I'd swear you were following me."

"Who was the guy in the alley?" you ask, buying time. For what, though? Surely there's no way out of here. "Him?" she sighs, wearily, "his name is – was – Ta'al Pierc. He worked at the Station, but he was secretly working for the Rebel Alliance. At least, he thought it was a secret. I've been feeding him information to smoke out Vermilion and the rest of the rebels. Pierc managed to break through the password protection scheme on the main computer, and took out some information that I didn't intend for him to see. He became more dangerous than useful."

"So you killed him." In cold blood. "Surely –"

"Surely I'm not allowed to go around killing people without a trial?

Don't be a fool, Havet. The Emperor's servants don't wait for lawyers and hearings and appeals; they just act. That's why we'll crush this Rebellion, and that's why you need to decide which side you're on."

If you have checked 552, go to 186

If you haven't, go to 198

173

Slowly, hands spread, you turn to face the assassin. She is sitting, legs crossed, at the foot of a pile of empty shipping cartons. She holds her blaster lightly in one hand. "I'm going to ask you some questions. Think carefully before you answer. Lying would be fatal."

"What did you just see in the alley?" You start to say 'Nothing!', thinking that would be what she wants to hear. But the words 'Lying would be fatal' were spoken with absolute determination. "I saw you kill a man," you reply. She smiles, pleased with the result. "Did you recognise him?" she asks. No, you'd never seen him before. "Do you recognise me?" Um – no. But you'll never forget her. She laughs at your clumsy reply. "Never is such a long time; you really need to keep thinking about how you're going to stay alive for the next few minutes."

"I'm Commander Diamond of the Imperial Research Station. The man you saw me execute –" She doesn't hesitate as she says it "– was a member of the Rebel Alliance. I have made it my mission to smoke out the rebels on Toprawa, and he wasn't the first I've killed. So, young man, will you help me get the others?"

"Me?" She laughs again, although you can see that there is no humour in it. "Yes, you. Are you a member of the Alliance already?" Oh, oh. This has to be another one of those "lying is fatal" questions. How are you supposed to answer this time? Yes, I'm a rebel (in which case she kills you) or No, I'm a good citizen (in which case, you're no use to her). You hear the blaster hum in her hand. "I'm waiting," she says flatly.

Check 565

If you tell her you are a member of the Alliance, go to 188

If you tell her you *aren't* a member, go to 204

174

The security guard is close at your elbow, as you turn swiftly. Your flight bag catches him in the chest, and he topples over. You slip your hand inside the bag, feeling the reassuring touch of your blaster. What now? The other guards are reacting, moving towards you. The first man is sprawled on the ground, angrily cursing your clumsiness. Is there any way out of this?

If you apologise to the security guard and surrender, go to 20

If you draw your blaster, go to 66

If you run for it, go to 127

175

Running quickly, you race out into the rubble-strewn area, trying to keep low. Grabbing a length of wire, you tie one end to a deeply-embedded fence post, then wrap the other round some heavy rubble. Making sure it is anchored securely, you let the scouts see you, then run off. You hear the whining of the speeder bikes as the scouts race after you. Any second now…

At over 80kph, the first bike's front wings hit the wire. The scout spills onto the ground and lies stunned. Having seen the first bike's mishap, the second guy tries to veer aside, but the front "sled" hits the wire, and the bike cartwheels over, slamming into a pile of masonry. There is a terrible explosion, and pieces of stone, bike and other debris fall all around you. Then all is still.

The stunned scout is in no mood for further resistance. Somewhere in the distance, you hear the shouts as the other guards from the check-point start closing in. Time to make a move, Havet!

Go to 86

176

You frisk the guy for his ID, which says that he is Vermilion, a merchant. Yeah, right. It looks like he'll survive. It's an ugly wound, but not a killing one. However, there is a great deal of damage. You know the risks of staying here, but you can't allow him to suffer unnecessarily. You guide the Force into Vermilion's body. After a moment, the critical point has been passed.

Except he'll be captured if you leave him here. In the distance, you hear sirens approaching. You hoist Vermilion onto your shoulder, and push out into the street, aiming for a building nearby. The odds on you getting away still look poor when a door opens in the basement. A woman appears. "In here! I'll hide you!" You take the stairs down, but you don't go into her apartment. Instead, you lay Vermilion down inside the doorway. "Thanks. I'll take my chances outside." You leave before the woman can argue. After all, how do you know if she can be trusted?

You evade the noose being thrown around the Monorail station by a fraction. Breathing hard from your exertions, you work out where you are from a few landmarks on the horizon. That's probably enough excitement for one day; how about finding somewhere to rest for the night?

Check 547

If you look for the Shuttle, and head back to the Spaceport District, go to 199

If you head back to the heart of the Commercial District, go to 169

177

Boba Fett watches as you drag out your blaster, almost fumbling the weapon. Fear and tension are eating into your desperate resolve, but you can't back down now. You level the weapon – still Fett doesn't move. What's his game? Does he think you can't shoot him down in cold blood? Can you, Havet?

There isn't time to find out. Your arm is suddenly paralysed with pain, and the blaster knocked from your hand. Seconds later, Fett's boot smashes into your body, and you are thrown to the floor, scattering chairs as you fall. The pain is terrible! You look up, and see that Al, the bartender and owner of this rat-pit cantina, has a large wooden cudgel in his hand. "Sorry, kid," he snarls. "We don't allow no shootings." Fett steps up to you, his blaster rifle pointed at your head. "Although they make an exception in my case," he says.

"If I thought I'd ever be back this way," Fett continues, "I'd have to kill you, kid. Instead, I'm prepared to be generous. You can leave, and you can learn. What you learn is this – never, ever, pull a blaster on someone unless you're prepared to use it."

Fett picks up your weapon and throws it to Al. "Off you go, boy," he says.

Remove the blaster from your equipment box

Check 566

Go to 34

178

Foolishly, you squander your advantage in the vain hope that the two scouts might not find you. The broken lock on the front door was always going to give you away! They come up onto the top floor, and spread out, checking every corner of the main room, and peering through the doors of the smaller rooms. The taller scout goes out of sight briefly; the other is checking the small store cupboard next to the room you are hiding in. Moments later, his footsteps are coming your way. You know both of them are very close, and you make ready to fight for your life.

If you choose to fight a combat, read 535, then use the combat rules in paragraph 601. Keep a note of this paragraph number so you can find your way back here.

If you win the combat, go to 146

If you lose the battle, go to 92

If you surrender, and you have checked 511, go to 54

If you surrender, but you haven't checked 511, go to 84

179

Plucking up your courage, you push open the door, and enter the building. From outside, it looked just like any office building in any city anywhere, but you soon see the difference inside. The foyer is large, and brightly lit. Surveillance cameras look down from every angle. There is a large reception desk, manned by efficient young women in uniform. Beyond them, the back of the foyer is blocked off by a high, transparent wall. The wall is pierced by several narrow gates, at which armed security guards check IDs, belongings and scan for concealed weapons or other contraband. This foyer, then, is as far as you get without them performing the first checks on your background. You see senior army officers, visiting businessmen and a queue of people much like yourself (looking for work), all being processed in the same fashion.

On the other side of the foyer from the reception desk, thirty or forty bored and unhappy people are sitting on plain chairs. Most have filled-in job applications in their hands.

A security guard walks up to you. "Report to reception," he barks. "Are all those people waiting to see if they can get work here?" you ask. He turns his head to look at them, and his face contorts into a superior sneer. He looks back at you with the same expression. "No-hopers. You need to be something special to get a job here. Report to reception. Have your ID ready."

If you don't have any ID, or don't want to show what you do have, go to 247

If you go to the reception desk, go to 208

If you leave the IRS building and go back towards the main highway, go to 99

180

It's not a bad wound, and – as you allow the Force to turn its power on the burned flesh – you can feel the worst of the pain subsiding. All the same, it would make sense to get some rest before you go racing around anywhere else.

Your attacker has disappeared. You can't be sure if you hit him or not. However, you know you can't stay here. Already it has been several minutes since the fight, and the noise must have alarmed the people on the street outside. A security patrol could be here any minute! You stumble out through the door. As you suspected, there are several people with frightened faces watching in your direction. They pull well clear as you run past, clutching your injured arm. You know they will report you if you try to get any treatment for that wound, so you'll have to settle for what you can manage to do yourself.

Breathing hard, you run along a few side streets, trying to confuse anyone following you. You can hear a siren in the distance. Fortunately, no-one seems to be heading in your direction, and you realise you are close to the Shuttle stop that will take you back to the spaceport district.

Wrapping some clean cloth about your wound, you head for the

Shuttle.

You have spent 2 Jedi Power Points treating your injury. Even so, you must reduce your Strength by 1 point.

Go to 199

181

There's no way you want to get involved in a battle with Boba Fett! You jump across the room, pushing aside the various humans and other creatures blocking your path. Behind, you hear chaotic shouts and curses, and several of the patrons of Al's cantina start following you. But you can't hear Fett. Perhaps, you think, he's going to let you escape?

And that's the last thing you ever think!

You can't outrun a blaster rifle, Havet! Time to start again.

182

It doesn't take you long to find Riverside, a smart street beside a dried up water-course on the south side of the highway. 182 proves to be a vid-palace; later today it will be showing some ancient horror vid. There are heavy chains on the doors, but a small side access is open. You enter cautiously, pausing to allow your eyes to get used to the darkness. The door opens directly into an auditorium, a small room with 50 seats facing the screen. The other doors are all locked. You take a seat at the end of an aisle, and notice that the auto-usher light is on. You drop a credit in the slot and select your order. "I don't mind popcorn," you call out, "but it tastes a lot better with a movie in front of it."

The screen comes to life. A voice introduces a short vid of Imperial terror-tactics. It then shows a blurred view of the Imperial Research Station. "In here, the Empire is developing more advanced terror weaponry." The film ends. A voice comes over the speakers. "We need volunteers to join the Rebel Alliance. We can offer you a chance to fight for your freedom. All we ask in return is that you get close to Facet Anamor, daughter of the Head of Research, and find out what she knows." A picture of a pretty blonde girl appears on the screen.

Check 616

If you have checked 525, go to 166

If you have checked 553 or 554, go to 197

If not, go to 211

183

Gritting your teeth against the pain, and aware of the speeder bikes roaring towards you, you reach deep into the strength of the Force, drawing on it to fight the injury to your ankle. The scouts bring their bikes in close, unsure of what you are doing, and one dismounts, ready to take you prisoner. Finally, you feel the pain subside in your foot, and you get ready to resist.

You have spent 1 Jedi Power Point to reduce the pain of your injury

If you fight, read 537, then use the combat rules from the beginning of the book. Remember this paragraph number so you can find your way back here

If you win the combat, go to 146

If you lose the battle, go to 92

If you surrender, and you have checked 511, go to 54

If you surrender, but you haven't checked 511, go to 84

184

This has stopped being fun… The crowd in the cantina push closer, warily eying the lightsabre, but determined to take you down. "Listen," you say, trying to place your back against a wall, "I'm no Jedi. I found it. I don't know how to use it or anything!"

"Then just hand it over!" snarls a lizard-faced creature with a rasping voice. Other voices offer their agreement. The crowd has pressed in so close now that you don't have room to fight back, even if you wanted to. Reluctantly, you snap off the activator, and the blade falls silent. The lizard-faced creature snakes out an arm, and snatches the lightsabre from your grasp. There is an immediate tidal wave of shouted demands, as all the patrons in the cantina start squabbling over the lightsabre. You are pushed to one side; of no consequence any more.

Losing the lightsabre is like losing an arm, but there is nothing you can do about it now. Stumbling away from the increasing tumult, you head towards the door.

Remove the lightsabre from your Equipment Box

Go to 34

185

You watch with a terrible fascination as the small fat man backs away from the mysterious shadow. He pleads for mercy: "I haven't done anything!" and then a hard voice, a woman's voice, replies: "You thought you could betray the Empire, Ta'al Pierc. You were wrong."

The man's eyes open wider, and he suddenly catches sight of you. "Please!" he cries, hands reaching out, begging for help. "She's going to kill me!!" But it's too late to do anything for Ta'al Pierc. You hear the soft cough of a heavily damped blaster, and the terrible sound of its impact. Pierc is thrown to the ground. Now there's just you and the shadow under the fire escape, the shadow who knows you witnessed everything thanks to Pierc's fearful scream.

Check 569

If you stay to face it out, go to 217

If you draw your blaster, go to 229

If you try to flee before she turns her attention to you, go to 307

186

Diamond shifts her weight slightly, and beckons you forward. "Don't be shy, Havet. I just want to see if you still have the bracelet I gave you." You pull back your sleeve and show her the device. "Good," she says. "Now, let me repeat the instructions I gave you – a luxury I rarely indulge in. Find the rebels. Do whatever it takes to be accepted into their 'Alliance'. Find Vermilion. And, when you've found him, press the transmitter. Is that understood?"

You nod. Off in the distance, you hear an engine cough into life.

Diamond hears it too. "I think that's all for now, Havet. Don't let what you've seen today prey on your mind. Do the job the way I told you to, and we'll all be much better off."

The engine revs, and comes closer.

Go to 300

187

It feels like the longest twenty or twenty-five metres of your life. You're sure that, at any moment, the assassin in the alleyway could step out and cut you down. You run to the front door, fear strangling your breath. No shot comes.

To your complete relief and surprise, you enter the main door of Al the Alchemist's.

Check 568

Go to 216

188

"Yes," you whisper, after a lengthy delay. "I'm a member of the Alliance." Diamond almost claps her hands with delight. You sigh inwardly; it always pays to keep a psychopath happy. "That's wonderful," she says, with an odd chime to her voice. "In that case, we can do business. Put this on."

She reaches into her tunic, and pulls out a decorative bracelet, set with semi-precious stones. You'd like to make a joke about never accepting gifts from strangers, but you don't. Instead, you fasten the bracelet around your wrist. It snaps shut, and you feel a warm tingle in your flesh. "That's an explosive cuff," she explains "It has a timer, and a remote detonator. If you misbehave, I'll turn you into a supernova. Understand?" You tug at the cuff, but it isn't going to come off your wrist. It doesn't take a wise man to guess that, if you try to cut it off, it explodes anyway. "It also has a built-in transmitter. To send for me, press the white stone. Go now, and find Vermilion. It shouldn't be too hard for someone inside the Alliance to track him down. When you find him, press the white stone, and I'll come and collect him. OK?"

Your choices seem pretty limited. Off in the distance, you hear an engine cough into life. Diamond hears it too. "Do we have a deal?" she presses. "If I help you, you'll take off the bracelet?" you ask. "You won't have to worry about it," Diamond insists.

The engine revs, and comes closer. "OK!" you mutter. "I'll do it." What choice do you have? "Good boy," she says, pouting like a big sister who has just made you agree to do all the chores (you never had one, but you've seen the type!).

Check 552

Go to 300

189

It looks like the guy will survive. You've hit him high up on the arm, near the shoulder. It's an ugly wound, but not a killing one. You slip his blaster into your pocket, and frisk him for ID. You find his card, which says that he is Vermilion, a merchant. Yeah, right.

You leave Vermilion on the floor, sprawled against the wall, moaning heavily. Without a backward glance, you go out to lose yourself in the crowd.

Check 547

If you look for the Shuttle, and head back to the Spaceport District, go to 199

If you head back to the heart of the Commercial District, go to 169

190

Checking to make sure no-one is watching (who knows what this guy is up to), you walk over. "New in town, son?" he asks. "Could be," you reply. "Then it could be I can help you," he replies, with a broad grin. He opens his coat, and you see he has several blank ID cards fastened to the linings. "Need any help with your ID?" Genuine Toprawan ID cards! Just what you need!

He picks up on your interest. You didn't reply – after all, he could be an Imperial agent – but your body-language must have tipped him off. "I understand," he says. "You don't want to talk about it. That's OK, but I can provide you with one of two answers to your problems. There's the expensive way, which gets you a new ID, but which can't be expected to last for ever. Then there's the cheap way, which solves your problems permanently."

That doesn't make sense. The second-rate choice is expensive; the best choice is cheap? Crazy. The dark-haired man, folds his arms over his chest, and waits for you to make up his mind.

Check 521

If you want to buy a new ID, go to 201

If you check out his second option, go to 221

If you've had enough of Toprawa City, go to 199

191

This is no time to be brave. You slip your blaster into the concealed holster under your arm, and leave your coat unbuckled. The gun feels heavy against your side, but kind of reassuring.

Check 507

If you also want to carry your lightsabre, go to 202

If you're ready to enter the cantina, go to 216

192

Even though it hurts like crazy, it's not a bad wound. Your attacker has disappeared. You're not sure if you hit him or not, but if he was going to finish you off, he would have done so by now. You collapse through the door. Alarmed citizens run away, calling for the police. Your head is swimming. Moments later, the street rushes up to meet you, and you hit the pavement hard. The light disappears; blackness closes in.

You have no sensation of time passing. In the same moment as you kissed the pavement, you wake up in a hospital. You're alive. The relief is enormous, but short-lived. At your side there is an enormous man, swathed in black, his face grotesquely framed by a grim, black helmet. His breath rasps like waves on a stony beach. He has something in his hand which he slaps into the other palm like a baton. A jewel winks at you in the overhead lights. It's your lightsabre.

So, your secret is out. The black-clad man is Darth Vader. His voice is like the end of the world. "Havet Storm," he says, turning the lightsabre over in his huge, gloved hand. "Would you like to tell me where you got this?"

Ooops. That just about wraps up your adventure. Perhaps you could give it another try?

193

Increasingly desperate, you decide the only way to get off the street is to blast the door. You shield your face as you squeeze the trigger. There is a loud report, and a black cloud of choking smoke. You move as if to step inside, but run head-first into the barrel of a blaster rifle. Choking, and half-blinded with shock, an armoured man staggers out from the doorway.

If you have checked 516, go to 223

If not, go to 205

194

It's a short, ugly brawl, but you're amongst those standing at the end. The Wookiee is close by. The monkey-humanoid has been killed, and the tall hammerheaded alien – an Ithorian – is wounded. There's no sign of the human who joined the fight on your side, nor of Boba Fett. Al rushes up, wailing about the damage, and moaning that three of the creatures you defeated hadn't paid their bills. "You'd better get out of here!" he shouts. "When word gets round about that toy you've found, everyone and his droid will try to take it from you!"

Al's right. You need to make tracks. But can you really ignore the wounded Ithorian?

If you leave immediately, go to 34

If you help the wounded Ithorian, go to 207

195

There is only one way to achieve what you want. Vermilion mustn't walk away with the knowledge he has gained. The fact clutches coldly at your heart, guiding your hand even though your eyes are closed.

The lightsabre strikes… In the moment of horror that follows, as you realise what you have done. The lightsabre drops to the ground. Its powerful beam snaps off, and all is silent. You reach out into the Force, looking for the strength to move your leaden limbs, but there is only a cold and sinister darkness.

To act as you have just done is to let the dark side into your soul. The Force only serves those who do not corrupt its power for selfish and murderous ends.

If you wish to start the adventure again, go back to 1

196

Boba Fett has a short start on you, but you have the means to change that. You run across to the nearby building where you stashed the speeder bike. Throwing off the cover, you leap into the saddle and gun the engine.

Market Street is easy to find – it's a busy road in Toprawa City, parallel to the main highway. No checkpoint blocks the way, and no-one can intercept a speeder bike with its throttle wide open. In fact, you even beat Boba Fett to Facet's address! OK. Now what are you going to do?

If you ambush Boba Fett, go to 213

If you go to Facet's apartment, go to 230

197

You interrupt the instructions, waving the metallic badge Facet gave you, proof of your employment at the IRS. There's a brief pause, then the voice continues: "I underestimated you, Havet. Very clever. The Alliance can really use your help." You're more than ready! "You know Al's cantina, near the spaceport? Hang around there as often as you can. Scarlett will meet you there." The speaker goes dead, and the house lights come on. You know a signal to leave when you see one. And you know exactly where you should go next.

If you go directly to the cantina as instructed, go to 216

If you check out the area around the cantina first, go to 99

Diamond shifts her weight, reaches into her tunic, and pulls out a decorative bracelet, set with semi-precious stones. She tosses it over. "It's an explosive cuff," she announces. "Put it on." You hesitate, and she gestures with her blaster. You close it on your wrist. "You've made a lot of trouble, Havet, now it's time to pay the price. If you cause me any more problems, I'll turn you into a super-nova. Understand?" You tug at the cuff, but it isn't going to come off your wrist. It doesn't take a wise man to guess that, if you try to cut it off, it explodes anyway.

"If you want to be rid of it, you have to do me a favour first. There is a small group of rebels on Toprawa. Their leader is Vermilion – a renegade who affects a blood-red turban. Vermilion is hatching a plot. It has something to do with the information Ta'al Pierc stole. Vermilion spent some time off-world, getting instructions from the Rebel Alliance; now he's back. Find him. The cuff has a built-in transmitter. Press the white stone, and I'll be with you in minutes."

You understand perfectly. "Good," remarks Diamond. Off in the distance, you hear an engine cough into life. Diamond hears it too. "Don't let me down." she says. "If I help you, you'll take off the bracelet?" you ask. "You won't have to worry about it," Diamond insists.

The engine revs, and comes closer.

Check 552

Go to 300

All things considered, you've had enough of Toprawa City for a while. There's no work, nowhere to stay and little scope for earning any credits. You'd be better off back at the spaceport; you won't stand out so obviously, and there might be casual work with a trader, or someone hauling supplies out to the port which would provide you with some immediate finance. It's too far to walk, so you take the Shuttle which runs back and forth between the commercial district and the port. A little warm sunlight shines through the window as you take your seat, and soon you are feeling drowsy, the long and fruitless day having finally caught up with you. Just as you are falling asleep, your Force-tuned instincts jolt you into full wakefulness. The Shuttle is pulling up at a road block! Craning your neck to

see through the windshield, you catch sight of several military types
with blasters and batons, flagging down the Shuttle.

If you stay in your seat, go to 225

If you leap off the Shuttle, go to 8

200

You look past the BlasTech EE-3 pointed right between your eyes,
into the face-mask of its owner. "Across the street!" you blurt out.
"A woman just killed a guy! She knows I saw it!" He looks out
through the ruined doorway. You get to your knees, but stop there as
he jerks the rifle in your face. "Looks like you're telling the truth,"
he says. "There is someone in the alley. So that's two people you've
managed to annoy in one day." Two? You look up into the man's
visor, trying to see his eyes, but all you can make out is the faint
reflection of your own face.

"Do you know who I am?" he asks. You shake your head. "My name
is Boba Fett," he continues, his final explanation. "You have two
choices. You can either go out there and face your friend in the alley.
Or you can stay and face me." Those are choices?

If you go back out onto the street, go to 212

If you'd prefer to deal with Boba Fett, go to 228

201

You're in no mood to play mind-games. "Look, I could use some
clean ID," you whisper, low enough so that not even a microphone
could hear. "But I've only got thirty credits; how can I afford one?"
The dark-haired man looks disappointed, but still gives you a big,
dopey grin. "No problem. My name's Carmine. I can arrange credit.
You get new ID, you get a job, you pay us back. After all, if you
welch on us, we can turn you into the authorities just like that."

He has a point. You follow him to a building a short distance away.
At the door, he grins into the surveillance camera above the entrance.
"Used to be a bank," he explains.

It takes three hours to make up a new card. A young slicer wakes up
a "sleeper" on the main Imperial database, and gives it your name.
"You're still Havet Storm," Carmine explains, "All we've done is

change the access point on the database; if anyone checks your ID, they'll find a clean, law-abiding record. They'd physically have to put the old records side-by-side with the new to realise it was the same person. Neat, huh?"

"First payment in a month, Havet," says Carmine, showing you to the door. "Don't be late. If you have a problem, call this number." He hands you a business card with a comlink number on it. "You advertise?" you ask, unable to believe it. "Just because you have the number, Havet, doesn't mean you know where I am." He lets you out of the bank.

Check 517 & 530

If you go back to the Commercial District, go to 227

If you catch the Shuttle back towards the port area, go to 199

202

You slip the thong of your lightsabre onto your belt. Under your coat, it is small and unobtrusive, but each time it slaps against your hip, you are reminded of its significance.

Check 508

If you also want to carry your blaster, go to 191

If you're ready to enter the cantina, go to 216

203

Along with several hundred other people who have spilled out onto the streets, you gape upwards at the space battle. Most of the time, all you can see are distant pulses of bright light, but a few ships venture lower into the atmosphere, and you watch tiny fighters swarming over larger Imperial vessels. The fighters are having a hard time of it, but they are gradually overwhelming the Imperial Corvettes. One of the larger Imperial vessels starts breaking up almost overhead, and escape pods and shuttles leap from its bays.

Fighters hunt down the shuttles one-by-one. The last, swinging low over the City, makes a run for the spaceport (from where ground-based fire is arcing upwards), but is hit and starts falling – directly towards you! Screaming citizens scatter, and you find yourself being dragged away by a large man with a powerful grip. Moments later the shuttle crashes into a building immediately adjacent to the cantina, and goes up in flames. By the time you lift your head, the battle has moved on. Al's place is burning furiously. You look around to see who saved your skin, but there's no-one there. Boba Fett has disappeared too. You've no idea what the battle was all about, but it did you a favour!

Check 580

Go to 99

204

Having seen what she does to people she thinks are members of the Rebel Alliance, you decide that Diamond wouldn't want to hear so say that you are, no matter what the truth is. Off in the distance, you hear an engine cough into life. Diamond hears it too. "That's a great pity," she sighs. "It means you are of no value to me, and yet I still have this problem of you being a witness to Pierc's accident."

The engine revs, and comes closer. "Goodbye," says Diamond, levelling the blaster at you.

To fight this combat, read 571, then use the combat rules from the beginning of the book. Remember this paragraph number so you can find your way back

If you win the battle, go to 250

If you lose, go to 236

205

You recognise the guy at once. His name is Boba Fett, the most notorious Bounty Hunter in the galaxy. And you just blew a door down on him. You blurt out the only excuse you can think of. "That woman in the alley! She's trying to kill you!!" Fett drags you through the doorway, then takes a cautious look outside. He must have caught a glimpse of the woman, because he ducks back, and readies his weapon. "If you're lying, kid, I'll find you and kill you. For now, beat it!"

Good idea. You pass quickly through the cantina, ignoring the angry questions of the other customers. As you head for the exit, you look back at the side door. Fett is checking his blaster rifle. For now, he has forgotten you. Next time, you can't expect to be so lucky.

Check 516

Go to 34

206

Despite your best efforts, you cannot hold off the mob in the cantina. You are dragged down, and fell your grip shaken loose from the lightsabre. Moments later, all is blackness.

Perhaps you should try again. Go to 1

207

The Ithorian did you a favour. You can't just leave him to die. Reaching out with the Force, you quell the pain raging in side him, and accelerate his body's natural defences, so that the healing process may begin. After a few moments, his breathing becomes more regular. The Wookiee growls appreciatively. You also realise that the human ally you had during the fight has reappeared. His grubby coat swishes against the floor as he walks over, tying a blood-red scarf around a superficial hand wound. He looks carefully at you as you rise to your feet.

If you have checked 521, go to 237

If not, go to 262

208

You walk across to the reception area. One of the bored-looking women behind the desks smiles a welcome, but it fades pretty quickly when she realises that you're not a high-ranking officer, or a rich merchant. "Can I help you?" she asks.

If you have checked 541, go to 220

If you have checked 550, go to 317

If you have checked 553 or 544, go to 222

If you want to ask about a job at the IRS, go to 232

209

The Imperial Officer slumps to the floor. You managed to defeat him quickly – there's no alarm from the Imperial Research Station. Leaping into his landspeeder, you set off after Boba Fett.

If you have already ticked one box on your Time Track, tick another

Check 586

Go to 226

210

You take off down the street, hoping you can put some distance between yourself and the killer. The area ahead seems to be filled with abandoned factories, and there aren't many people about. You think about turning back, but a glimpse of the dark-haired woman working her way along the street behind you changes your mind. Trouble is, she knows this city, and you don't. She's herding you towards your death, Havet. There doesn't seem to be much you can do about it.

If you have checked 526, go to 240

If you haven't checked 526, go to 279

211

"How do I find Facet Anamor?" you call out. "She's also in charge of Personnel at the Station; if you get a job there, you'll meet her. She also likes to shop in the City, or to sit in cafes drinking fruit juice and chatting. Perhaps you could use your 'charm'." The hidden voice uses a lot of sarcasm on the word 'charm'. From where you sit, the owner could use a few lessons himself.

You hear a faint click. The sound system has been turned off. Looks like it time to go. You hit the auto-usher for a refund, but nothing happens. "Some Rebellion," you shout, "stealing Credits one at a time!" No-one answers.

So, Havet, are you going to go along with this slightly seedy plan? What was the idea again? Get close to Facet Anamor and then trick her? Not very honourable work, is it?

If you go off to catch the Shuttle into Toprawa City, go to 72

If you go back towards the spaceport, go to 99

212

Caught between a rock and a hard place, you decide you'd better go back out into the street. Boba Fett strikes you as the kind of mindless killer you can't talk out of violence. Maybe, just maybe, you'll stand a better chance with the woman in the alley?

That hope lasts about 2 seconds, all it takes for her to appear from the alley and aim her weapon at you. Whatever you witnessed down that dark by-way, it is just about to cost you your life.

Your adventure is over. If you're ready to start again, go to 1

213

You find a place opposite the entrance to Facet's apartment building on Market Street, and get ready to ambush Boba Fett. Sure enough, after a few moments you hear his landspeeder approaching. Annoyingly, he doesn't pull up in front of 525 Market; instead he parks down the cross-street a way, sitting in the landspeeder, lights out. He has a full view of her front door. If Facet comes out, he has a clear shot at her.

If you wait for Facet to come out, check 584, then go to 264

If you open fire on Boba Fett now, read 585, then use the Combat Rules from the beginning of this book. Remember this paragraph number so you can find your way back

If you hit Fett with either of your first two shots, go to 271

If he hits you, go to 269

If you both miss, go to 283

214

You tell Facet that Boba Fett is outside, and that he was searching for her. She looks incredulous. "Do you think the Rebels have hired him to kidnap me?" she asks. You doubt it, but you say nothing. "We can slip out through the secret exit. Will you help me, Havet?" You grab her bag and throw it across your shoulder. She leads you back down the stairs, and through the kitchens. At the back of the house, a cleverly concealed door opens onto a dark alley. You slip out, and try to steer your way through the gloom.

You have gone no more than a few yards when you realise you have lost your grip on Facet's hand. You call her name, trying not to let your voice carry. Blundering around, you reach the front of the building. Where is she? You find no sign of her anywhere.

Suddenly, though, you spot of a darting shadow rushing towards you. Boba Fett! Knowing that you can't let him find Facet – and that he has every reason to kill you – you get ready to meet him once again.

If you open fire on Boba Fett now, read 585, then use the Combat Rules from the beginning of this book. Remember this paragraph number so you can find your way back

If you hit Fett with either of your first two shots, go to 271

If he hits you, go to 269

If you miss twice and he misses you, go to 283

215

"Thanks," you say gripping both ends of the bracelet and pulling. There is a huge explosion.

Havet's adventure has ended. If you'd like another try, go to 1

216

The sign above the entrance says the cantina is called Al The Alchemists'.

If you have checked 580, go to 77

Otherwise, if you have you checked 516, go to 9

If you haven't checked either of these, go to 218

Everything falls silent. You know you should run, that the killer isn't going to want to leave witnesses, but your feet are rooted to the spot. You wait, watching. The shadow finally steps out from under the fire escape.

If you have checked 514 or 552, go to 238

If not, go to 282

218

As you push open the door, you wonder just what Alchemy Al brews up in here. The smell is disgusting! You wrinkle your nose in disgust. Which proves to be a minor social error, since a tall Wookiee, who is just inside the door combing some gruesome fluid out of his fur, seems to think you were complaining about the way he smells. Perhaps you could explain?

Perhaps not. You quickly duck out of his way, and into the middle of the cantina. Al's place is typical of any watering-hole this close to a port. Creatures of every race in the Empire are pressed close – too close in some cases – celebrating old contracts and making new ones. Hustling for a buck. If you had anything to sell, this would be the place to sell it – before someone stole it from you.

It occurs to you briefly that you're much too young to be in a place like this. But it's too late now. You might as well stay now you've come this far. There's hardly enough room to swing a Katalian Ape, but you spot a small space at one end of the long counter, where one man is standing in the gloom, nursing a long glass of something. You push your way over, tripping over some octopod's legs and fall against the counter. The barman fills a tankard with something before you even order.

If you drink it, go to 231

If you ask the guy at the counter what it is, go to 94

219

"Vermilion!" you gasp. You recognised the man at once; the white coat and the turban are a dead give-away. He pulls you into the building. "You know who that is behind you, kid?" he asks, continuing without waiting for the answer. "Diamond, the Security Chief at the Imperial Research Station. Why is she after you?" You tell him about the little man she murdered in the alley. "Ta'al Pierc," whispers Vermilion, sadly. "One of our best agents. If not for him…"

You have reached a laundry room at the back of the building. Vermilion motions for you to be quiet while he opens the back door fractionally. There is an echoing blast and he is thrown back as the door is shattered. "This way!" he calls running back towards the front of the building. He turns into a corridor, and then through an open door. As you enter the room, he pushes the door closed, and throws a heavy bolt across.

He bends to lift a rug from the floor, and you see that there is a trap-door. "I had hoped to keep this secret for a while longer," he murmurs. "Still…" He lifts the trap. "Listen. Down here, there's a passage. If you turn left, you can get back out onto the street not far from Al's. If you follow me, well, you'll have see… What I can tell you is that if you come with me, you'd better be prepared to join the Rebel Alliance. We've lost enough resources already today – I'm not prepared to waste any more on you."

If you go with Vermilion, go to 239

If you head back towards the spaceport and the cantina, go to 299

220

The woman at reception looks at you scornfully as you pull the card from your pocket. She takes a look at it, and her eyebrows arch in surprise. "Oh!" she gasps, mouth wide. "I'm sorry, Mr – Mr – I, I –" You put the poor girl out of her misery. "Just tell Miss Anamor I'm here."

"Of course!" she shrills, a little too loudly (boy, have you ever spooked *her!*). She keys an internal com unit. "Could I have your ID?" You hand it over, and the girl swipes it through the slot at the side of the unit. Let's hope your ID stands up to the test.

"He's here to see Miss Facet," says the girl into the unit. "Of course, I'll tell him." She hands back your ID, but not Facet's card. "Miss Facet isn't actually in her office at the moment. However, if you proceed directly to the security point, someone will meet you." The girl smiles again – much more brightly this time – and gestures in the direction of the checkpoint.

There are four or five gates at the checkpoint, each manned by hard-faced security personnel. However, a sixth gate opens as you approach, and an officer beckons you forward. You look across at the poor devils waiting in line for their turn to be searched; several of them glance back at you, wondering how it is that some scruffy urchin gets in straight away while they –

You reach the gate. The security man takes your ID, and swipes it through another reader. You see surveillance cameras trained on you from the front and sides, building up a 360° picture of your face. More security guards scan monitors, some reading sensor output, others checking the results of the ID check. Others are lurking in the background, heavily-armed.

Remove the check on 541

If you have checked 511, go to 249

If you have checked 513 (but not 511), go to 260

If you have checked 510 (but not 511 or 510), go to 234

If you haven't checked any of these, go to 278

221

Your curiosity gets the better of you. "OK," you ask, "What's the easy option?"

"I didn't say it was easy," says the man, "I said it was cheap. Fancy a drink? I've some Star Racers in the cooler." At last – your favourite drink! "The name's Carmine." After a moment's hesitation, you tell him your name. He smiles. "Popular name, that. Havet, I mean, not Smith." Carmine leads you to a tall building a short distance away. At the door, he grins into a surveillance camera above the entrance. "This used to be a bank," he explains. According to the sign over the door, the building is now occupied by the Tenson Printing Company. You're tempted to ask "who are they?" Carmine sits you down, and pulls another chair up close. "Before we have our little chat, Havet, tell me – what do you think of the Empire?"

Oh, oh. This feels like one of those no-win questions – when you get it right it's deadly and when you get it wrong, it's fatal. Great. And he hasn't even given you the Star Racer...

If you answer "I think it's a fine institution. I love the Emperor

with all my heart, and I think Darth Vader is the right leader for our time", go to 235

If your answer is "Well – er – that is, you know, it's sort of – um – you know…", go to 329

If you answer "The Empire is vile, corrupt and run by murderers!", go to 417

222

You hand over the metallic badge Facet gave you. The young woman places it into a reader. After a few moments, she checks the readings, removes the badge and tries it again. "I'm sorry," she says. "This badge hasn't been activated yet. My records show that you're not supposed to be starting your employment for a few days yet. Why don't you call back later."

Go to 99

223

"You!!" growls Boba Fett. "Hi!" you smile brightly, "how's it going?" He looks at you as if you are mad (not far wrong there, eh Havet?), and in that moment of hesitation, you dodge past him. He must have been sitting right up close behind the side door, because there are broken chairs across the floor, and a Nalroni trader sits against the wall, nursing a bump on the head. You vault over them, and find your way over a narrow rail into an alcove at the end of the room.

Fett doesn't react. You hear him speak to the Nalroni. "We'll finish our conversation later, Karaff. Right now, I have to kill that brat." You try to find as much shelter as you can behind tables and other furniture. It seems like every eye in the place is on you. After all, it's not every day people shoot their way into a cantina, and then start building a barricade. Not *every* day.

You've escaped from one homicidal nutcase, and found yourself a substitute. What next?

If you use your lightsabre to hack through the wall behind you, go to 75

If you draw your blaster, go to 90

If you use Arf to set up a decoy, go to 103

You cross towards the vacant seat. The blonde girl pushes absently at the salad until you approach. She glances at her chronograph occasionally. It looks like she's been waiting for someone. "Hi!" Not your most original opening, but it will have to do. "Anyone sitting here?" She makes a big show of looking over the table at the empty seat. "Not that I can see," she replies. You start to explain what you really meant, but she laughs and tells you to sit down.

She's very pretty (lovely deep blue eyes!), a year or two older than you, and she has a great sense of humour. It turns out she has been waiting to have lunch with a guy she works with. This guy doesn't sound too much like competition – it comes up in conversation that he's a small fat guy in the Records Department – and he can't be too bright to miss a date with a girl like this.

You eat your meal together, and chat about nothing in particular. "My name's Facet," she tells you after a while. "I work in the Personnel Department at the Imperial Research Station. What do you do?"

Check 515. Read 539. Remember to come back here after

If you tell her that you are looking for work, go to 327

If you tell her a lie, go to 338

If you change the subject, go to 350

You sit tight. Moments later, the shuttle pulls up at the checkpoint, and three unpleasant-looking security guards get on. Looking out the window, you can see stormtroopers mixed with the security guards, and scouts mounted on Aratech speeder bikes. Escape isn't an option.

The guards start checking IDs. "What's this all about, Officer?" asks a businessman (rather him than you!). "Trouble at the spaceport." mutters the guard. The businessman groans – he's probably late for his flight already. "I'd have thought," he continues, an air of superiority in his voice, "you'd be checking people *leaving* the port." The guard stiffens, then leans forward to grasp the man's shirt. "I'd have thought you should keep your fat mouth shut!" he hisses. The businessman slumps back in his seat, and doesn't utter another word. Very wise too.

Moments later, the same guard is right in front of you. "ID, kid," he snaps.

Find the number you have checked beside your ID in your Equipment Box.

If the check number is 517, go to 52

If the check number is 520, and you have also checked 511, go to 40

If the check number is 520, and you have also checked 510, go to 27

If the check number is 520, but you haven't checked either 510 or 511, go to 65

If you have no ID (or you want to pretend you haven't), go to 15

226

You arrive at Facet's apartment on Market Street. There's no sign of Boba Fett, although you can see a landspeeder which looks like his parked a short distance away along a cross-street. Acutely aware that he could be anywhere, watching, you park immediately outside Facet's door, and try to keep low behind the landspeeder as you reach for the entry-phone.

Check 584

Go to 248

227

The evening is drawing in as you head back into the Commercial District. Office workers are making their way to the suburban shuttles and the Rapid Transit stations. A few beggars and street traders hustle them for credits, keeping a wary eye out for the police. Things must be bad on Toprawa if there can be this many poor people in its capital city!

You realise you are wasting your time here. If you're going to find a decent place to rest your head, you'll do better out towards the spaceport, where life is less expensive, and there is more chance of finding someone hiring off-world labour. So, you head back to the shuttle pick-up bay. There's a long queue of commuters, and you notice that cafe over on the corner is still open. You could maybe kill 30 minutes in there, and have a much more comfortable ride home. Or maybe you should just get going?

If you want to catch the Shuttle immediately, go to 199

If you visit the cafe, go to 340

228

"I can't go back out there," you explain. Fett finds this almost funny. "You're more afraid of her than you are of me? This is worth looking into." Fett reaches over and searches you with his free hand. "Just so you don't get the idea to shoot me in the back." He pushes you away from the door. "I don't expect to ever see you again, kid. If I do, you'll be sorry." That's for sure.

Fett grabs hold of the Nalroni trader he was talking to. "You go first, Karaff. Let's see who we're dealing with over there." They step outside. You don't even want to look. Instead, you make your way past the stunned customers in the cantina, and head for the front door.

Check 516

Go to 34

229

There's a cold slick of fear on your skin as you fumble to draw your blaster. The shadow under the fire escape barely seems to move, but you never manage to complete the action. The silenced blaster coughs again, and you feel a burning shock in your hand as you are hit.

The blaster falls to the floor somewhere. Through the pain, you force yourself to start running. You've more than met your match this time, Havet! Run for your life!

Remove the blaster from your Equipment.

You have been wounded. You must either spend 2 Jedi Power Points to start the process of healing your hand, or reduce your Blaster Skill and Lightsabre Skill by one until you can get proper medical attention.

Go to 102

230

It's time for you to meet Facet. You can put your charm and good looks to work.

Finding 525 Market Street is no bother; Market Street runs parallel to the main road out to the spaceport, just a block north. It's a fairly posh looking apartment building, by the look of it. In your tired old clothing, you feel distinctly out of place. There's an entry-phone by the door. It doesn't have a list of names, just one button. Does Facet own the whole place? You press the button, and an electronic voice sounds from the speaker.

Have you checked 572? If you have, go to 248

If not, go to 310

231

You take a cautious sip. The drink smells like an animal which died of something terrible, and it smells better than it tastes. "Yeccch!" you retch. "That's terrible!" You turn to the guy at the end of the bar for confirmation. "Don't you think this stuff is terrible?" He doesn't move. "Actually," he replies, "I think it's a fine drink. Won't you take another, and toast the Empire with me?"

"I don't think so!" you reply assertively (the guy must be a nut to drink any more). "You won't drink to the Empire?" he asks, glowering at you; or, at least, coming as close to a glower as you can wearing a full-face helmet. "Or you won't drink with me?" Oh, oh. Isn't this conversation heading in a rather negative direction all of a sudden? "Actually –" you start, but he interrupts immediately. "Are you saying that you won't drink to the Empire with me… with Boba Fett?"

Check 516

If you reply: "Yes sir, sorry sir", go to 123

If you answer: "You're not Boba Fett; he's much uglier than you", go to 129

If you choose "Sorry, never heard of you. Perhaps I'll remember you from now on", go to 17

232

"I've come about some work," you tell the woman behind the desk. Her well-trained smile droops a little; she's heard the same thing before. She pulls a folder from a drawer. "Read this," she orders. "When you're called, go to the checkpoint. Fill out the forms while you're waiting"

Forms? On paper? This kind of thing is ancient history, the kind of nonsense they got up to before the Old Republic! It dawns on you quickly that this process isn't designed to match anyone with jobs, but to make things as tedious and pointless as possible, so that most applicants will just give up and go away. You, of course, are made of sterner stuff.

Which is why, several hours later, you're still sitting in the most uncomfortable chair science could devise. No-one has paid you the slightest attention. The daytime shift at Reception has gone home, leaving the place crewed by non-sentient beings from beyond the grave. A guard wanders over. "OK. That's it for today. Off you go." He waves his weapon vaguely to prove he means it. "But we haven't seen anyone!" says an unwise man along from you. "You've seen me, haven't you?" grins the guard. "So, come back tomorrow, and see who else you can see."

Moments later, you're out on the street, as bone-weary as if you had run twice round the planet.

If you search out a hostel and get some sleep, go to 50

If you want to keep looking around, go to 99

233

You cannon off the man in the doorway, and rush into the building. There had better be a back way out! It takes you several attempts to find the right passageway, and then you rush through the laundry and open the back door... You never see the shot that finishes your adventure on Toprawa. There is just a brief moment when you realise that the killer out-thought and out-ran you. Then oblivion.

Better luck next time. To start again, return to paragraph 1

An urgent chime sounds on one of the monitors. The guards stiffen with tension, turning their blaster rifles in your direction. One of them reads the information off the screen. "Mr Storm's ID has a Code 510 tag, sir. Security Infringement at the spaceport. Report filed by Corporal Kiell, Port Security Detachment. Cross-reference shows no follow-up report; Corporal Kiell relieved of duty." The officer takes a hard look into your eyes. "Caught trying to bring something illegal onto Toprawa, Mr Storm?" he asks. "We all do it. Wipe that record, Trooper. Miss Facet wouldn't want her guest bothered by every patrol on the planet over a customs offence."

You thank the officer, and watch as the blemish at the spaceport vanishes from your file. Thank heavens for friends in high places! "You must leave all weapons with us, sir," the officer continues. "Also, that…" He's pointing at the cavernous pocket where you store Arf. You pull the droid out; better you leave him here than let them do a thorough strip-down search on him…

Remove the check on 510

Read 549

If you have checked 508, go to 280

Otherwise, go to 297

You're not at all comfortable with Carmine's question, but you decide this isn't the time to take chances. Your answer is a very respectful one, praising the Empire and it's leaders. Carmine's face is completely impassive. "A fine, proper answer," he says at last. "I'm sure we all appreciate what the Emperor is prepared to do for us. No sacrifice too great, eh?"

He makes a big show of looking at his chrono. "Actually, I have a pressing appointment. Could we have this chat later? I know you'll understand." Seconds later, you're back on the street, like he couldn't get rid of you soon enough. What a strange guy! What a time-waster!

If you give up on the City, and grab the Shuttle back out to the port, go to 199

If you want to look round the Commercial District some more, go to 227

236

You didn't stand much of a chance against Diamond. In no time at all, she has swatted you like a fly. You feel your strength ebbing away. She steps over your broken body. "Such a waste," she sighs. "If you had your time again, wouldn't you have played our little game my way?"

Would you? Right now, you'd give a lot to find out…

Your adventure is over. Start again from paragraph 1, and try to keep out of Diamond's hair this time…

237

"Havet!" the man grins. "Fancy seeing you again!" You look him over. That ugly coat and the scarf should have tipped you off at once. "Carmine."

"In the flesh!" he beams. "And I see you didn't tell me everything about yourself when you we met before." He takes a closer look at the wounded Ithorian. "It's been a long time since I heard of anything like that. You saved his life!" You try to tell him that the Ithorian did you a favour, and that you just needed to repay it. "Don't be modest, Havet. I know what you are. That lightsabre… the way you saved this man's life. You're a Jedi, aren't you?"

Great! The secret is out. The way Carmine likes to talk, it'll be all over Toprawa by morning. "So?" you challenge him. "So, why don't we have a talk about it?" OK, you're prepared to listen. "No, not now. I have to help our friend here get to a doctor, and you need to disappear from here before the police arrive. Go to 182 Riverside. It's an old vid-theatre. We'll talk there."

Carmine picks up the wounded Ithorian with the Wookiee's help. "See you soon!" he beams.

If you slip out the side door and head for the address he gave

you, go to 182

If you want to keep out of Carmine's nutty schemes, go to 34

238

Seconds later, you are face-to-face with the killer. Her close-cut black hair frames an emotionless face. You find yourself unable to look away from her strange, colourless eyes. There can be no mistake – the murderer is Diamond, the Head of Security at the IRS. "Fancy seeing you here, Havet," she says, and then adds with as much sincerity as a Gallian cobra: "Such a coincidence. I wonder how many more times we'll be brought together like this?"

If you have checked 552 in your Data Bank, go to 337

If not, go to 318

239

You agree to go along with Vermilion. Scrambling through some rubble-strewn alleyways and through a few doors in and out of buildings, you reach a narrow side-street, somewhere off the spaceport highway. Vermilion stops, and points along a wider street which follows a dried-up river course. "That's Riverside. You want 182, on the east side. You can't miss it." Vermilion straightens his turban and brushes dirt from his immaculate white coat. "Aren't you coming?" you ask. "It's better if we separate here, Havet. I'll see you again later."

Vermilion takes a last look around, then scoots off around a building and out of sight. What a weird guy he is. If he's any indication, are the Toprawan Rebels people you really want to get mixed up with?

If you search out 182 Riverside, go to 182

If you go back the way you came, go to 99

240

The killer has nearly all the advantages; she knows the area, and she seems very experienced at tracking down her quarry. However, you have one advantage she can't match.

You sprint into the abandoned factory where you left the speeder bike. Thank the stars – it's still here! Pulling off the cover, you leap into the saddle and fire it up. Within seconds, you're blasting back out onto the street. The killer leaps out of your way, then fires a few shots at your rapidly retreating form. One of them hits the bike, and it starts leaking coolant. Looks like this is your last ride – but at least you'll be alive at the end of it!

Remove 526

If you stay close to the spaceport, go to 99

If you head into the City, go to 72

241-243

The code is an advanced version of Q2800, heavily seeded with personalised short-cuts and password requests. It looks like the program is for testing the effects of a massive power surge through some kind of resistance package; a kind of building-sized spike protector. It isn't like anything you've ever seen before. You struggle for about 30 minutes, then Facet leans over and shuts the monitor off. "Never mind, perhaps a data entry job would be the best thing after all."

She sounds disappointed. Did she think you were some kind of computer hot-shot? Well, no matter, you've got a job. Facet taps some details into a machine, and out pops one of those green metallic badges. "Take this," she says. "It won't be active for a few days, while we do some background checking on you." Oh, oh! "Just to make sure you've never been in any trouble with the authorities." Whew! Is that all...

"Call back, after Ninthday. Show that at Reception; they'll tell you what to do next." You take the badge, and slip it into a pocket. "OK," smiles Facet, brightly, but still showing a tinge of disappointment. "Is that it, or is there anything else I can do for you?"

Add the green badge to your equipment, and check 553

If you want to ask Facet for a date, go to 33

If you're ready to leave, go to 47

244-245

The code is an advanced version of Q2800, heavily seeded with personalised short-cuts and password requests. The program is for testing the effects of a massive power surge through a power suppression system; the kind of thing you'd get if you had a blow-back from some kind of particle beam or energy weapon. The energy they're talking about is huge!

It takes 20 minutes, but you find the error. There's a feedback loop, which would slowly exaggerate the effect of a particular piece of control equipment. At first, the test results would be pretty accurate; then they would slowly corrupt the data, making it appear that the control systems were having a greater effect that would really be the case. You point the error out to Facet, and suggest a correction. She seems quite impressed, though you're not sure how much she understands. "I'll pass that on," she says.

From where you sit, the Empire owes you one. Facet turns to a second machine, and taps in some details. Out pops a blue metallic badge, similar to the green one you're wearing. "OK," she says. "You're hired. This won't be active for a few days, while we do some background checking on you. Call back, after Ninthday. Show that at Reception; they'll tell you what to do next." You take the badge, and slip it into a pocket. Facet smiles. "Welcome to the Imperial Research Station. Is there anything else I can do for you?"

Add the blue badge to your equipment, and check 554

If you want to ask Facet for a date, go to 33

If you're ready to leave, go to 47

246

The code is written in Q2800. Simple. The program tests the effects of a massive power surge through a suppression system; the kind of thing you'd get if you had a blow-back from some kind of particle beam or energy weapon. The energy they're talking about is huge!

It takes 10 minutes to find the error. There's a feedback loop, exaggerating the effect of control equipment. At first, the test results would be accurate; but they would slowly degenerate, making it appear that the control systems were more effective than they really were. The 'error' must have been built in deliberately. Sabotage! You also see a password bypass patched onto the code. You point out the error to Facet, and suggest a correction, but you don't voice your suspicions about the sabotage. She seems quite impressed. "I'll pass that on," she says.

From where you sit, the Empire owes you one, and – if they don't pay you back – you now know how to break through the access passwords on their computer system. Hmmm. You'll have to think about how you're going to use that information. While you consider your options, Facet turns to a second machine, and taps in some commands on its keyboard. Out pops a blue metallic badge, similar to the green one you're wearing. "OK," she says. "You're hired. This won't be active for a few days, while we do some background checks. Call back, after Ninthday. Show that at Reception; they'll tell you what to do." You take the badge, and slip it into a pocket. Facet smiles. "Welcome to the IRS. Is there anything else I can do for you?"

Add the blue badge to your equipment, and check 554

Also check 555

If you want to ask Facet for a date, go to 33

If you're ready to leave, go to 47

247

The security guard looks at you suspiciously. "You do have your ID, don't you?" he asks. "Um –" you reply. The guard grabs your arm and leads you towards the end of the foyer. Elbowing aside a few of the people in the line at the gate, he calls to the officer. "Staff," he says. "You won't believe me, but this moron has come *here* without any ID."

The Officer looks at you as if you were growing wings in front of his eyes. "Another one? Are all Toprawans completely thick?" One of the more dignified members of the queue narrows his eyes at this remark, and you shrug your shoulders. The man hitches his belt, a dark red affair made from animal skin, and scratches his beard.

"Hey! I'm talking to you!" the Staff Officer shouts. "It's an offence to leave your domicile without your ID. Would you like me to tell you what the punishment is for being caught without ID?" You tell the Officer that you've just flown in from Korphir, and that you must have left your ID in your other suit, and that on Korphir you didn't have to carry ID all the time, and – "Enough!" he shouts, even more loudly. "OK," he says to the Troopers at the gate. "Let's get a visual screen of the guy, and run the sensors over him."

"But I was here first!" complains red-belt, bristling with rage. The Staff Officer ignores him. The security guards pull you in front of the cameras.

If you have checked 513, go to 260

If not, go to 328

248

In a brisk electronic drone, the entry-phone demands to know who you are. "Havet Storm," you answer. "I'd like to leave a message for Facet –" Facet's voice cuts in, sounding edgy and hurried. "Havet? Come up." The entryphone buzzes, and you push open the door. There is a large entry hall, and a set of stairs climb ups to the next floor. Facet's voice echoes down from above – "Up here!" You trot up the stairs.

Facet actually does own the entire building! The upper floor contains a huge ballroom, complete with a stage big enough to house an orchestra. In one corner of the room, Facet throws clothes into a bag. She looks very unhappy, and quite frightened. "I'm really pleased to see you," she says. "Have you heard? There was a battle over the city!" How were you supposed to have missed it? "My father says the Rebels will launch an attack. I'm going to stay at the Station."

If you have checked 584, go to 214

If you haven't, go to 265

249

An urgent chime sounds on one of the monitors. The guards stiffen with tension, turning their blaster rifles in your direction. The Officer glances at the monitor. The operator opens his mouth to speak. "That's nothing to worry about," the Officer snaps. "Notify the appropriate agency."

He turns back to you. "You're overdue on tax payments, Mr Storm," he says. How's that possible – you've never paid any tax…? "Call at the Imperial Revenue Office in Toprawa City within 48 hours." His voice is tense. "Maybe it's a rebate," you joke. "I doubt it," he replies.

You pass through the gate. The Officer returns your ID, and gives you a separate, green metal card. "You are cleared only for the Green Areas. Do not leave the Green Areas or an alarm will sound. If an alarm sounds, stand perfectly still, you will be intercepted within seconds. If you are found moving outside the Green Areas you will be shot. Understand?" You nod. "Leave all weapons with us," he continues. "Also, that..." He points at the cavernous pocket where you store Arf. You pull the droid out; better you leave him here than they spend time doing a thorough strip-down search on him... "Room 330. This Trooper will accompany you."

The guard, instead of leading the way, falls in behind you. That doesn't feel right. Nerves jangling, you set off towards the elevators. A black-bearded man in a smart black suit, set off with an appalling red belt, stands at the doors. The elevator arrives at the same time you do, and the man gestures for you to go in. "After you," you offer. He nods his thanks and gets in. You follow, and the guard makes a point of stepping past you, to stand at your back once more.

The elevator rises to the first floor, then stops. No-one is waiting. The man in the red belt steps forward to look both ways along the corridor. As you turn to watch him, you realise the guard is slumped on the floor! What in all the galaxy –? "Give me a hand," says the bearded man. He drags the guard out of the elevator, frowning when you don't help. "They'll miss him quickly; we have to get you out of here now. Take this pass –" he hands you another metallic green card "– use the gate at this end of the foyer. My people will make a disturbance. Go through then."

You're supposed to see someone about a job! "Go on!" urges the man, retreating to the corridor.

Read 549

If you ignore the bearded man, go to 330

If you wish to go elsewhere within the Station, go to 28

250

Without an action replay, you don't know *how* you did it, but you've defeated Diamond! Her body armour gave her some protection, so she isn't badly hurt, but she is down, and stunned.

You ought to check her out, or maybe – no, you can't think of killing her while she's like this. Instead, you content yourself with going through her pockets. You find a red security pass, like a metallic badge; a heavy duty blaster; a strange box which looks like some kind of remote transmitter, and a fortune in high-denomination credits. Well, well. You pocket the lot.

That engine you heard earlier seems to be getting closer. You step back from the unconscious body. The noise seems to be coming from the other side of that stack of cartons...

Add the following haul of treasure to your Equipment Box.

A blaster – check 573

A red security card – check 574

A transmitter – check 575

Go to 300

251-257

You try to help Vattali as much as you can, but the equipment is very unfamiliar to you. "Keep steady on that contact" he says. He uses a small drill to open a hole into another part of the lock. You hear a dull click, and Vattali smiles widely. "There. You can take it off."

Go to 215

258-259

Time drags while you steel yourself, trying to keep your hands perfectly still. The electronics repairman tutts and clicks, and whistles every now and again. He digs out a small fuse-gun, and starts welding parts of the bracelet together again. "I thought we were taking this thing off?"

"I don't wish to alarm you," he trills, "but the bracelet contains a modest quantity of explosive. I have cut the lock, which has armed the detonator. If we remove the bracelet, it will explode, unless I can disconnect the thermal charge from – ah!" What? WHAT!?

Go to 266

260

An urgent chime sounds on one of the monitors. In perfect synchronisation, all the guards stiffen with tension, and turn their blaster rifles in your direction. The Trooper operating the console leaps back in alarm, pulling a blaster from a holster at his belt. The Officer is almost as surprised by this as you, but he manages to step back, so that he doesn't block anyone's field of fire.

"This is the guy they filmed at the spaceport," the guard exclaims, his voice high with tension, and the blaster in his hand trembling. "The one who opened fire on the Port Security Detachment." Ah! So that's it. The Officer smiles, dreaming of promotion. "Good work, Wychov!" He motions for some of the other guards to step forward. "Search him!" You are quickly disarmed. The Officer points at the cavernous pocket in your coat where you store Arf. "Take the droid too…"

"Where do we take him, sir?" asks Wychov, who looks a lot calmer now that you're unarmed and there are five other weapons trained on you. "Where else?" the Officer replies. "Something like this, and Commander Diamond will want to see him for herself."

The guards march you off. As you pass the other gates, all eyes are on you. In particular, you notice a black-bearded man in a smart black suit, set off with an appalling red belt, who watches the events intently. "I'd stay and chat," you explain, "but I'm late for an appointment."

Remove all weapons and Arf from your Equipment Box

Go to 330

261

You try to subdue the Officer quickly, but he dodges your first blow and calls for help. Moments later, you are caught in the savage glare of a searchlight, and Imperial soldiers are rushing out of the IRS to capture you.

Not quite the way you wanted to get inside. Try another route. Go to 1

262

The man in the red scarf sticks out a hand. "Carmine," he says, offering you a toothy grin. You fight off the temptation to reply 'but I didn't knock' and introduce yourself. He takes a closer look at the wounded Ithorian. "It's been a long time since I heard of anything like that. I – I didn't know any of you people were still alive. But that lightsabre… the way you saved this man's life. You're a Jedi, aren't you?"

Great! The secret is out. "So?" you snap, irritably. "I know some people who could use talent like yours," he says. "Good people. Go to 182 Riverside and we can talk." Carmine picks up the wounded Ithorian with the Wookiee's help. "It's the truth, Havet. We can help you, and you can help us. How about it?"

If you slip out the side door and head for the address he gave you, go to 182

If you keep well clear of Carmine's friends, go to 34

263

"Help me get it off!" you shout. The Rebel Technician doesn't seem very keen, but you keep on at him. Pity, really. As he goes back into the case with the cutter, he makes just one very small mistake – but it's the last one either of you ever make.

Whew! The bracelet had a bomb in it? Does that give you clue about what to do when you start again?

264

You settle down to wait for Facet to come out, keeping a close eye on Boba Fett's landspeeder. After a few moments, you catch sight of a woman walking along the sidewalk beside Facet's building. Did she just come out of a back door? One moment the street was clear, the next, there she was!

Have you checked either 514 or 565? If you have, go to 275

If not, go to 286

265

Facet continues packing. "You shouldn't have come here, Havet," she says. "The Rebels might be looking for you too. Go now; try to stay low until the fighting is all over. Imperial reinforcements will be here soon – they'll soon sort out the rebels!"

"Can't I come with you?" you ask. She shakes her head, tossing her blonde hair. "I can't do that, Havet. Security. You understand, don't you?" She shuts the case she has been packing, and pulls on a short jacket. Together, you leave the huge upstairs room, and make your way down to the door. Facet looks out through the entry porch camera. "No-one. Go now, Havet. Good luck." She opens the door, and ushers you outside.

Well, that was very friendly. In fact, you can't think of anything less friendly. Oh, oh – yes, you can. It's coming towards you right now, powered by its jet pack, and with its blaster rifle aimed in your direction. Boba Fett!

You must fight Boba Fett! Read 588, then use the Combat Rules from the beginning of this book. Record this paragraph number so you can find your way back

If you hit Fett with your first shot, go to 271

If he hits you, go to 269

If you both miss with your first shots, go to 283

266

"There!" says the blue-skinned repairman. You hear a click, and the pressure on your wrist falls away. You open your eyes to see the bracelet lying on the shop counter. "Nova! – you scared the heat out of me!" you blare, very shaken. The repairman isn't offended. "Nasty piece of work, that," he trills. "Double-spring mechanism; you think you have to hold it down, but it's sprung from both ends – you have to hold it *still!* Very hard to defuse."

"Is it safe now?" you ask. "Not really," he replies, cheerfully. "There's a timer, but I think that hasn't been set. There's also a remote activator, which can be activated by a transmitter on a tight frequency. I haven't isolated that. I don't fancy poking around inside that thing any more than I've done already." You share the emotion. "OK. Thanks. I owe you." He shakes his head. "Just take it away with you! That's enough payment for me!"

You can get rid of the bracelet if you choose – just cross it off your Equipment list

If you keep it, change the check number to 589

You leave Vattali's shop. If you go back towards the spaceport, go to 99

If you catch the Shuttle into the City, go to 72

Great! No doubt about it, Diamond is walking right towards you. You'd better try and shift out of sight before she sees you.... She doesn't, not at first. Boba Fett does. He leaps up in his landspeeder, and braces his blaster rifle against the windshield. "I knew I'd flush you out!" he calls, and then opens fire.

You must fight Boba Fett! Read 591, then use the Combat Rules from the beginning of this book. Record this paragraph number so you can find your way back

If Fett hits you with his first shot, go to 277

If he misses, go to 293

268

You return to consciousness slowly, as if you have been asleep for hours. In fact, it can only have been a few moments. There's no sign of Diamond or Boba Fett, but Facet is kneeling at your side, stroking your head, and patching your wounds as best she can with a makeshift first aid kit. "Havet!" she cries as you wake up, her deep blue eyes full of tears. "You're alive! What happened?" Good question. You try to answer, but you only get as far as "Boba Fett...". You feel pretty rough!

"I can't leave you here," she says, determinedly. "I'll take you with me to the Station. Can you make it?" Good question. You stagger to your feet with her support, and she carries you to Fett's landspeeder (man, she's strong for an office girl!). Moments later, you're on your way.

If you have ticked a Time Box already, tick another

Go to 285

269

He was just too good for you. You missed your first shot by a light-year, but Fett was almost spot on with his. The searing heat burns you, and you fall, spilling your weapon in to the street. You fight the pain as much as you can, drawing on your Jedi strength, but you need more time than Boba Fett is going to allow you. You hear him walk over to where you are sprawled, tunic smouldering, your hand groping towards your weapon. Fett kicks it away.

"You've had this coming,brat!" he snarls levelling his weapon. You close your eyes, but the death blow doesn't come, not yet anyway. Fett spins round, hearing feet running along the street towards him. You open your eyes, and see a black-haired woman rushing towards you, weapon drawn, her clear eyes flashing with determination. "Diamond!" exclaims Fett. Like you, he doesn't know what she's doing here. Has she come to rescue you, or to claim the right to execute you yourself? The answer surprises you, but not as much as it surprises Boba Fett. She aims her stun gun at him – and fires!

Boba Fett vs Diamond! To check out the match-up of the century, read 593, and use the combat rules from the beginning of the book. Record this paragraph number so you can find your way back here.

If Boba Fett beats Diamond, go to 290

If she beats the Bounty Hunter, go to 312

270

"What did you have in mind?" you ask. She plucks your weapon from your hand. "I had hoped you would lead me to Vermilion. Instead, I find you skulking round here, chasing that air-head, Facet Anamor, and brawling with Boba Fett. Where is Vermilion? Remember, don't lie to me." Something tells you that wouldn't be a smart thing to do. "He's planning an attack on the Imperial Rcsearch Station," you tell her. "Good. When?"

"60 minutes after I arrive," you tell her. That gets her interest! "Then we mustn't delay things any longer, must we?" She pulls you to your feet and frisks you lightly. "Come on, Havet," she says. "Where are we going?"

"To the Imperial Research Station," she laughs, brutally. "Where else?"

Go to 274

271

It must be one of the best shots you have ever made. Although your attack doesn't penetrate his armour, you shake Fett up, and he goes to the floor heavily. Move a little closer, and you can finish him off once and for all. As you close the gap, he struggles to his knees, and tries to pull the blaster rifle out from under his legs. A wounded animal is often the most dangerous.

You see his head move suddenly. Someone behind you? A clever bluff? No, your Jedi senses warn you that there is someone there, someone even more dangerous! You dive to the floor, rolling off the sidewalk and into the shelter of a parked vehicle. As you rise up, weapon at the ready, you see who has crept up behind you. A slender figure, tucked into a dark jump-suit; short black hair; a taut, severe face; and clear, crystalline eyes...

Have you checked either 514 or 565? If you have, go to 284

If not, go to 295

272

This Jedi thing must have something going for it after all. You are on a roll! Diamond collapses, out cold. You truss her up with her belt. She'll make a fine prisoner for the Rebels.

After one last check to make sure no-one else is going to attack you, you rush to Facet's apartment. The entryphone plays a recorded announcement back at you. There's no-one home. Curse it. Facet must be at the IRS already. You leave the building, and grab Diamond's limp form, throwing it into your vehicle. Gunning the engine, you set off to find Vermilion.

Go to 294

273

The first loser in the three-way battle between you, Fett and Diamond is the raven-haired woman. She screams horribly, then falls still.

Continue the battle with Boba Fett. Read 597. Record this paragraph number so you can find your way back here.

If you beat Boba Fett, go to 296

If he beats you, go to 314

274

Diamond drives you to the IRS building in just a few minutes. As you arrive, you sneak a glance around. Somewhere nearby, Rebel eyes will be watching. In a minute or two, Vermilion will know that you've arrived here with Diamond, not Facet. What will he do? Diamond takes you through the security gates, getting you badged up with a Green Security pass. She then whisks you to a distant wing of the building. All the areas you pass through have Green Security status. She opens a door opposite the elevator with an electronic code punched into the door lock.

You enter someone's living quarters. There are soft toys everywhere. Surely – "I know what you're thinking," smirks Diamond. "but these are Facet Anamor's quarters." She picks up a furry toy animal, strokes its ears, then tosses it aside. "I'll see if she's around. She can entertain you while I deal with the Rebels." She leaves the sitting room through a door on the far side.

You look out of the window. The Communications Centre is very close by! You can also see the labs, in a building adjoining this one. You have almost decided to try and find your way there when two things happen. First, Facet comes in. "Havet!" she calls. "Diamond said you were here but I didn't believe her. Is it true there's going to be an attack?"

Before you can answer, the second event occurs. There's gunfire close by, and an alarm sounds. Vermilion must think you have betrayed the attack to Diamond, and ordered his forces to begin the assault at once! That means you have less than 30 minutes before they blow the place up! Facet winces, but stays calm. "We're as safe here as anywhere, I suppose," she announces, opening up a cooler. "Drink? she asks.

Add a Green Security Pass to your Equipment Box (unless you already have one). Check 553

Look at your Time Track. Tick all the boxes up to and including the one which says "Read 595"

If you accept a drink, go to 291

If you have checked 590 and you offer to make the drinks, go to 313

If you attack Facet, go to 331

275

Your pulse is racing. The black-haired woman is none other than Diamond, the Research Station's Head of Security. What's she doing here? Checking up on Facet? Looking for you? She's coming right towards you. There really isn't any way she can fail to see you where you are currently hiding. You either have to move, or take action now!

Tricky choice, Havet! If you try to change position, go to 267

If you fire at Boba Fett, go to 287

If you fire at Diamond, go to 298

If you wait, go to 311

276

Fett draws the short straw in your three-way battle. He staggers back against his vehicle after a direct hit. Diamond ceases fire at once. "He's down, Havet," she calls. "You ready for a truce, or do I have to get rough with you too?" She stands up, and moves towards you.

If you wait to see what she has planned, go to 270

If you fight her, read 594, and use the combat rules from the beginning of this book. Record this paragraph number so you can find you way back here

If you beat Diamond, go to 272

If she beats you, go to 292

277

There's nowhere to run. Boba Fett fires. He doesn't hit you cleanly, but the searing heat burns you arm, and you fall, spilling your weapon in to the street. You fight the pain, drawing on your Jedi strength, but Boba Fett isn't going give you time to recover. He walks over to where you lie, tunic smouldering, your hand groping towards your weapon. Fett kicks it away.

Go to 289

278

It seems to take forever for the security guard to check your ID. Sweat breaks out on your forehead. At last, there is a small 'beep' from the console, and he tells the Officer you're clean. The Officer checks the sensor display, and nods to the guards to let you through.

"You'll have to leave all weapons with us, sir," the officer continues. "Also, that..." He points at the cavernous pocket where you store Arf. You pull the droid out; better to leave him here than have them spend time doing a thorough strip-down search on him...

Read 549

If you have checked 508, go to 280

Otherwise, go to 297

279

Running blindly on, you wind up in a pitch-black building, a complete dead end. Your heart is hammering, and you find it hard to breathe even though you are desperate for air. She's out there! And all you have is the shelter of the dark in this empty, derelict building. Sadly, that proves to be too little. While you have your weapon ready to cover the sole entrance, the killer takes more drastic measures. A gas grenade bounces on the floor in front of you, spewing its choking plume of smoke. Within seconds, you feel the ground slipping from under your feet. The last thing you think of, as the darkness comes in, is that if you ever wake up, you might find yourself thinking you were better off dead...

Rather than discover what the killer has in store now that she has caught you, why don't you start a new adventure. Go to 1

280

You realise what you have done, but a fraction too late. As you step beyond the transparent wall, blasters are levelled at you from all directions. The Security Officer lunges forward, his hand grabbing under your coat. Oh, man! You were carrying your lightsabre on your belt! They picked it up on the sensor scan; if you had hidden it in Arf, you would have been safe.

"I don't believe it!" the Officer laughs, looking forward to his promotion. "A Jedi lightsabre! Where did you get it from?" Naturally, you start telling him a story about how you found it on Korphir, and how you've no idea what it is or how it works, but he isn't going to buy that story. "A Jedi! I thought you people were all dead! When I report this, Lord Vader will want to reward me personally!" The smile vanishes from his face. "I expect he'll want to see you as well."

This is one of those situations you can't fight your way out of, Havet. Perhaps you should start again?

281

"Are you sure?" you ask the Rebel Technician. He rolls his big, wild eyes; he's pretty shocked himself. "Sure, I'm sure! If we'd tried to take that thing off, we'd be all over Toprawa City." Great. "There's no way to take the thing off without it detonating?" He shakes his head. Perfect. "It's worse than that," he adds. "It's attached to a remote system; someone, somewhere has a transmitter detonator. They just press a button…" Absolutely wonderful!

"OK. Thanks," you say quickly. What next? You know who put that bracelet on you; so the key must be inside the IRS, right? And that's where Vermilion wants you to go anyway, right? So??

Check 572 if you haven't already done so

If you have checked 525 and you want to visit that location, go to 230

If you have checked 553 or 554 and you want to go to the IRS, go to 163

282

The black-haired woman steps past the body of the murdered man while you stand there, mouth open, still unable to comprehend what you have seen. She takes a long, hard look at you. "Think you'd make a good witness?" she asks. You give a weak, half nod, trying to think of something you can say. She doesn't wait to hear. As she raises her deadly weapon, the last words you here are: "So do I."

Curious about what you have stumbled across? Perhaps you should start again!

You and Boba Fett must be having an off day. Your first couple of shots go wide, and he misses you too (don't complain; did you see what his rifle did to the wall?). You are watching him line up his next shot, when you both hear someone running. A woman has appeared, a lithe figure with short black hair and clear eyes, armed with a stun gun. "Diamond!" exclaims Fett.

You'd better take advantage of the surprise to open fire, Havet? But on who? Tricky choice, Havet!

If you fire at Boba Fett, go to 287

If you fire at Diamond, go to 298

284

"Diamond?!" you gasp. The approaching figure is indeed the Imperial Security Commander. She ignores your levelled blaster, and moves over towards Boba Fett. What in all the galaxy…? He looks up at her, head rolling with the effort, just as surprised and curious as you. Then she shoots him, once, with a stun gun, and he goes down heavily. "That's another favour I've done you, Havet," she grins, wetting her lips with her tongue. "Don't you think it's time you paid me back?" She steps towards you.

If you wait to see what she has planned, go to 270

If you fight her, read 594, and use the combat rules from the beginning of this book. Record this paragraph number so you can find you way back here

If you beat Diamond, go to 272

If she beats you, go to 292

285

You drive to the IRS with Facet. Parking outside, you watch a security guard rush from the Reception Building to drive it away. You know that somewhere nearby there is a pair of eyes watching your arrival. In a minute or two, Vermilion will be informed that you've arrived.

Facet takes you through the security gates, getting you badged up with a Green Security pass. She then whisks you to a distant wing of the building, which houses some living quarters. All of the areas you pass through have a Green Security status. Facet opens a door opposite the elevator doors with an electronic code punched into the door lock.

You enter a pleasantly-furnished apartment, with soft toys strewn all over. "We're as safe here as we can be," she says. She crosses the room, opens up a small bar and asks: "Drink?"

Add a Green Security Pass to your Equipment Box (unless you already have one). Check 553

If you accept a drink, go to 291

If you have checked 590 and you offer to make the drinks, go to 313

If you attack Facet, go to 331

286

You've no idea who the dark-haired woman is, but as she reaches the corner, Boba Fett calls out a name – "Diamond!" Diamond. What a pretty name. "What do you want, Fett?" she answers, briskly. Fett strolls over towards her. "I'm looking for a brat, his name is Havet Storm. I thought if anyone would know where to find him, it would be the Head of Security here on Toprawa." Diamond picks imaginary lint from her sleeve. "I know him," replies Diamond. She does? "He's with the Rebels." You are? "They're hatching some kind of plan to attack the Imperial Research Station. If this Havet Storm survives, you can have him."

Boba Fett pauses to consider this. "Good," he says. "There's a bar along the street from here," Diamond adds. "Wait there. I'll send word." Fett agrees, and marches off down the street. When you turn back, the mysterious woman has disappeared.

There's no point hanging around here any longer! You make your way to Facet's front door.

Check 584

Go to 230

287

You open fire on Boba Fett.

Read 591, and use the Combat Rules from the beginning of the book. Record this paragraph number so you can find your way back here

If you hit Fett with your first shot, go to 271

If you miss, go to 293

288

The attack starts well enough. The security guards in the Reception Building are bowled over like ninepins in a hurricane. Stepping over fallen bodies, and crashing through the gates, you follow two other Rebels into a computer facility on the first floor. Two desperate Imperial Officers and a stormtrooper attempt to block your path.

Read 601, and use the Combat Rules from the beginning of the book. Record this paragraph number so you can find your way back here

If your team wins the combat and you have checked 555, go to 316

If you win the combat but you have not checked 555, go to 333

If you get hit, go to 344

289

You figure you're about a nanosecond from death at Boba Fett's hands when the bounty hunter suddenly stiffens, his eyes glazing over. He topples to the ground, landing heavily. How…? The answer is made obvious at once. Diamond. She has a stun gun in her hand, which she must have used on Fett while he was getting ready to kill you. Why? Does she want the 'honour' of killing you herself? A black mist comes over you. Faced with the two most dangerous people on Toprawa you didn't really stand much of a chance, did you Havet?

Read 592

Go to 268

290

After a short, savage battle, Boba Fett beats Diamond. She lies still, twisted awkwardly on her back in the road. He leans against a traffic sign, breathing hard. "Just you... and me... now, Havet," he gasps.

Tough break, Havet. Give it another shot. Return to 1

291

You accept the drink Facet offers. At last – a Star Racer! It tastes fantastic – well worth waiting for. You could just sit here for hours sipping one of these. "Havet," says Facet, after a short while. "I'm worried about my father. I'm going through to the computer room in the labs to see if he is there. Will you wait here?" She leaves without waiting for your answer. You relax for a moment. Of course, you are supposed to be helping transmit the information the Rebels have captured up to Princess whatshername. You'd better get back to work, Havet.

Tick another box on your Time Track

If you search Facet's quarters, go to 315

If you follow the direction she took, go to 332

292

Your mother always said you should never fight with girls – and she was right! Diamond dodges every blow you try to land on her, then drives a blow into your arm which almost breaks the bone! Stunned, you drop your weapon, and surrender. "Very wise," she snarls, not even breathing hard. "You should play rough games in the street, Havet. I'm taking you the Imperial Research Station. Don't cause me any more trouble!"

As if you could!

Read 598

Go to 274

293

Your first shot went wide, taking a lump out of a building. Out of the corner of your eye, you see Diamond level her stun gun – but not at you! She's aiming at Boba Fett!

Read 596, and use the Combat Rules from the beginning of the book. Record this paragraph number so you can find your way back here

Who is the first to get hit?

If it is Diamond, go to 273

If it is Fett, go to 276

If it is you, go to 293

294

Driving quickly, you reach the vicinity of the Imperial Research Station in no time. You park the vehicle on a side street, and then go looking for Vermilion. As you suspected, once Rebel eyes have spotted you on the street, someone is sent to find you.

Vermilion has set up his HQ in an ice cream parlour. He isn't there when you arrive, but Carmine is. You get the idea that Carmine is some kind of deputy of Vermilion's. He fidgets with his scarf as you tell him what happened outside Facet's apartment. "Fancy an ice?" he asks, rummaging in a chill cabinet. "No," you reply. "You haven't got a Star Racer in there, have you?" He hasn't.

"So, you can't get inside the Station?" he asks after a while. "Not unless you have a clever idea," you answer. The meeting with Facet was the only plan you had. Why wasn't she at her apartment? "Well, we'll just have to take our chances." Carmine signals to an aide. "Give the word, we're going to attack at once."

You join a Rebel group planning to hit the main Reception Building. The last moments pass agonisingly slowly. At last, you hear a buzz through the headset of the helmet you have been given, and you set off, clutching a blaster rifle. The attack is on!

Tick all the boxes on your Time Track, up to and including the box marked "Read" 595

Check 599

Add a blaster rifle to your Equipment Box and Check 600

Go to 288

295

The black-haired woman moves faster than Vipergrass. She fires her stun pistol at you, and the world explodes into bright flashes of green and white, while your legs take it upon themselves to fold up. You hit the ground harder than you have ever fallen before, though you don't feel a thing. The woman steps past you, and over to Boba Fett, who is still trying to gather his strength so he can get to his feet and continue the fight. She zaps him too. Fett goes to sleep like a switch has been thrown on him. She removes his weapons (it takes her quite a while), then rolls him into the gutter.

Now her attention is back on you. She checks you quickly for weapons, then looks at your ID. "Havet Storm." She can read, then. "Have I heard of you? Do you even know who I am? My name is Diamond. I'm Head of Security at the Imperial Research Station. Which is where you're going, right now." You're in no position to argue.

Check 565

If you have already ticked a box on your Time Track, tick another now

Remove all blasters from your Equipment box

Go to 274

296

Unbelievable! You've beaten them both! Boba Fett and Diamond are both laid out on the ground, and you have barely a scratch on you. Maybe this Jedi thing is worth something after all! You truss the woman up with her belt. She'll make a fine prisoner for the Rebels. Boba Fett you ignore. He looks pretty beat up. He'll live, but he won't enjoy it.

After one last check to make sure no-one else is going to attack you (let 'em try!), you rush to Facet's apartment. The entryphone plays a recorded announcement back at you. There's no-one home. Curse it – Facet must be at the IRS already. You turn back from the door, and grab Diamond's limp form, throwing it into your vehicle. Gunning the engine, you set off to find Vermilion.

Go to 294

297

Obeying the officer's instructions, you leave your weapons in a metal container. You place Arf in as well. You pass through the gate, where the Officer returns your ID, and gives you a separate, green metal badge. "You are cleared only for the Green Areas. Do not leave the Green Areas or an alarm will sound. If an alarm sounds, stand perfectly still, you will be intercepted within seconds. If you are found moving outside the Green Areas you will be shot. Understand?" You nod. Green is safe, anything else is the business end of a blaster rifle. Got it.

"Personnel is on the third floor." He gestures along the passage behind him, where you can see a row of elevators. You pin the metal ID to your coat, and set off for the third floor. Moments later, you are standing outside a door marked "Facet Anamor; Personnel Director". The third floor is filled with offices, and crowded with busy people. You were met at the elevator by a polite, uniformed woman, and brought here. She keys the door panel, and a green light appears beside her finger. "You may go in," she says.

The office is simply furnished, but Facet has brightened it with holo pictures and flowers. She rises from the workstation at which she was seated, and comes over to shake your hand. "I'm glad you've come," she says. "I have a feeling we're going to get on well together."

If you have checked 551, go to 308

Otherwise, go to 339

298

From what you've seen, Boba Fett is just an ugly bully with chip and a rocket launcher on his shoulder. Diamond is *real* trouble. Aiming carefully, you fire at her first.

Read 602, and use the Combat Rules from the beginning of the book. Record this paragraph number so you can find your way back here

If you hit Diamond with your shot, go to 273

If you miss, go to 293

299

"No hard feelings," you say shortly afterwards, after you have descended through the trapdoor, "but I'm better off on my own." Vermilion looks disappointed, but he doesn't argue. "OK, kid. Play it your way. If you ever need to find me, try looking for a guy called Carmine in Toprawa City, or hang around Al's place. It attracts some interesting people." Yeah, right.

Vermilion turns away, and scrambles over a rubble heap, disappearing almost at once. You head the other way, and come out in the basement of a derelict building. Diamond is nowhere to be seen.

Go to 99

300

The engine you heard before revs loudly one more time, and then you catch a brief glimpse of a powerful fork-lift thumping into the back of the pile of cartons. In a half-second, Diamond is buried under a tide of boxes. You stand there, almost unable to move.

"Let's go!" The voice is urgent. You see it belongs to a man wearing a smart, dark suit, set off with a lurid red belt. He has jumped from the fork-lift and is heading for the exit. "Do you want to still be here when she comes out from under that pile?"

No, you can honestly say that you don't.

If you have checked 557, go to 319

If not, go to 346

301

You look the security guard in the eye, dropping your voice to a dead calm. "There's no need, Officer," you smile. His eyes seem to lose their focus. "You don't need to detain me at all."

"On second thoughts," he replies, "there's no need to detain you at all." So far, so good. You concentrate a little deeper. "In fact, you'd far sooner I just moved along and left the terminal."

"In fact, it's probably best if you moved on." The guard gestures for you to go forward through the gate. The tension of the situation has left you shaking like a Wind-drone... Wasn't the point of coming here to make a new start, to avoid having to face up to the Jedi curse? Great start, Havet!

Go to 46

302

You reach deep inside yourself, drawing on your Jedi powers. Something in the back of your mind reminds you that this is just a lowly security guard. He doesn't warrant this level of overkill!

It's too late now. You can feel the strength of the Force welling up inside you...

Go to 301

303-306

You reach deep inside yourself, drawing on the full might of your Jedi powers. You realise in your heart that you are over-reacting, that this is just a lowly Imperial drone going about his business, but your anxiety has got the better of you. The Force sweeps through you like a tidal wave. This is the curse you were born with; the power that you have always dreaded. After the last time, you swore you wouldn't use it again! Now here you are, three minutes after landing on Toprawa, and you've yielded to the temptation once more.

Check 501

Go to 301

307

This isn't a good place to be, Havet! Putting on a burst of speed your old school athletics coach would have been proud of, you hurtle back along the alley, back the way you sauntered in. You don't dare look, but you can hear the killer behind you. What have you got mixed up in? Find out later! As you exit the alley, you realise the street is too empty, too open, to find any hiding place. You'd do better to trust to your speed, and take off. What you need is somewhere you can shake her off your tail!

Go to 142

308

Facet chatters as she pours you a cold, sweet drink. She has been to the theatre in Toprawa City ("Terrible! What a dump!!"), and she has mixed with what passes for the social elite on the planet ("All they wanted to do was complain about their precious economy!"). Worst of all, she has had the most terrible time getting decent staff to work at the Centre ("I sometimes wonder if there's a single engineer or programmer left in the Empire!"). It's a hard life.

Without pausing, she asks: "What am I going to do about this awful man who wants to kill me?"

It takes you a moment to gather your wits. As far as you remember, no-one has threatened to kill anyone. Facet becomes tetchy when you mention this. "You don't understand, Havet. Vermilion has been stirring up trouble for my poor father ever since we arrived. He blames us for all the problems they have here! Is it our fault the trade routes have been cut? Is it our fault that there are no jobs? No! It's all the fault of Vermilion's rebels – terrorists and cut-throats, the lot of them!"

She sits back behind her desk, pouting. "You see, Havet? If Vermilion is following me, it must be because he wants to use me to get back at my father! You'll help, won't you?" Oh, oh – she isn't going to cry, is she? "Um – sure. What do you want me to do?"

"Well, Vermilion leads a group of rebels in Toprawa City. Couldn't you make contact with them? Get on the inside? Then, if they don't leave me alone, we could call the police, or something." Facet opens a box while she is talking, and pulls out a metal bracelet, on which there are a number of small studs. She slips it over your wrist, and you hear a slight click as the lock snaps shut. "It's a transmitter!" she whispers. "If you find the rebels, press the white stone, and help will be on its way." You look at the bracelet – it's quite attractive, as jewellry goes – and you wonder if it wouldn't look better on the other hand. When you pull at it, however, it refuses to come off. "There's a key," Facet says. She searches in the box. "I must have left it at home. I'll give it to you the next time we meet. Please don't break the bracelet – it's really very valuable!"

Wow! You must have made quite a hit with Facet. Perhaps you could push your luck and try for a reward for being so helpful!

Add the bracelet to your equipment and check 556

If you want to ask for some work, go to 339

If you want to ask for a date and you haven't already checked 525, go to 33

If you want to leave, go to 47

Despite the risks, you find yourself pouring out your hatred of the Empire. Strange, really, because you hadn't realised that's the way you felt. You've always hated what is hidden inside you, your Jedi past, but you've never realised how much you feel the Empire is to blame for the hatred that your heritage attracts. After all, it was the Empire who actually killed your father and grand-father, right? Even if this Jedi thing is so bad, can that really justify their they murders?

Carmine lets you finish. He looks genuinely sympathetic. "We can help you, Havet. A few of us have been – well – planning something. A gesture, a piece of resistance. Have you heard of the Rebel Alliance?" You confess that you haven't. "Well, we don't have time for the full sales pitch now," says Carmine. "Let's just say there are others who hate the Empire just as much as you do. There's going to be a war, Havet. Who knows, maybe it's will start right here on Toprawa."

"What's that to do with me?" you ask. "We need people to join us, to fight with us," replies Carmine. "What do you say, Havet?"

How ironic. You spend all day tramping the streets of Toprawa City, looking for work, and this man is trying to sign you up for an unpaid crusade against the Empire. Maybe it makes sense – if it meant a place to hide, a bed, food. But how could you live amongst these "rebels" and keep your terrible secret safe? Sooner or later, they'd find out you were a Jedi. What then?

No, it isn't worth the risk. "I'm sorry you feel that way, Havet," Carmine replies when you turn down his offer. "If you ever change your mind, call this number." He hands you a business card with a commslink number on it. "You advertise?" you ask. What kind of rebellion has printed stationary? " Just because you have the number, doesn't mean you know where I am. This place will be just another empty building in the morning."

"One more thing," he adds. You are given a new ID Card. "Same name, same visual. It's just coded differently, so that when they swipe it through the reader, they find a record that's cleaner than your best clothes after washing day."

He shows you to the door. "Think about what I said!" he grins, and steps aside to let you out.

Check 517 and 530

If you go back to the Commercial District, go to 227

If you catch the Shuttle back towards the port area, go to 199

The metallic whining voice of the entry-phone crackles from the speaker. "No-one can come to the door right now. Please call again at another time. These premises are guarded by the Imperial Security Services." So much for the date... Still, maybe she didn't mean tonight. The invitation was pretty vague. She might still be at work – perhaps you could hang around...

No, there's no point. You can always come back another night.

If you wander into Toprawa City, go to 169

If you go back in the direction of the spaceport, go to 99

311

You wait, trying to make yourself as small as possible in the hope that Diamond doesn't see you. Some hope. She makes a big show of walking past, then whips round to hold a stun gun against your head. "Havet!" she whispers, "What a lovely surprise!" She frisks you quickly and efficiently, then hauls you from your hiding place with surprising strength.

Once you're out in the open, Boba Fett sees you at once, and leaves his landspeeder. Diamond positions herself so that he can see clearly that you're her prisoner. He halts, still several paces away, blaster rifle propped on his shoulder. "I have business with this boy, Commander," he announces coldly. "So do I," replies Diamond, evenly. "And Imperial business takes precedence over any personal quarrels you may have."

Boba Fett considers this for a while, then shrugs. "He'll keep. If he doesn't suffer any fatal accidents while in your custody, perhaps you'll let me know?" He turns away. Diamond watches him carefully as he lopes back to his landspeeder. He throws the car into a tight U-Turn, and roars away towards the spaceport.

"You have a dangerous knack of making very powerful enemies, Havet." You can't deny it. "Is that what you are, Commander?" She comes as close to an amused laugh as you have seen. "Me? I'm not your enemy, Havet. I'll prove it. What were you hoping to do here – meet Facet Anamor? OK, I'll take you to her; she's at the Imperial Research Station."

Of course you can't trust Diamond, that much is obvious. At the same time, unless she's telling you a pointless lie, what can you gain from resisting her? So, you say "thank you" as politely as you can (with a blaster rammed against your spine), and follow her to your wheels.

Go to 274

312

You watch the battle, fighting the pain from your own wound, drifting so close to to unconsciousness that the fight seems unreal and distant. Two deadly killers circle and stalk each other; you're reminded of the courting rituals of Athetian spiders. Finally, however, Diamond gets an angle on Boba Fett, and pops him with the stun gun. It isn't a clean hit, but he staggers under the jolting impact, and she aims carefully to hit him again. Fett puts a few more dents in his antique armour as he crashes to the ground.

Diamond's brow is slick with sweat, and she breathes deeply. Your eyes remain fixed to the weapon in her hand. She can't finish you off with that, so what will it be? A knife? A blow to the neck? You feel your grip on consciousness loosen as your brain decides it would rather not be around for the finale of this fight. The last thing you remember as you slip away are Diamond's clear, determined eyes. They seem to be mocking you...

Read 592

Go to 274

313

"Let me," you offer, sounding a bit abrupt. Facet looks surprised, but steps back from the bar anyway. You tell her to take a seat, and she obeys. Oh, man! She's got a Star Racer in the cooler! You lick your lips, and crack the seal on the tube. Good manners prevent you from taking a pull straight away, but you can almost taste its sharp, warm tang. At last! It takes real willpower to mix Facet's drink first; three parts citrus juice, one part local bitters, ice and just a small vial of sleeping draught to taste. You hand her a long glass, and she drinks deeply.

As for you, well, you've finally got your hands on a tube of Star Racer. Nothing is going to stop –

There is a thump behind you, and you jump out of your skin. The tube falls to the floor, and breaks on the tiles under the bar. NO!!! You look round, ready to scream at Facet, but she has fallen from the couch and lies in a heap on the floor. You rush over to check her pulse. She's alive, but her running lights have been switched off – she doesn't stir when you call and only groans slightly as you lift her onto the couch. That sleeping potion must have been strong stuff!

You don't have long. Find that data the Alliance wants, and get to the Communications Centre.

Check 603

If you search Facet's quarters, go to 315

If you search Facet, go to 334

If you leave her quarters, go to 345

314

In a three-way battle between a Bounty Hunter who's a trained killer; a high-powered Imperial Officer who's a trained killer; and you, guess who came third. You go down, wounded, but not fatally, not yet. You hear firing continue. Sooner or later, Diamond or Boba Fett or both is going to come over to finish you off. It hardly seems worth living for.

You've had it for this adventure. Go back to 1, or create a brand new character

315

You search Facet's quarters. The sitting room is comfortable, well-equipped and well-furnished, but there's nothing unusual. The kitchen is much the same. The bathroom is equally unrevealing (except you find a bottle of the perfume Facet wears – mmmm, it smells good). Finally, there's the bedroom. A computer terminal, more soft toys, more clothes than anyone in their right mind would ever want, a vast collection of fashion data cards, and – Now that's interesting. Facet wears contact lenses; there's an empty case on the bedside table. Why would someone with her money wear contacts in this day and age, when she could have corrective treatment? And what's this? Loose blonde hairs on a small, round wooden block. Um – is Facet going bald?

Tick another box on your Time Track

If you check out the terminal, go to 336

Otherwise, you're done in here. If you have checked 603, go to 335

If you haven't checked 603, go to 347

316

After a brisk fight, the Rebels take control of the computer room. As you draw breath, an idea pops into your head. You leap into a seat in front of a console. "Come on, Havet!" yells one of the other rebels, "we don't have time to play computer games now!"

"Leave me!" you shout. "I've had an idea!" A Rebel Officer arrives, bleeding from a head wound. "Havet! – the Imperials are regrouping! Diamond got loose, and she's back directing their defence. We need every man!" You don't even look up. "If this works, I can do more damage my way. Check with Vermilion – he'd understand!" Cursing your name, the Rebel Officer departs.

The original plan was that you should get yourself on the inside. OK, so things didn't work out perfectly, but you have thought of a way round it. These computers control the security badges all the Imperials wear. What if you were to activate one? Wouldn't that mean you could wander anywhere you wanted in the building? Maybe find Facet Anamor, or her father?

Using the password patch Ta'al Pierc had placed on the Imperial computer, you break into the security badge program. You slip your badge into the slot beside the console, and it pops out moments later, officially activated. OK. Now all you need is a uniform from one of the dead guys, and you're in business!

Check 604

If you haven't already checked 553, 554 or 574, add a Green Security Badge to your Equipment and check 553 (you can take a badge from one of the dead Imperial Officers)

If you try accessing more Imperial files from this terminal, go to 341

If you look for Facet's quarters, go to 353

317

You hand over your completed application forms. The girl takes one look at them, and drops them into a shredder at the side of her desk. "Those are out of date," she says, pulling a folder from a drawer. "You need these," she says, with a mocking smile. OK. You get the idea. There's no way you're going to spend another day in the torture-chamber furniture they provide for no-hopers like you, filling in forms no-one is ever going to look at. You pop the new folder into the shredder. "Thanks for your help," you smile, and leave.

Moments later, you're back out on the street. So, nothing doing there. What next?

Remove check 550

If you catch the Shuttle into Toprawa City, go to 169

If you want to keep looking around locally, go to 99

318

Keeping you covered, Diamond reaches into her tunic, and pulls out a decorative bracelet, set with semi-precious stones. She tosses it over. "Put it on." You hesitate, and she gestures with her blaster. Fair enough; you close it on your wrist. "That's an explosive cuff. It has a remote detonator, which I possess. If you cause me any problems, if you tell anyone what you have seen here, I'll turn you into a supernova. Understand?"

You tug at the cuff, but it isn't going to come off your wrist. It doesn't take a wise man to guess that, if you try to cut it off, it explodes anyway. "If you want to be rid of it, you have to do me a small favour. There is an irksome group of rebels on Toprawa. Their leader is Vermilion, a vain man, who wears a blood-red turban. You should be able to find him easily enough. Vermilion is planning an attack on the Imperial Research Station. This fool –" she indicates Ta'al Pierc's broken body – "gave him some information."

"Find Vermilion. He likes to drink in Al's cantina, or you might meet up with his friends in Toprawa City. When you find him, press the white stone on the underside off the cuff, and I'll be with you in minutes. Just track Vermilion down, and you'll be free? Understand?"

You understand perfectly. "Good," remarks Diamond. "Don't let me

172

down. Now get out of here, or I'll finish you as easily as I finished this poor fool."

Check 552

If you leave the alley and go to Toprawa City, go to 169

If you head for Al's cantina, go to 216

If you think things would look better after a good night's sleep, go to 50

319

You chase after your rescuer. "Scarlett!" you yell, "wait up!" he looks back with an angry fire in his eyes. "Tell everyone who I am, why don't you!" he hisses. Ooops. "You know who that was trying to kill you?" You tell him that you got the idea. "You may not have any friends, kid, but you've made some top-drawer enemies!" You have run far enough, and Scarlett slows down, pulling you into a small convenience store selling third-rate produce.

"Why was she trying to kill you?" he says, filling a bag with fruit. You give him an account of what you saw in the alley. Scarlett looks deeply unhappy. "Pierc, eh?" He shakes his head. "We can't afford to lose people like that. Not when all we have to replace them is the likes of you."

You realise that this is some kind of invitation. Scarlett wants you to become part of the Rebel Alliance. "What do I do?" you ask. He ponders for a moment, then uses a marker to write an address on a small, soft-skinned fruit. '182 Riverside' it reads. "Memorise that address," he says, "then eat it. You look like you need the calories."

He heads for the front door, checking to make sure Diamond is nowhere in sight. "This is where we split up. Go to Riverside. Otherwise, you're on your own." He skips out of the door. You take another look at the address, and then eat the fruit.

If you set off for Riverside, go to 182

If you think a night's sleep would be better for you, go to 50

You tap the entry code for the door into the keypad. It slides open, and you step through, into the Blue Zone.

If you have checked 554 or 574 *and* 604, go to 342

If haven't done this, go to 355

321-323

You try your Jedi Mind-Influence on the Captain. He doesn't have a lot of resolve, and you can feel him bending to your will. "Look," you say, trying to sound wonderfully reasonable, "you don't want to waste time over this…" The Captain repeats your words to the other security troopers at the check-point. "We can't waste time chasing this, Sergeant" he drones, flatly. "I don't want to have to arrest every kid who comes through here with a minor flag on his ID. Let's get him back on the shuttle and get this traffic moving, OK?"

The other guards look surprised, but you don't get very far in the Imperial service questioning Captains. The Sergeant, however, isn't convinced. "But, sir –" he argues, looking into the officer's curiously dull eyes. "We can't just ignore it!" He grabs your shoulder, and your concentration wavers. In that moment, the Captain throws off the effects of your influence.

He's groggy, and the other guards are unsure what they're supposed to be doing. Are you their prisoner, or what? Your last chance to escape might be right here and right now!

If you choose to fight, read 523, then use the combat rules from the start of the book. Record this paragraph number so you can find your way back here.

If you win the combat, go to 81

If you lose, go to 92

If you surrender after the combat has begun, go to 84

If you don't want to fight, but you have checked 513, go to 48

If you don't want to fight and you have not checked 513, go to 60

You use your Jedi Mind-Influence on the Captain. He doesn't have a lot of resolve, and you feel him bending completely to your will. "Look," you say, trying to sound wonderfully reasonable, "you don't want to waste time over this…" The Captain repeats your words. "We don't have time for this, Sergeant" he drones. "We can't arrest every kid who comes through here with a minor flag on his ID. Let's get him back on the shuttle and get this traffic moving, OK?"

The other guards look surprised, but you don't get very far in the Imperial service questioning Captains. The Sergeant opens his mouth as if he is going to argue, but you have the Captain shutting off his protest almost before it can be uttered. "Sergeant, you have my orders!" The Sergeant salutes, and leads you back to the shuttle. Partway there, when you're pretty much out of sight, he grips your arm tightly. "I don't know how you got to be so lucky," he hisses. "If it were me, I'd have run you down to the detention centre and shaken you until the truth fell out."

"Well, *Sergeant*," you reply, "the *Captain* sees things differently." He stiffens, but you can see he knows that – for now – he has to let you go. "Keep making enemies like this, kid. That way, one day, one of us will get to teach you a lesson." The Empire seems to have an endless supply of jerks, so he might be right. You climb back on the shuttle and it eases away from the check-point. Your fellow passengers look straight-ahead, their faces a mixture of frustration and relief. But you look right into the eye of the Sergeant, and wave him goodbye.

Go to 86

327

"I've just arrived from Korphir," you tell her. "It was time to move on – family troubles, you know!" Facet nods – but you're glad she doesn't know what your family problem is! "So, I'm looking for work here." She laughs. "Well, you're lucky you met me! No-one else is looking for people at the moment, but the IRS are still short-staffed." You chat about what the Imperial Research Station does, and Facet tells you it's "government stuff" and mentions a "big project".

"Come over," she says. "Show us what you can do… who knows, maybe we could end up working together!" Next moment, having glanced at her chrono, she leaps to her feet, dropping some credits on the table. "I'm late – I have to go," she says. "Let me pay for this meal – I bet you're finding Toprawa pretty expensive!" That's for sure… "Come to the IRS sometime, and ask for me." She hands you a card with her name and the IRS address and comms number on it. By the time you've glanced at the card, she's heading for the door, giving you a friendly wave.

Alright! This could be the best news you've had since you arrived on Toprawa. So, maybe you should wait round here for a while, find somewhere where you can make yourself a little more presentable, then head over to the IRS.

While you mull it over, someone takes Facet's chair. He grins, in a very unfriendly fashion, his eyes dark and piercing under the dark red swirl of his turban. He abruptly takes the card from your hand and reads it, then reaches down with his other hand to grip your wrist. You realise this guy has been watching Facet since you first arrived. "I think we should talk," he says.

Check 541

If you try to break free, add your Strength Rating (from your Character Sheet) to the number 110. That is the number of the next paragraph you should read (so, if your Strength is 2, go to paragraph 112). Go to that paragraph now.

If you allow him to take you wherever he wants, go to 11

328

The surveillance cameras map your features from front and side, building up a detailed image on one of the monitors behind the gate. You watch as the operator keys the commands to search against the planetary data-base. A few agonising moments pass by, then the operator turns to the Officer and tells him there is no match. The Officer gives you the once over one more time. "OK. Get out of here. And find your ID before you do anything else!"

You assure him that's just what you'll do. He signals to one of the patrolling guards to escort you from the building.

Back outside on the street, you notice a man wearing a red belt watching from the other side of the road. As you walk away from the IRS, he follows, until you are about 200 metres away. He crosses the street, and drops in just behind you. "If you've got problems with our friends in the Empire," he says, his voice no louder than a murmur, "I may be able to help you."

If you listen to what he has to say, go to 32

If you ignore him and go back towards the spaceport area, go to 99

329

What a question! What do you think of the Empire!! How are you supposed to give a virtual stranger an answer to that? It's a 50/50 chance that if you say the Emperor is a boon to all mankind, Carmine will turn out to be some of crazy revolutionary; or if you go on about injustice and oppression, he'll turn out to be the Emperor's kid brother or something.

When in doubt, stall.

Carmine listens as you gabble on about how you've never really thought about it, about how you're just a kid, about how you just want to live your life right and keep out of trouble with everyone. He grins widely. "The same answer I'd have given, Havet, if I were you."

"How come?" you ask. Carmine doesn't answer your question directly. Instead, he straightens his clothes with the flat of his hand, and stands up. "Sooner or later, son, you'll have to come down off the fence. When you do, you're going to need a few friends. I'm just proving what a friendly bunch we can be, in case you decide to jump our way." And which way is that, you wonder. "You'll know, when the time comes," he laughs, as if he has read your mind.

He hands you a business card with a comlink number on it, but no address. "I move about quite a bit," he comments, "but you can always find me through that number." He shows you to the door. "Think about what I've said!" he grins, and steps aside to let you outside. You try to think of something to say in return, but Carmine is already closing the door.

Check 530

If you go back to the Commercial District, go to 227

If you catch the Shuttle back towards the port area, go to 199

330

Commander Diamond's office is in a room on the third floor. An outer office is occupied by two armed stormtroopers and several security guards. You are taken through under close escort. The office is lit only by the light which spills in from the doorway. You are taken to a rugged-looking chair in front of a dark, plain desk. The guards filter back out, and the door is closed, leaving you alone in the pitch darkness. You notice, by the way that the closing of the door shut off all sound from the outer office, that this room is completely sound-proof.

OK. So what next? It's been several years since you were afraid of the dark, and the brief moments before the door closed allowed you to familiarise yourself with your surroundings. What's to stop you getting up, and looking around for a weapon or a tool, something you can use to escape? What's to stop you?

"Stay in your seat." The voice, which seems to have come from out of nothing, makes your heart leap. The surprise alone nearly jolted you out of the chair!

A light comes on, directed into your eyes, like in some ancient vid-film. This is all a joke, right? Then the voice comes again, as brittle as jagged glass, and you realise no-one is laughing.

"Havet Storm. Do you know, I think I know less about you than about anyone else on Toprawa? You're an enigma, a mystery. And yet you have managed to cause more trouble in a few standard hours than all the rebels on the planet." The background lighting comes up. Like a phantom, Diamond materialises in front of you, clad in a tight black outfit, crossed once by a broad, violet sash. Her close-cropped hair gleams, as if wet. Her colourless irises fix on you, and her broad slash of a mouth grins.

"What am I going to do with you, you naughty little child?" You swallow, hard. This would be a bad time to make a bad joke, wouldn't it? "You could adopt me." Diamond laughs loudly. "Do you know," she replies, "I think I might!"

She steeples her fingers in front of her face, elbows resting on the desk. "It is quite within my power and jurisdiction to have you killed," she announces, in the same tone of voice normal people use to tell you the time of day. "Do you love the Emperor, Havet? Are you loyal to the Empire? Of course not. Here on Toprawa, there are many disloyal citizens. On some other worlds, there are others. Some of these malcontents have banded together to form a 'Rebel

Alliance.' They think a fine-sounding declaration and some acts of terrorism will somehow topple the Emperor's rule. They are wrong. They need to be shown that they are wrong.

"Our scientists have been working on the means by which we shall persuade these 'rebels' of the error of their ways. A great scientist, by the name of Bevel Lemelisk, is constructing a death star – a kind of super-weapon. Here on Toprawa, in this very station, we have been working to perfect the control and power suppression systems for the death star's principle weapon, a super laser, capable of destroying whole worlds. Druth Anamor, the chief scientist at this station, completed our work in the last few days. An Imperial ship is en route here to pick up the data, and take it to the Imperial shipyards so that it can be built into the death star."

You squirm a little in your seat. Doesn't all this sound a little, y'know, classified?

"Why am I telling you this?" Diamond asks, as if she has read your mind. "Simple. I know that the Rebel Alliance knows all this already. A traitor, named Ta'al Pierc, warned them about the death star, and the renegade bandit Vermilion has discovered that a ship containing the death star plans will be here in a very short time. I suspect that the rebels will try to intercept the ship. The Imperial Fleet of Lord Vader, sadly, cannot arrive here in time to prevent it.

"I also know the Toprawan rebels will attack the Imperial Research Station. What I don't know is where, or how. I should very much like to know that, Havet. Which is where you come in.

"I want you to penetrate the Rebel Alliance, and to discover everything you can. I want you to help me lay a trap. If we can wipe out these traitors, then we can stop them getting hold of Druth Anamor's work, and perhaps find out what the rebels intend to do if they get hold of the death star plans. We can deal such a defeat to these rebels that we may not even need a death star to crush all of them like bugs!"

Diamond laughs, with that same fragile, barbed quality with which she speaks. You suspect she isn't dealing from a full deck, but you refrain from mentioning it to her. "Find Vermilion, or some other rebel leader. It shouldn't be too hard. You attract trouble, Havet. I expect they'll fall over themselves to find you.

"Which leaves one question in your mind." Actually, you can think of several, but never mind. "Why should you help me?" She rises from her seat, and walks slowly around the corner of her desk. "The answer you should give is 'because I'm a loyal subject of the

Empire.' However, since we know that you're not, let me give you another reason." Like a flash, her hand disappears inside the sash, then reappears, clutching what appears to be an electronic bracelet. She clamps it round your wrist before you can so much as twitch.

"It's an explosive cuff, Havet. If you don't help me, the first thing I shall do as soon as the alarm announces the rebel attack is to detonate it." You tug at the cuff, but it isn't going to come off your wrist. It doesn't take a wise man to guess that, if you try to cut it off, it explodes anyway. "It has a built in transmitter. If you need me, access the white key on the underside. I'll never be far away. In fact, that's another good reason why you should do what I say, Havet. Because you'll never know where I am, how close I am, until –"

Silence. You sit rigid, waiting for her to speak again, but nothing comes. You turn in your seat and – nothing! She has vanished into thin air.

Guards enter the office and escort you out. You stumble along between them, your mind a blur. It'd be easy to think you imagined that whole conversation, but you haven't. On your wrist, you can feel the warm reminder that it was all very real. Downstairs once more, they remove the green badge, and propel you towards the door.

Check 552

Go to 45

331

This isn't something you're going to feel proud about later, but you feel there isn't time for anything else. Jumping on Facet, you strike her once, and she lapses into unconsciousness. It was much easier than you thought. Honestly, Havet, wasn't there a better way to deal with a young woman than that?

You remove her blue security badge. You then look around for something to tie her up with, but there isn't anything. Perhaps she has a belt in her wardrobe?

Unless you already have one, add a Blue Security Badge to your Equipment Box and check 554

If you want to search Facet's quarters, go to 315

If you want to leave her quarters, go to 345

332

You open the door of Facet's quarters as quietly as you can. Looking down the hall, you can see she has reached a set of doors. Beyond the doors, you can see that the passage leads to more residential areas, and that this is a Blue Zone, which means you need a blue security badge to pass through. She taps the number 320 into the electronic lock. The door opens, and she walks through.

If you approach the door into the Blue Zone, go to 320. Otherwise, check 605

If you go back and search Facet's quarters, go to 315

If you take the elevator to the lower floor of the accommodation area, go to 345

333

You beat that group of Imperial soldiers, but there are plenty more where they came from. The Rebel attack is hopelessly outgunned. A small group fight their way through to the Communications Centre, but are ambushed there. Eventually, you too are cut down.

So close, Havet, but not quite. What could you have done differently?

334

You search Facet, but all she has on her of any use is her Blue Security badge.

Unless you already have one, add a Blue Security Badge to your Equipment Box and check 554

If you want to search Facet's quarters, go to 315

If you want to leave her quarters, go to 345

335

Having finished searching Facet's bedroom, you go back out into the sitting room. For a second, you hesitate, unable to believe your own eyes. But it's true. Facet has gone.

How is that possible? She was sleeping like a baby! Where has she gone, and why hasn't she raised the alarm? Just what is going on here?

If you give Facet's quarters an even more detailed search, go to 358

If you leave, go to 345

336

You switch on the power, and the terminal in Facet's room comes alive.

If you have checked 555, you may wish to read that paragraph again now

Otherwise, go to 348

337

Diamond walks over, slowly, keeping you covered with her blaster. She seizes your wrist, and pulls up your sleeve to reveal the bracelet she gave you. "I see you're still wearing my present," she purrs. "How sweet." As if you had any choice! "I had hoped you might have found Vermilion by now," she says, stepping back. "It's very important. I'm told he likes to drink in Al's cantina, or you might meet up with his friends in Toprawa City. You haven't forgotten our arrangement, have you?"

Of course not. "Good. Don't let me down. I'd hate to have to deal with you like I dealt with this poor fool. I'll be waiting for your call."

If you leave the alley and go to Toprawa City, go to 169

If you head for Al's cantina, go to 216

If you think things would look better after a good night's sleep, go to 50

338

Almost without thinking, you tell Facet a lie, as if something was warning you not to get too close. By the time you have finished spinning out your tale about your cousin/uncle/friend owning a light freighter on which you are the navigator/co-pilot/engineer, you have contradicted yourself so many times that Facet can see that it is a complete falsehood. She checks her chrono.

"That's really interesting," she says, flatly. "Look, I'm sorry, I have to get back to work." She gets to her feet, leaves some money for her meal, and heads for the door. Perfect.

If you follow her to the door and apologise, go to 349

If you wait and let her go, go to 360

339

"Do you have any idea about what kind of work you want to do, Havet?" Facet asks, operating her keyboard. "Um – something with computers?" you offer. "Programming? Trouble-shooting? Data entry?" Facet laughs, then asks what programming languages you are familiar with, what kind of work you've done in the past. You tell her, adding a few embellishments. She's quite impressed, taps a few keys, then swings the monitor round in your direction. There are several lines of complex computer code in front of you, and more scrolled off the bottom of the screen. "Take a look at that, Havet," says Facet. "What's wrong with that code?"

To see how well you do with this test, look at Havet's Technical Skills score on your Character Sheet. Add that number to 240, and that is the number of the next paragraph you should read (so, if your Technical Skills score is 4, you would go to paragraph 244). Go to that paragraph now.

340

You feel in your pockets, looking to see if you can afford a snack in the cafe. All this walking around has given you an appetite! It takes you about half-a-second to decide – you're not going to go hungry just because things haven't worked out yet. Sooner or later you'll earn some credits, and things will be OK.

You trot over to the cafe, and take a seat. A grey-skinned guy with a shaggy pelt of black hair takes a hard look at you. He's cleaning the tables down and stacking chairs – looks like he's getting ready to close. Ha! – he's probably realised you're not going to be a big tipper, either!

If you have checked 525 or 541, go to 352

If you haven't checked 525 or 541, but you have checked 515, go to 12

If you haven't checked either, go to 43

341

You try to access other Imperial programs from this terminal, but to no avail. Different terminals have different physical connections; this one just can't access the main research programs, or any other useful information. You switch off. You have to penetrate deeper into the Station, to find a way to reach Facet's father or the main research labs. Time is pressing!

Tick another box on your Time Track

Go to 353

342

You're in the Blue Zone, in the upper part of the accomodation area. So far so good. You check out the area, and realise that Druth Anamor – Facet's father, and the Head of Research at the Station – has a large apartment just along the hall, while Diamond's living quarters are just inside the door from the Green Zone. At the end of the building, a private elevator descends down towards a walkway, which connects to both the Communications Centre and the main labs.

If you enter Druth Anamor's apartment, go to 367

If you enter Diamond's apartment, go to 356

If you want to check out the elevator, go to 378

343

Unbelievable! You have your lightsabre back! It must have been brought to Diamond after you lost it before. And now you have it back. You feel more complete that you have felt for some time. No matter how you feel about being a Jedi, you realise that to be parted from this one link to your grandfather is more than you can stand.

Of course, it's obvious Diamond must have some plan in mind if she has just left this here for you to find. Your senses are jangling with instinctive fear, but you know you can't back down now. You have to go on.

Your hand reaches out, and opens the door from Diamond's quarters. The passage, marked in the deep blue of the middle security band, stretches off into the distance.

Put your lightsabre back in your Equipment box and check 508

Go to 342

344

The battle in the computer room is short and brutal. The crack of blaster rifles fills your ears, and you catch the stench of plasma. The room is wrecked in short order. Sadly, so are you. A lucky shot, and you're cut down. You'll never know if the Rebels achieve their objectives.

Well, maybe you will. Are you ready to give it another try?

345

You decide to leave Facet's quarters. The place could be swarming with Stormtroopers any minute. You open the door carefully at the thought. The passage leads to a door, and beyond that to part of the Blue Security Zone. You're more likely to find what you're looking for there. Or maybe there's another route you could try?

If you approach the door, go to 365

If you take the elevator down to the lower floor, go to 354

346

"Who *are* you?" you demand as you chase after your rescuer. He leads you on a fine chase through the streets, finally halting outside a boarded-up library. He activates his comlink. You listen as he makes the call; this doesn't seem to phase him one bit.

"Scarlett here," he says as the connection is made. "Pierc is dead. Diamond got to him. She was chasing a boy – I think he's a witness." He pauses, listening to whoever is at the other end. "If you think he can be trusted," he continues. "This could be one of Diamond's traps." Another pause. "OK. I'll send him to you." He replaces the unit.

"You know who that was trying to kill you? OK. If the Empire wants you dead, then you need our help. Go to 182 Riverside. If you pass muster, we'll look after you. If not…"

Scarlett refuses to answer questions. "I don't know the first thing about you, kid. For all I know you could be Darth Vader without the hat. Just do as you're told, and we'll see what happens."

Check 557

If you set off for 182 Riverside, go to 182

If you ignore Scarlett's dramatic warnings and look out for yourself, go to 99

347

Other than the stuff you've already checked out, your search hasn't turned up much. Surely there must be something in Facet's quarters you can use?

If you want to intensify the search, go to 358

If you've finished looking, go to 345

348

Would Facet have access to any more files from her terminal, you wonder?

If you want to access the Personnel files, go to 381

If you want to access the IRS floorplan, go to 370

If you want to try accessing other Imperial files, go to 359

If you are finished at the terminal, and you have checked 603, go to 335

Otherwise, go to 347

349

Before Facet opens the door, you catch up with her. "I'm sorry," you say, "I got myself into a mess back there." Her eyes flash, showing her disappointment and anger. "I'm don't like being lied to, Havet," she insists, and opens the door. You follow, trying to find a way to apologise properly. Facet crosses the street, heading for the escalator at the Monorail station. She looks back over her shoulder as she hears the approach of a train, and stops abruptly. "I have to get back to work. I don't have time for liars, and I don't want to hear any lame excuses, OK?" That seems to be that. She walks away, leaving you alone on the pavement.

You look back at the cafe – it suddenly occurs to you that you didn't actually pay for your meal – and notice someone watching you closely, partially hidden by one of the tall columns which supports the Monorail. As you catch his eye, the man turns away, and jogs along the street. You catch sight of his red turban. His attention is on Facet now (she has reached the escalator), but he makes a few quick glances in your direction, as if he was concerned that you might... what?

Who would be interested in your conversation with Facet? In fact, why would anyone be interested in you at all? Unless, of course, it's not you that someone was interested in, but Facet. Yes, there's no doubt about it. The man is stalking Facet, following her into the station. As she takes the escalator, he disappears through a door leading to the stairway.

If you follow Facet up the escalator, go to 53

If you follow the man up the stairs, go to 64

If you decide it's none of your business and head back into the Commercial District, go to 169

350

The last thing you want is to get into a discussion about your background, so you grope around for a subject. It comes as a surprise to you when you ask Facet for a date. "My word!" she gasps, equally surprised. "You're a fast worker!" You wonder if you've blown it, but Facet seems genuinely amused. She pulls a lipstick from her bag, and a napkin from the table dispenser. "You can find me here most evenings. I work pretty late, but you could stop by, at eleven maybe. Can you dance?"

"Sure," you say, taking the napkin. It's news to you, but you would have agreed if she'd suggested wild storn-ray wrestling. "See you soon, then!" she smiles, heading for the door.

You lean back, and survey the napkin as if it were a priceless antique. The chair jolts abruptly, and you try to correct your balance. It takes a moment for you to realise that it didn't tip over on its own, but because a tall man in a dark red turban has grabbed the back of your coat. He grins, in a very unfriendly fashion. You realise this guy has been watching Facet since you first arrived, and that he saw her give you the napkin.

"I think we should talk," he says.

Check 525

If you try and break free, add your Strength Rating (from your Character Sheet) to the number 110. That is the number of the next paragraph you should read (so, if your Strength is 2, go to paragraph 112). Go to that paragraph now.

If you allow him to take you wherever he wants, go to 11

351

You get caught in no time. It looks like they can monitor the location of everyone in the building through the badges. A guard intercepts you as you look for a staircase. "Mind the coat," you bluster as he drags you along the hall, "I've got an appointment in Room 330."

Nobody laughs, least of all you.

Go to 330

352

Sitting in the almost empty cafe, you remember that the last time you were here, you met Facet. She gave you her address, and said you should call round, right? So, are you going to?

You'd prefer it if you had some time to think about it, and to remember what a good-looker Facet is. Sadly, you don't have time. You host rushes you through the meal, hovering over you as you eat the last few morsels, then whisking the plate away and taking your money.

Anyone would think he was in a hurry to see you go. You can take a hint

You may wish to look at 525 or 541 (whichever one you have checked) before you decide what to do next.

Otherwise, it's time to head back out of the City. Go to 199

353

It proves ridiculously easy to track Facet down. You hardly see a soul as you run away from the main battle, into a deserted wing of the building and up the elevator to the residential floor. OK, maybe all the security personnel are busy with the Rebels, but how can it be this easy to just run around a vital Imperial plant like you belonged here?

All of the areas you pass through have a Green Security status, but your badge seems to be doing the job of keeping you out of trouble with the many sensors you pass. As the elevator doors open, you find yourself opposite the door of someone's living quarters. Facet's. Which means you're only problem is how to gain entry – the door is protected by an electronic lock which needs a key or a code sequence. Unless, of course, you could just ring the bell...

"Come in!" calls a familiar voice. Oh, come on... You enter a pleas-antly-furnished apartment, with soft toys strewn all over. Facet comes into the sitting room from another door, rubbing her long blonde hair as if she has just washed it. Is she surprised to see you. "Havet?! How did you get in here?" Think quickly. "Diamond sent me. The Rebels are attacking the Station; she sent me up here to guard you." Which explains how you got the badge and the blaster rifle. Perhaps. Facet seems ready to believe you, though. "That's thoughtful of her," she says. "And I'm glad that means you're safe too." She crosses the room, opens up a small bar and asks: "Drink?"

Why not?

If you accept a drink, go to 291

If you have checked 590 and you offer to make the drinks, go to 313

If you attack Facet, go to 331

354

You call the elevator, and ride it down to the ground floor. The only doors away from where the fighting is going on are securely closed, and any attempt to go through them is going to set off alarms all over. You spend a few moments searching fruitlessly for another way to reach the Communications Centre or the main Laboratory, but without any luck. You were better off upstairs, you realise, and you have wasted precious time.

Tick another box on your Time Track

If you return to search Facet's quarters more thoroughly, go to 347

If you check out the door into the Blue Zone, go to 365

355

You step into the passage. You manage barely three or four paces before an alarm sounds. You just about hear the clicks of electronic locks shutting, isolating you in this part of the building. Lights further down the hall go off, while you are bathed in a harsh spotlight. An electronic voice intones a warning: "Warning. You are not cleared for access to this area. Stand perfectly still. You will be intercepted within seconds. If you are found moving in this area, you will be shot." A repeat of the grim announcement begins. You take out the speakers, and the sensor arrays in this part of the hall.

You guess that it is most likely that the security intercept will come through the doors from the Green Zone, and that they won't be as brisk as usual, because of the alert caused by the Rebel attack. You are right on both counts. As you reach the door, you hear the soft metallic click of the lock unbolting.

Two security guards are pushing through the door, blasters extended, as you attack.

Read 607 and use the Combat Rules from the beginning of the book. Record this paragraph number so you can find your way back

If you defeat the two guards, go to 366

If you lose, go to 377

356

You search Diamond's quarters. You make a number of interesting discoveries about the Security Commander. One, she likes tropical fish – she has a huge tank along one wall of her sitting room. Two, she likes weapons. Her cupboards are full of them.

The third discovery – well, that's going to need some thinking about. In a small cabinet, locked until you carve it open, you find a blonde wig and a case with cosmetic contact lenses. Blue lenses. Now who do you know with blonde hair, blue eyes and who has quarters right next door to these? Just thinking about it makes your head spin.

So you don't think about it, and rifle through her collection of weapons instead.

Have you checked 556 or 552? If you have, go to 398

Otherwise, do you have your lightsabre? If you do, go to 368

If you don't, go to 343

357

You grasp Druth Anamor by the throat. "I ought to kill you," you hiss into his face. "If nothing else, it would prevent you creating any more weapons." Dr Anamor mocks you, sneering. "You won't kill me, young man. You don't have the blood for it. I know the type; you're not ruthless enough." You make another attempt. "Are you prepared to risk your life on that?"

"There is no risk," he grins, his yellow teeth bared. "To be a killer you must be mad, stone-hearted, or dedicated to a great cause. You're not mad, you're just reckless. You can kill easily enough when the madness of battle is upon you, yes – but not like this, not in cold blood. Nor are you cold-hearted. I'm told you have a great fondness for my daughter, Facet. This proves that you are too compassionate to make a great warrior.

"And what great cause do you serve? A Rebellion? A rising of ungrateful, backward non-entities against their Emperor? Ha! That is not a cause to kill for. Let me tell you a story. There was once a man, an old man, who had a young daughter. The days when he could kill in the name of the Emperor were over. All he could do was design weapons for others to use. And the greatest weapon, his most powerful creation, was his daughter. He dedicated her life to his cause, and trained her in the arts of murder, subterfuge and tyranny. When he had taught her all he knew, he sent her to the Commission for the Preservation of the New Order, who trained her to become the Emperor's servant, his armoured hands, crushing all those who stood against him. Finally, this daughter went into the Imperial Security Bureau, where she learned even more, and where she rose rapidly through the ranks to become a Commander."

"You're talking about Diamond," you add, wondering where this is leading. "I'm talking about my daughter," he cackles. "I'm talking about Facet! She is Diamond!!"

Whoa! Just what are we getting into here?

"It's true," he continues, relishing your discomfort. "My sweet, innocent daughter, the girl who makes friends with homeless young men, and disenchanted Imperial hirelings, is also the woman who seeks them out, and slays them!" He laughs loudly. Inside your body, you can feel a great tide of anger rising in you. "She puts on a wig, some pretty contact lenses and a soft smile, and they rush to tell her their secrets. Little do they realise that they have summoned their own nemesis! Ta'al Pierc confided in her – and betrayed the Toprawan Rebels' plans. Once she had squeezed him dry, she eliminated him!"

"Do you understand now, boy, how I know that you can never kill me? Because I have bred a true killer, a perfect assassin! And you're afraid of her!!"

In fact, right at that minute, you've never been less afraid in your life. Angry, yes; close to burning up with fury. But not afraid. There is evil here. The same type of evil that claimed your grandfather all those years ago. And you can get rid of it, right here and now. In fact, if you don't you think you might just go mad!

Tick another box on your Time Track

If you slay Druth Anamor, go to 383

If you release your grip, go to 393

358

You search Facet's quarters again, even more thoroughly. You patience is rewarded. After a lengthy exploration of the walls of her bedroom, you find a hidden lever, which activates a secret panel. Beyond, there is a narrow passage.

You follow the passage, and reach the far end, groping your way through the darkness. Another panel opens into another bedroom. You look around carefully before stepping in. Draped over a chair, you see a bright sash. Your Jedi instincts ring the alarm bells immediately. The last time you saw that sash, it was being worn by none other than Commander Diamond.

Tick the next box on your Time Track

Go to 356

359

You give it everything you've got, but this terminal just won't access the information you were looking for.

Tick the next box on your Time Track

Go back to 348

360

You feel a complete idiot for the way you spoke to Facet, but it's too late to do anything now. You can tell from the way she spoke, and the stiff carriage of her walk that she is very angry with you for lying, and the door bangs as she slams it behind her.

You've had that feeling before when you think everyone is looking at you? You've got it now.

Dropping a few coins onto the table, you get ready to leave. As you push your chair back, you cannon it into someone. You start to apologise – haven't you made yourself look stupid enough? – when you realise it is the guy who seemed to be watching Facet earlier. You both halt, eyeball to eyeball. He seems to be checking you out.

"Sorry," you mutter, pulling the chair from the aisle to let him pass. "No," he says, quietly. "After you." Fair enough. You turn your back on him and head for the door.

You're pretty sure now that the guy is keeping a close watch on Facet. Maybe it's none of your business; maybe she wouldn't thank you for sticking your nose in anyway. Maybe you should ignore her and the mysterious stranger in the red turban, and get on with finding a job.

Outside, you spot Facet walking along under the Rapid Transit Monorail, heading for the escalator. She's about sixty metres away, but you're sure it's her. Behind you, the door closes, without the man in the turban having left the cafe. Your Jedi senses are ringing like an alarm bell.

But just what are they warning you about?

If you follow the girl to the Monorail station, go to 53

If you want to see what the man in the turban gets up to instead, go to 7

If you want to get back to looking for a job, go to 169

361

"You disgust me more than anything I have ever known," you tell Anamor. You can see this doesn't impress him, but it feels better to have said it. You throw him into a chair and tie him up with some fibre optic cable. "You aren't even worth killing." You find an electronic key in his pocket and slip it into one of your own; it might be useful.

He giggles insanely. "An enemy spared is an enemy doubled." You finish the last knot, making it as tight as you can. He winces with the pain. "If you survive, it will be because we have failed. If that's the case, I don't care if you get the chance to attack me again." He howls like a wild dog on a leash as you head for the door. "Where are you going?!" he yells. You walk back and gag him. "For the throat," you reply, and set off to find the rest of the Rebel forces.

Add the electronic key to your Equipment. Check 606

Go to 378

362

Even with the aid of his powerful exoskeleton, Druth Anamor is no match for you. The mad old scientist collapses, breathing his last out on the floor. "Diamond..." he gasps. "Revenge..." You grip him by his lab coat, and give him the once over to make sure he hasn't got any more concealed weapons. A small key tumbles to the floor. You pick it up. "She'll get her chance," you tell him, as you watch him die. It's as if someone somewhere closes a door on a chilling and evil wind. You feel warmth creep back into your tired limbs.

Even as you consider your options, the room shakes. A violent
explosion rips through the building nearby. The Rebels must be
close, and their explosive charges are already threatening to take this
place apart. The terminal screen dies as power is shut off. "Fair
enough. I have an appointment with Diamond anyway," you say,
heading for the door. Outside, smoke is starting to fill the passage,
and you trot with due pace to the elevator at the end of the hall.

Add 4 Jedi Power Points to your current total

Add the electronic key to your Equipment. Check 606

Go to 378

363

The sensors mounted in the ceiling sniff at you as you run along the
passage.

If you have checked *both* 574 and 604, go to 369

If not, go to 382

364

The surviving technicians have had enough. You've caused more
mayhem in their lives than they would ever have thought possible.
Hands raised, they whimper for mercy.

"I want the plans for the weapon you've developed, the one for the
death star." They look at each other; you look at the dead bodies on
the floor and they get the message. "On the table," the least heroic
says, pointing at a grey transit tube. Of course; they had it all packaged up ready to transfer to the Imperial convoy before it was
ambushed. The fact that it is still lying around makes you nervous,
but you're so sure this is all a trap that a little extra paranoia can't
hurt. You pop the tube. Eighteen small data discs, labelled and in
order. The super laser.

You place the tube in one of your coat's many pockets, and pull Arf
from his appointed home. "You've done well so far," you tell them.
"Stay smart and you might live long enough to feel good about it. Sit
down under the benches; this place is bound to take some incoming
rounds. Don't, whatever you do, stick your head outside. Or my dog

will kill you." Arf growls threateningly.

It might work. Besides, you fuse the door lock as you go out. You slip Arf back into your pocket – he's too valuable to leave behind, so you'll just have to hope that your bluff isn't called. Anyway, you have the super laser plans, as planned. If Vermilion's people have held up their end... It's time to go see. Jumping into the landspeeder, you race off towards the Communications Centre.

Add the plans to your Equipment Box, and check 608

Go to 388

365

You walk up to the security door between the Green and Blue Zones. A keypad is set into the wall, which requires the correct three-digit code to open the door.

If you have checked 605, you may wish to read that paragraph again and go to the paragraph number it indicates

Otherwise, if you have your lightsabre and wish to use it, go to 379

If you decide to wait here, go to 387

366

The two guards go down in seconds. One of them drops a comlink. He was obviously meant to report in on the alarm. You key it to transmit, trying to think what you should say. "Is that you, Bariilas?" comes a snatched query. There's a great deal of gunfire in the background. "Sure..." you reply. You hope that Bariilas' commander is under too much pressure to worry about proper communications procedure, and that the background noise is masking any differences in your voice. "What was it?" he asks. You improvise. "One of the rebels was blundering round up here and –" The voice cuts in. "You get him?" You look down at the two fallen Troopers. "No problem," you reply. "Good!" The link goes dead. Seconds later the lights return to normal. With the sensors out, you shouldn't have any more difficulties.

Go to 342

The door into Druth Anamor's quarter is locked, but you fry the electronic keypad, and it jolts open on the short-circuit. The room that appears before you is very – red. Druth Anamor's quarters aren't anything like his daughter's. Instead of fluffy cushions and floral prints there is just red silk, red satin, red steel. Just about the only thing in there that isn't red is you, the glowing computer terminal on the desk, and Druth Anamor himself.

The man is not a walking advertisement for a career in applied science. His skin is deathly white, mottled in places with grey marks, like bruises without any colour. He has a brutal slash of a mouth, like a scar, set with jagged yellow teeth. As for his body, as he rises to his feet you see that it is thin and wasted, and that he wears an exoskeleton to help him move. You hear the servos whine as they propel him stiffly to his feet. His eyes glisten with excitement. You notice they are very pale, almost as colourless as the rest of him.

"You must be Havet Storm," he rasps. "My daughter told me all about you." You've never been keen on meeting girlfriends' parents, and now you know why. Druth moves closer, taking painfully slow steps. "Is she here?" you ask, glancing anxiously at the other doors. "No, we're alone. I think she hopes to catch up with you later." Right.

"So, you've decided to join the Rebel Alliance?" He pronounces the word "rebel" as if it hurts him to say it. "You? A Jedi?" What?! How did he know that? "We've learned a great deal about you over the last few hours, Havet Storm. I must say, I'm surprised to find that you would take the side of rebels against your master, the Emperor, and his dark lieutenant, Darth Vader."

It's been quite a surprise for you too.

If you threaten Anamor to get the information you need, go to 357

If you push past him to use his terminal, add your Tech Skill score (from your Character Sheet) to 370. This is the number of the next paragraph you should read (so, if your Tech Skill is 5, you would read 375). You can spend Jedi Power Points to increase your score temporarily

If you wait to see what Anamor does next, go to 380

368

Unbelievable. All these blasters in Diamond's rooms, and not one of them charged up. Isn't that unbelievably careless – or unbelievably smart.

You take a last look around. The room is spartan, spotless and functional. It fills you with foreboding. Reaching for the door release, you know you'll be glad to get out into the hall.

Go to 342

369

You thunder along the covered passageway towards the distant Research Lab. A few of the people you pass look round at you, but the local alarms are silent, and if you didn't have an authorised pass, the speakers would be screaming blue murder, right? These Imperial servants might not be used to seeing a guy in a floor-length coat running loose around the place, but with a Rebel attack about to tear the place to pieces, they have other things on their minds.

So, you reach the Labs without interruption. There are several very worried-looking technicians carrying stuff out of the Labs to a waiting ground car, with two stormtroopers on watch. They stiffen as you approach, but they don't halt you. Time for some clever fast-talk.

"Who's in charge here?" you snap. A worried-looking scientist-type steps forward. "Commander Diamond wants to know why this stuff hasn't been loaded yet." He bristles with indignation. "We've only just started," he wails. "Well, hurry up! This area could be overrun at any minute!" You hand him one of the cases stacked by the door. You hand another case to one of the other technicians, then pass two more to the stormtroopers. You get everyone busy humping stuff onto the ground car, then you ask: "Where are the records for the super laser?" They all stop, and turn to look at you. Naturally, you have them covered. The stormtroopers look very sheepish when they realise you have their blaster rifles.

You herd them into the Labs. One of the braver scientists tries to hide a grey transit tube which was lying in a rack on the table. You pop the tube. Eighteen small data discs, labelled and in order. The super laser. Of course; they had it all packaged up ready to transfer to the Imperial convoy before it was ambushed. The fact that it is still lying around makes you nervous, but you're so sure this is all a trap that a little extra paranoia can't hurt.

You place the tube in one of your coat's many pockets, and pull Arf from his appointed home. "You've done well so far," you tell them. "Stay smart and you might live long enough to feel good about it. Sit down under the benches; this place is bound to take some incoming rounds. Don't, whatever you do, stick your head outside. Or my dog will kill you." Arf growls threateningly.

It might work. Besides, you fuse the door lock as you go out. You slip Arf back into your pocket – he's too valuable to leave behind – and hope that they don't call your bluff. So, you have the super laser plans, as planned. If Vermilion's people have held up their end, this crazy mission might still turn out alright… You grit your teeth, and set off towards the Communications Centre in the landspeeder.

Tick another box on your Time Track

Add the plans to your Equipment Box, and check 608

If you wish to take one of the blaster rifles, add it to your Equipment Box. Check 609

Go to 382

370

You pull a diagrammatic plan of the Station off the computer. It is spread over a wide site, but the areas you want are actually close together and nearby. The living quarters of several of the senior civilian managers at the Station occupy two floors at the top of a long, flat-roofed building, attached to the Reception Building. It is divided in two; the most senior people are in the Blue Security Zone – these include Druth Anamor and Commander Diamond, both on the top floor. Diamond's quarters are, in fact, right next door to Facet Anamor's, on the other side of the divide between the Green and Blue Zones. At the end of the building, a private elevator, which only serves the top floor, descends to ground level, where two wide, covered walkways connect to the main Research Laboratories and the Communications Centre.

Most of the main military buildings and the heavy testing labs are scattered elsewhere on the site.

You memorise the layout. The Rebel attack is designed to penetrate the ground floor of the Reception Building, then out across a landing field to the Communications Centre. That's where most of the defenders will be. Your route lies in another direction.

Go to 348

371

You ignore Druth Anamor, and drop into the seat in front of his terminal. Surely you'll be able to access the files you want from here. He stands some distance behind you, mocking you with quiet laughter as you try to find your way through the maze of security checks and program trees. Even with Ta'al Pierc's patch in place, there is still a lot of work to be done – the higher functions of the computer network seem to be protected by a different system altogether.

Tick another box on your time Track

Go to 372

372

The Station's most secure files are guarded by a sophisticated password system. You can't even find a menu through which to track them down. Without knowing the right place to look, or the name of the files, or what answers to give to the password checks, you're groping in the dark. Finally, a wrong answer at one of the checks actually shuts the terminal down. As the screen goes dead, you bang the desk in frustration. Druth Anamor cackles with glee.

Your blood is hot. You feel like strangling him, or at least dangling him out of the window until he tells you how to access those files! His invention will kill billions; might his own death not save some small proportion of those lives?

Tick another box on your Time Track

If you threaten Druth Anamor, to force him to give you the plans, go to 357

If tie him up and leave him here while you go to the main labs, go to 361

If you attack him, go to 383

373

You discover quickly that there is a microwave connection to the Research labs, linking Druth Anamor's terminal to the files you want. Your first problem is that you have no idea of how to find your way through the intricate path of connected programs to get to those files.

Tick another box on your Time Track

If you abandon the attempt, and want to threaten Druth Anamor, go to 357

If you keep going, go to 374

374

It takes several precious minutes to figure out how to track down the files concerning the super laser on Druth Anamor's terminal. There are thousands of linked pieces of information; test reports, feasibility studies, junked plans. However, buried deep in the main research database, you find a package of linked files, a summary of all the work on the control and damping systems for the super laser, along with a complete schematic of the weapon itself. Druth Anamor utters a derisive snort behind you. "Careless of you," you mutter. "That package was put together when we were preparing the transfer of data to the Imperial convoy. You've done well to find it, Storm – laying your hands on it is another thing."

Tick another box on your Time Track

If you abandon getting the files, and attack Druth Anamor, go to 383

If you keep going, go to 375

375

You stare hard at the screen of Anamor's terminal. The password patch Ta'al Pierc placed on the lower-level computer functions doesn't work on this higher level stuff. You need time to adapt it, to transfer it over to this terminal, and then to worm its way into the lab database. Your work as quickly as you can, and the reward comes after about ten minutes – tapping in Pierc's code, you watch with satisfaction as all the password checks are blanked. Druth Anamor gasps at your skill. "How did you know how to do that?" he curses. "You're just a kid."

"This is nothing," you reply. "You should see me on Mega-Sonic 3000. Now that's a tough computer game." Just one prompt is left. No clue as to what it is, just an annoying call for a last piece of information. What is it?

Tick another box on your Time Track

Go to 376

376

You are within an ace of getting the information you need. Linked to the main lab database, Anamor's terminal has accessed the files, and the password system has tumbled thanks to your rapid rewiring of Ta'al Pierc's patch program. You've even found some disks to copy the information onto, and stored them in the output magazine. Now there's just a last, annoying prompt, a mysterious blinking cursor asking for – what?

And then it hits you. You know just what this is. The tracker ball attached to Anamor's terminal is also a DNA reader – it needs his finger on the button. He has backed away from you, almost to the far side of the room. Perhaps, you could wrestle him over here?

If you have checked 560, go to 395

If you haven't, go to 400

377

You are overwhelmed by the Imperial guards. Your weapon is taken from you, and they drag you off to a room in another part of the Blue Zone, throwing you into a chair. One of them operates a comlink. Diamond's face appears on the screen.

"We've captured an intruder –" the Trooper begins. "So I see. Hello, Havet. Things can't be going too well for you if you have been defeated by these poor excuses for fighters. Give him a drink, Trooper!" The young soldier hurries to obey. "The Rebel attack seems to be directed towards the Communications Centre," Diamond continues. "That's where I am. If, by some strange and marvellous fluke, you manage to escape, you will join me here, won't you?"

Fat chance of that, you think. Diamond directs her attention to the Troopers. "Operate the nerve gas valves on corridors 9, 11 and 13 of the Green Zone. Now." The two young soldiers cross to the control panel, and reach for the controls. There is a blinding flash of light, and both of them are stunned by powerful jolts of electricity. As your eyes recover, you see Diamond's cruel, taunting face disappear as the link is broken.

You know she is playing with you, and that you are barely in any shape to fight back. Even so, you have to go on to the end. Picking yourself out of the chair, you go back out into the Blue Zone, and look for the stairs back up to the residential area.

Tick another box on your Time Track

Add 1 Jedi Power Point to your current total.

Remove any blasters or blaster rifles you have from your Equipment Box; these have been taken away

Go to 342

378

You enter the elevator at the end of the Blue Zone.

If you have checked 606, go to 396

If you haven't, go to 407

379

You don't have time to play games with code numbers and electronic locks. Activating your lightsabre, you hack through the door. A guard on the far side gets the shock of his life as you come through the burning door.

Read 611 and use the Combat Rules from the beginning of this book. Record this paragraph number so you can find your way back.

If you defeat the guard, add a Blue Security Badge to your Equipment Box (unless you already have one), and check 554. Go to 342

If you lose, remove *all* your weapons and go to 377

380

At a speed you wouldn't have believed possible, Druth Anamor leaps across the grossly decorated room, his taloned hands reaching for your throat. All that slow, agonised movement you saw when you first arrived was faked – the exoskeleton propels him faster than a landspeeder! You crash to the floor, almost buried under his weight. He has one hand fixed on your throat, and the other poised over your face. An ugly, barbed probe protrudes from his fist. He starts pushing down, and it takes both of your arms to hold his one, servo-assisted hand back. "In times past," he grunts, " they used to drill holes in the heads of mad people, 'to let the demons out.' What demons are there in your head, Storm? Shall we find out?"

Add your Strength score (from your Character Sheet) to 400. That is the number of the paragraph you should read next. So, if your Strength is 4, you would read 404. Feel free to spend any Jedi Power Points you have left to increase your Strength score for this struggle

381

You access the Personnel Records. Nothing too surprising here. It shows Druth Anamor as the Head of Research. He's held some other senior research posts in the past, and stands quite high in the Imperial scientific hierarchy. It looks as if the Emperor is quite fond of him.

His daughter, Facet, is about ten months older than you. She has such a slender record, that you might wonder if she really exists! She certainly doesn't deserve her important administrative position as Director of Personnel. Daddy must have got her the job. Her assistant is twice her age, and a hundred times better qualified.

As for Commander Diamond, there is little about her beyond her name, rank, and position as Head of Security. She doesn't even have a payroll number! The only interesting fact you can discover is that she arrived on Toprawa almost exactly at the same time as Facet Anamor.

Return to 348

382

The moment you set foot onto the walkway leading to the Research labs, a local alarm starts to wail, drowning out the more general alert outside. An electronic voice calls out: "Warning. You are not cleared for access to this area. Stand perfectly still. You will be intercepted within seconds. If you are found moving in this area, you will be shot." You keep running, ignoring the message as it repeats. Other people on the walkway freeze as ordered, looking at their red security badges suspiciously, as if fearing they might be the offender. You rush past.

So much for being intercepted within seconds! The Station garrison must be fully stretched dealing with the Rebel attack. You actually reach the Research Labs before you hit any trouble. Two stormtroopers are at the main doors, guarding a number of technicians who are loading up a landspeeder. You have a fight on your hands.

Read 612, and use the Combat Rules from the beginning of the book. Record this paragraph number so you can find your way back

If you take out the two Stormtroopers, go to 364

If you lose the Combat, go to 384

383

No matter how great the evil you face, if you give into hate and anger, you let the dark side into your soul. The Force cannot be a power for retribution, only for the preservation of all that is good. Havet has taken a step onto the dark path, from which there is almost never any way to turn back.

Let the Force guide you to a new beginning, back at paragraph 1

384

Oh, man! So close! Sadly, the stormtroopers have defeated you.

Try again; perhaps you could create a new character, with different attributes

385

At the very last hurdle, you have failed in your adventure. Diamond has won it all. She has defeated you, crushed the rebellion on Toprawa, and recaptured the plans. Up in space, a lonely spaceship will arrive, listening for the transmission which will begin the epic story of Star Wars. Sadly, that transmission never arrives, and Princess Leia will turn back from Toprawa, without ever having recorded those fateful words – "Help me, Obi-Wan Kenobi, you are my only hope."

Give the game another try; with the information you have acquired, you should beat Diamond with one more attempt

386

You burst into the Communications Centre. The main room is packed with equipment, all lit in the ghostly blue glow emitted by the overhead lights. Dead Imperial soldiers lie all around, and more than a few Rebels. You search desperately – there's no sign amongst them of either Vermilion or Diamond. The game can't be over yet. Scarlett appears from behind a console, having rigged a rapid repair to some damaged equipment. "Havet!" he yells. "Am I glad to see you! Have you got the super laser plans?"

Have you checked 608? If you have, go to 388

If not, go to 394

387

You spend several fruitless minutes trying to figure out the entry code on the door, then you catch the slight sound of someone operating the keypad on the other side of the door. You listen to the tones – 3-2-0. A half-second later, the door swings open.

An security officer walks through, hesitating as he sees you. You are pressing the keypad, making it look as if he just beat you to the punch in entering the code. You laugh: "Snap!" He looks suspicious, and you can see he's about to step away from the door and allow it to close. "Crackle!" you shout. He looks at you as if you were some kind of madman, but steps forward, allowing the doors to close, but walking straight into your swinging blow aimed at the side of his head. "Pop."

Now, what was that code again?

Tick another box on your Time Track

Go to 320

"I've got the super laser plans!" you shout, pulling out the transit tube. "Where's Vermilion – he has the rest!" Scarlett grins. "Vermilion? He'll be right here." He stands up, and pulls the hideous red hide belt he wears through the loops of his trousers. It has a fastening on the inside, and he undoes it, revealing a secret pocket. He removes a row of data disks, and places them on the Communications Console at his side. Then he does a curious thing – he peels the belt wide open, so that it becomes a wide band, like a scarf. He removes the clasp, and then starts winding the belt around his head, just like... it was... a... turban. He pulls off his beard.

"Vermilion." The Rebel leader and several of the other Rebels laugh loudly. "I'm sorry, Havet. I would have told you... I just wasn't sure if I could trust you. Diamond has been chasing me so hard lately, I adopted these disguises so I could move around freely. She never came within an ace of catching me."

"Until now," comes a cold clear voice. You whirl round, as does Vermilion and the other Rebels. Several fake panels have fallen down from the walls, and a squad of stormtroopers has surrounded you. Diamond rises up from behind a dummy fuse box like a stage magician rising through a trap door. "Let me see," she says, counting on her fingers. "Vermilion, the death star plans, Havet Storm. All a girl could ever want." She turns to the stormtroopers. "Kill them."

The first shots ring out. In your stupor, you realise that Diamond's first shot is coming your way. It looks like your time is up. "NO!" yells Vermilion, throwing himself at Diamond. He hits her, hard, but as they land you hear the thump of her blaster. Vermilion's body jumps half a metre into the air, and falls sickeningly on the floor at your feet. Diamond's clear eyes meet yours. The final battle begins.

Read 613, and use the Combat Rules from the beginning of the book. Record this paragraph number so you can find your way back

If you defeat Diamond, go to 389

If you lose the Combat, go to 385

389

Diamond falls staggers back, clutching at her wound. Her eyes fill with tears. For a moment, they look almost blue in the strange light.

"Daddy," she gasps, slumping backwards.

You turn quickly, wading into the stormtroopers. They have lost their stomach for the fight with the death of their commander, however, and the few surviving rebels help you make short work of them. You rush over to Vermilion, turning him over onto his back. His wound is ugly; it looks fatal, but you find just enough strength within you to stabilise his condition for a moment. "The... plans..." he breathes hoarsely. "Frequency 1215... Codeword... Skyhook." You feel him ebbing; what you'd give to be able to help him though these last few moments. But the priority are the plans, and you know Vermilion cannot rest easily until they have been transmitted. You lower him gently into the tender arms of a young woman named Surna, a rebel you watched throttle a stormtrooper with her bare hands a few seconds ago.

You grab the disks Vermilion laid on the console, and load them into the input magazine of the Data Compressor. You add the schematics for the super laser, and start the process of preparing a burst transmission at high speed. As soon as the ready light comes on, you key the microphone and call out "Come in Skyhook! Come in, Skyhook!" A woman's voice comes over the speaker; calm, measured and full of determined strength. Must be the Princess. "Skyhook here!" she replies. "We have only moments! Prepare to copy!"

You check that the burst is ready, and that the frequency is clear. "Ready and copying," Leia announces. "Go ahead." The burst begins. Now it's just a matter of time. You post a few guards, then go back over to Vermilion. Surna is crying. "He's dead," she weeps. "He heard the burst start... told me to buy you a Star Racer." You look back. The transmission has ended.

You pick her up, and lead her to the door. "We ought to go and get one, then, because it looks like the bad guys are getting ready to launch a counter attack." The other Rebels hurriedly place some explosive charges, then follow you from the building.

If you have checked 589, go to 409

If you haven't, go to 399

390

You just don't have the strength to fight off Druth Anamor for long. He pummels you into the ground. You wait there, broken and ready for death, but the final blow never comes. "I don't deserve this moment," he cackles. "Diamond is the one who planned all this. Go, find her – and she will have the trophy she most desires." He carries you out into the hall, and dumps you on the floor, tossing a small electronic key onto your back. "You don't have time to indulge your pain, Havet Storm," he gloats. "Your nemesis awaits you!"

Check 606

Go to 378

391

You release Druth Anamor, refusing to sink to his level. A wash of strength comes over you, as if you had been cleansed by your experience. You push him back. "This place stinks of evil," you say, your voice quiet. "I need some air." Dumping him to the floor, and disabling his exoskeleton, you leave his foul apartment, and go out into the passage. The air is indeed sweeter out here. You breath it deeply, then head for the elevator.

Add 3 Jedi Power Points to your current total

Go to 378

392

The fight takes too long. More guards arrive, better armed, and even more determined.

Read 615. Use the Combat Rules from the beginning of this book. Record this paragraph number so you can find your way back here.

If you defeat the guards, go to 366

If they defeat you, go to 377

393

You release Druth Anamor, refusing to sink to his level. A wash of strength comes over you, as if you had been cleansed by your experience. You push him back. "This place stinks of evil," you say, your voice quiet. "I need some air." You look again at the terminal on his desk. Is there any way you can get what you want through that?

Add 2 Jedi Power Points to your current total

If you use the terminal, add your Tech Skill score (from your Character Sheet) to 370. This is the number of the next paragraph you should read (so, if your Tech Skill is 5, you would read 375). You can spend Jedi Power Points to increase your score temporarily

If you tie Anamor up and leave, go to 361

394

"No," you gasp. "There wasn't time." Scarlett bangs the console. "For all our sakes, Havet, you have to get those plans! Look, I haven't finished programming the communications link yet. Try one more time. We still have a few seconds." Seconds? But the Research Lab is half a kilometre away! "There's a landspeeder parked outside. Take it and go!" You find the vehicle just where Scarlett said it would be. You rev it up, and drive across the open space of a landing field. A guard tower spots you, and rips up the metallic flooring around you with laser fire, finally hitting the landspeeder's engine. The car dies as you aim it at the walkway leading towards the Labs. You dive through the gap. You're still about 200 metres short of your goal.

If you have checked *both* 574 and 604, go to 369

If not, go to 382

395

If only Arf wasn't damaged. You could have used the DNA reader on his back. What rotten luck. Oh well, you'll just have to drag Anamor over to the tracker ball…

He realises what you intend before you do. As you turn, he seizes a lamp, and heaves it across the room. It missed you by a yard – but that wasn't his intent. It crashes into the monitor, and the computer shatters in a spray of polymers, ceramics and sparks. "You're a bad loser, Anamor." He snarls, like a cornered animal. "You're about to find out how bad," he answers.

Go to 380

396

You slip the key you found in Druth Anamor's room into the waiting lock, then key for the ground floor. The elevator descends quickly. The doors open on a covered area, just outside the main building. Two covered walkways extend away from you. One leads to the distant Research Labs, a brutish-looking building about a kilometre away. A small electrically-powered cart sits close by, but you find that its batteries have been drained, and it isn't connected to the charger. No easy ride, then. The other walkway leads to the much nearer Communications Centre, a white structure, bristling with antenna and dishes.

The sounds of battle are closer than ever.

If you go to the Research Labs, go to 363

If you head for the Communications Centre, go to 386

397

On a spaceship not that far away, a young woman bends down over an R2 unit, and begins a recording.

"General Kenobi, years ago you served my father in the Clone Wars. Now he begs you to help him in his struggle against the Empire. I regret that I am unable to present my father's request to you in person, but my ship has fallen under attack, and I'm afraid my mission to bring you to Alderaan has failed. I have placed information vital to the security of the Rebellion into the memory systems of this R2 unit. My father will know how to retrieve it. You must see this droid safely delivered to him on Alderaan. This is our most desperate hour. Help me, Obi-Wan Kenobi, you're my only hope."

She places a data tape into the droid for it to record, and gives it further instructions. From close by, the sounds of battle rattle round the ship. Leia sends R2D2 on his way.

For a moment, she feels a sense of loss. Down on Toprawa, she knows, brave men and women have given their lives to transmit the plans she has placed within the droid. The price has been very high indeed. But she also feels a strange exhilaration. An epic adventure has begun.

You made it possible, Havet! Congratulations! Go to 408

398

Tucked behind the only picture on the wall of Diamond's room, you find a small electronic key, made of the same strange metal as the bracelet you were given. You activate it, and the clasp on the bracelet falls open. Thank the Force!

Remove the check on 556 or 552, and check 589 instead

Do your have your lightsabre? If you do, go to 368

If not, go 343

399

There's fighting all around, but your group manages to get clear of the Communications Centre. You're halfway to the perimeter fence, virtually home free, when a ragged voice halts you. You turn back, unable to believe your ears. Diamond – still alive! She's swaying on her legs, battered and bloodied, but still defiant.

Did you check 556 or 552 at any point in the game? If you did, go to 410

If not, go 411

400

Then it occurs to you – there's no need to have Anamor's DNA. You unplug the tracker ball, and pull Arf from his home in your coat. Slipping open the hatch on his interface panel, you unspool a connection, and plug him into the terminal. Then you place your finger on the DNA reader on his back. Arf comes to life, barks happily, and sets about by-passing the terminal's own reader. Seconds later, the data transfers itself onto the disks, and you have the super laser plans in your hands. You find a transit tube on the floor by the desk and drop them in.

Behind you, Druth Anamor issues a roar of rage. "Shut up," you snap, turning round to face him, "there's nothing you can do –"

You have the plans. Check 608

Go to 380

401-404

You just don't have the strength to hold Druth Anamor back for long. It's an ugly way to end your adventure.

So close! Perhaps a different character would do better?

405-406

Druth Anamor tries to drive the probe into your head, but you kick out with your legs and lever him over to one side. He crashes to the floor, hard. Moments later, you are both on your feet, ready to do battle, breathing hard. "I underestimated you, Storm," he gasps. "Never mind," you reply. "It's the last mistake you'll ever make."

Read 610, and use the Combat Rules from the beginning of this book. Record this paragraph number so you can find your way back here

If you defeat Druth Anamor, go to 362

If he defeats you, go to 390

407

This is too much! The stupid elevator doesn't work! It must need some kind of key!

You don't have time to go looking for it. There's a service hatch in the floor. You open it, and begin the rough climb down to the ground floor. It takes several minutes, and another few seconds pass by as you prise open the doors at the bottom of the shaft.

The doors open on a covered area, just outside the main building. Two covered walkways extend away from you. One leads to the distant Research Labs, a brutish-looking building about a kilometre away. A small electrically-powered cart sits close by, but you find that its batteries have been drained, and it isn't connected to the charger. No easy ride, then. The other walkway leads to the much nearer Communications Centre, a white structure, bristling with antenna and dishes.

The sounds of battle are closer than ever.

Tick another box on your Time Track

If you go to the Research Labs, go to 363

If you head for the Communications Centre, go to 386

408

A few hours have passed. You're sitting in the ruined bar of Al's cantina, nursing the longest, coldest Star Racer the Alchemist could find. It tastes wonderful. You drink a toast to Vermilion/Scarlett/Carmine. Sitting at your side, Surna echoes the sentiment.

Al is dusting, which seems a pretty pointless task. He's talking of opening the place up again. "By the way, Havet," he says. "Someone was in here asking after you. Someone we'd both prefer to do his drinking elsewhere." Boba Fett. "What did he want?"

"You, of course," explains Al. "He's in a big hurry. Some kind of big bounty on a guy who welshed on a deal with Jabba The Hut. Says he wants to take care of you before he leaves."

So, you haven't quite finished all your business here on Toprawa. Sooner or later, you and Boba Fett will come face to face again. But not right now! You take another long pull on your Star Racer. "He'll keep," you say. "Meanwhile, you haven't got another one of these stashed away somewhere, have you Al?"

The adventure continues in the Lost Jedi Book 2: *The Bounty Hunter*. On sale now!

409

As you leave the Communications Centre, you see Diamond's body, half buried by shattered equipment. You slip the bracelet onto her wrist, and snap it shut. "I don't take presents from strange women," you tell her unhearing form.

Check 614

Go to 399

"It's over, Diamond!" you shout. "You've lost!" She staggers again, falling against the fractured covering of the walkway. "You think so?" she calls back, coughing on blood and hate. She holds up a small transmitter. "Do you know what this is, Havet? It's vengeance!!"

She presses the button.

Do you still have 552 or 556 checked? If so, go to 412

If you have checked 614, go to 413

If you haven't checked any of these, go to 414

411

"It's over, Diamond!" you shout. "You've lost!" She staggers again, falling against the fractured covering of the walkway. "Don't be so sure" she calls back, coughing on blood and hate. "Every book has its sequel." How true. "What makes you think you'll be in mine?" you ask. She pulls herself upright, running on sheer guts and pride. "You'll never be free of me, Havet. Enjoy this moment of triumph while you can. Next time…" One of your fellow Rebels has heard enough. He raises his rifle, and takes aim. He never gets close to hitting her. Wounded or not, Diamond slips out through a hole in the side of the walkway and is gone.

Go to 397

412

There's a savage explosion. You don't hear it properly, because you're at the centre of it.

Well, you won – but you didn't live to enjoy it! Play the game again if you want to win properly, or turn to 397 for a look at what might have been…

413

There's a savage explosion. The walkway fills with smoke and noise. You take shelter until the carnage becomes quiet again, then walk back along the battered tube to where Diamond had been standing. Even now, though there is a lot of blood, there is no sign of her body.

"You're a tough lady, Diamond," you shout out into the open space beyond the walkway. "Next time, I hope I blow your head off." Distant gunfire is the only reply. You trot back down the tunnel to the others. "Let's get out of here," you say. "No point winning if you don't live to enjoy it, eh?"

Go to 397

414

Somewhere in the distance, there is a fresh explosion. Diamond looks in the direction it came from, and then back at you. You roll up your sleeves so she can see you don't have the bracelet any more. She howls with rage and frustration. She pulls herself upright, running on sheer guts and pride. "You've made a fool of me, Havet. Enjoy this moment of triumph while you can. Next time…" One of your fellow Rebels has heard enough. He raises his rifle, and takes aim. He never gets close to hitting her. Wounded or not, Diamond slips out through a hole in the side of the walkway and is gone.

"Is there going to be a next time," asks Surna. "Oh, I do hope so," you reply.

Go to 397

415

The guy poking around Al's bar must be the rebel you were told to look out for when you visited Riverside. He introduces himself as Scarlett. "You must be Storm," he says. "What news do you have for me?"

If you have checked 525, 553 or 554, go to 140

If not, go to 118

416

"Hello, Scarlett," you sigh. You're beginning to get a little irritated with him. "I'm surprised to see *you* here," he replies. "Working for the Empire yet?"

You spin round to confront him. "What's your problem, Scarlett? What does it matter to you what I'm doing?" He throws up his hands in mock surrender. "Hey – take it easy! I just wanted to talk. Look, let's go somewhere private. I can really be a nice guy if you let me."

If you go with Scarlett to hear his explanations, go to 49

If you choose to find a meal instead, go to 141

417

Carmine stares at you, waiting for your answer.

If you have checked 616, go to 309

If you haven't checked 616, go to 418

418

Despite the risks, you find yourself pouring out your hatred of the Empire. Strange, really, because you hadn't realised that's the way you felt. You've always hated what is hidden inside you, your Jedi past, but you've never realised how much you feel the Empire is to blame for the hatred that your heritage attracts. After all, it was the Empire who actually killed your father and grand-father, right? Even if this Jedi thing is so bad, can that really justify their they murders?

Besides, after what you were told at Riverside, you know that there is an alternative, and it's your guess that Carmine is a member of the Rebel Alliance, just like Scarlett. You voice your suspicion, and Carmine raises his eyebrow in surprise. "I hope you don't make a habit of accusing people of being rebels, Havet. The Empire doesn't need any help hunting for us."

"I'm just looking for a way to fight back," you assert. "We need people to join us, to fight with us," agrees Carmine. "What can you do to help us, Havet?" You are reminded of what the voice at Riverside asked you to do. Carmine nods as you think. "Nothing's changed, Havet. We have to get someone onto the inside at the IRS, and we think Facet is the key. You have to work on her, gain her trust."

"I'll find a way," you insist. "Good," smiles Carmine. "If you need to contact us again, try hanging round Al's cantina, near the port." Can't you just come here? "We move around a lot, son. This place will be just another empty building in the morning." He leads you to the door. "One more thing," he adds. You are given a new ID Card. "Same name, same visual. It's just coded differently, so that when they swipe it through the reader, they find a record that's cleaner than your best clothes after washing day. Good luck." You step outside, and the door closes behind you.

Check 517

If you go back to the Commercial District, go to 227

If you catch the Shuttle back towards the port area, go to 199

DATA BANK

501

Using your Jedi powers to such an extent is an exhausting business. You will exhaust your strength quickly if you keep this up, although you can recover Jedi Power Points by resting, and in some other ways. Remember, also, that other Jedi – as well as some of those who hate the Jedi – can sense disturbances in the Force, such as the one you have just caused by your actions. Be careful!

Continue with your adventure.

502

A good night's sleep is one way to restore your energy, so that you can use your Jedi powers at their full power.

Restore your Jedi Power Points to their Starting Level.

Continue with your adventure

503

You take another long look at the guy in the turban. He is tall, with tanned skin, deep brown eyes and a few days growth of beard on his chin. He wears a turban, much like the desert-dwellers on your home planet, and a long white jacket over a patterned shirt and light-coloured leggings. Wonder what he's done to get into trouble? Smuggling, probably – or maybe he's a spy, this being a military planet and all. Well, that's his problem. You need to keep well away from Imperial hassle.

Continue with your adventure

504

Isn't there something familiar about the guy at the counter. You take a longer look as he finishes his drink, his eyes following the blonde girl as she walks to the door. It comes to you at once. He was at the space-port, the smuggler the security guards were watching. Is it just a coincidence that he's turned up in this cafe? What's his business with the girl?

Continue with your adventure

505

There are 4 security guards for you to deal with. Each has Combat Skill 1 with a Blaster. The fight starts **Close-Up**.

Continue with your adventure

506

There are 10 security guards in the immediate vicinity you must deal with. Each has Combat Skill 1 with a Blaster. Another dozen will arrive in less than a minute. The fight starts **At Range**.

Continue with your adventure

507

You are armed with a blaster, which you keep in a holster under your arm, where it is easy to get hold of. It is a standard BlasTech DL-18, a civilian issue side-arm. It isn't going to do much harm to armoured stormtroopers, but it's perfectly effective otherwise. Although it is legal to carry a weapon, you really need a license on Toprawa, which is a sensitive military base.

You could keep your blaster stashed in a bag, where it is less likely to be found.

If you wish to change the location of the weapon, change the box you have ticked on your Character Sheet, and check box 532

In Combat, if you use your blaster, add the dice roll to your blaster skill. You must be At Range

Continue with your adventure

508

You are carrying your lightsabre, the weapon of a Jedi. Even though you are frightened of your Jedi heritage, and have promised yourself not to use your Jedi powers in case you are uncovered, you cannot bring yourself to get rid of the weapon your grandfather left for you.

In the hands of a properly-trained Jedi, the lightsabre is a powerful weapon. You have had to train yourself, but you think you know how to handle the weapon correctly.

The question is, dare you? Although the Jedi are rumoured to be extinct (something you know isn't quite true), there are plenty of people round with long memories of what they were like, and what the significance of a lightsabre is. On your belt, there is no way you can disguise it, but you can use it immediately if you get into trouble. If the wrong person catches a glimpse of it, however, you could be in serious trouble. You could carry it in Arf's secret belly-hatch instead, where it would be out of sight.

If you wish to change the location of the weapon, change the box you have ticked on your Character Sheet, and check box 529

In Combat, if you use your lightsabre, add the dice roll to your lightsabre skill. You must be Close-Up.

Add 1 to all attacking dice rolls when you use a lightsabre in Combat.

Continue with your adventure.

509

You take a longer look at the man beside you in the cafe. He is tall, with tanned skin, deep brown eyes and a few days growth of beard on his chin. He wears a turban, much like the desert-dwellers on your home planet, and a long white jacket over a patterned shirt and light-coloured leggings. No-one you know, but something about you has set your senses tingling.

Continue with your adventure.

510

Now that the security guard has swiped your card through the data reader at the spaceport, you're on file here on Toprawa. Just what you need. If you have another run-in with the law, or take a job with a reputable company, they'll demand to see your ID. Who knows what will happen then?

Continue with your adventure

511

Something tells you that you made a big mistake getting into trouble at the spaceport. What did that woman call herself? Diamond? Well, you suspect that you'll regret having her as an enemy. It would be a really good idea to postpone your next meeting for as long as you can. Trouble is, you can't expect to postpone it for long – without ID, you'll be in instant trouble if you're stopped.

Continue with your adventure

512

Disarmed, no ID, hardly any money and it's not even lunch-time. What else can go wrong?

Cross off your blaster and ID from the Equipment Box on your Character Sheet. If you leave the space-port now, you must also cross off your Lightsabre. This means you cannot equip yourself with these weapons during the rest of the adventure.

Continue with your adventure

513

After that fracas at the space-port, the authorities have your face on tape, and they'll know your name, date of birth and shoe size faster than a Lanthan Panther can do 100 metres at high altitude with a tail wind and a turbo-jet pack. If anyone on Toprawa takes the time to check your ID, you'll be dead meat.

That should be a real incentive to stay out of trouble. Your problem is that the same rules apply to several other activities, such as getting a job. You need new ID, and you need it fast.

Continue with your adventure

514

Of course, you realise at once who the black-haired woman is. The first time you saw that face, it was offering you the kind of invitation you really couldn't turn down. Or, maybe, one you should never had dared accept.

Diamond; Head of Security at the Imperial Research Station. The sort of Imperial servant other Imperial servants jump to obey. The woman who thinks you were connected somehow with that guy at the spaceport – Vermilion, or whatever his name is. And now, the woman who knows you have just witnessed her murdering the little fat man in cold blood.

Continue with your adventure

515

Something tells you that you'll remember the blonde girl for quite a while. She has the most electric blue eyes, and her long blonde hair falls in waves over her shoulders. At a guess she's be nearly a year older than you. She's the most beautiful woman you've ever seen – just thinking about her makes you feel strange.

Continue with your adventure

516

Just an average night out at Al's cantina. The man you turned from a name on the news reports into a deadly personal enemy is none other than Boba Fett. There are all kinds of stories about Fett which come back into your mind now that you have met him face-to-helmet; he's the most feared Bounty Hunter in the galaxy, and one of the most deadly humans (if that's what he is) anywhere in the Empire, possibly excluding Darth Vader and a few other Imperial servants. His armour is loaded with concealed weapons and other devices – wrist lasers, flame-projector, rocket and grenade launchers. He has killed, enslaved or vanished thousands of people for money, and quite a few more for pleasure. No-one has ever seen his face, or knows anything else about him...

Short of spitting in the Emperor's eye, there isn't anything you could have done more likely to get you killed than make an enemy out of Boba Fett.

Continue with your adventure

517

You slip your new ID into a pocket. If it holds up, you should be able to get through any check-points without trouble.

Change the check number beside your ID (on your Character Sheet) from 520 to 517

Also, delete check 510 if you have it

Continue with your adventure

518

The business card has a standard Toprawa 10-digit code, followed by a 3-digit access code – number 530.

If you're using communications equipment, and you want to call the number on the card, read 530

Continue with your adventure

519

Facet scribbles down her address, 525 Market Street. "Meet me here at eleven!" she says. You pocket the card, trying to think of something clever to say, but Facet is already gathering her things and getting ready to leave. "I have to get back to work; I'll see you later!" With that, Facet leaves the cafe.

Check paragraph 525

If you want to continue with your adventure, do so now

If you decide to kill some time and then go directly to her place, go to 230

520

You have your ID card, as issued on your home world when you turned 14. It has your picture, and a sample of your DNA encoded digitally. Bar-coded information can be read off the card through any security check-points scanner.

Failing to carry or produce your ID on an Imperial world is a criminal offence, with a 10-year penalty.

Continue with your adventure

521

It strikes you that there was probably something very wrong about that guy hustling the fake IDs. Not wrong as in illegal – that's obvious – but wrong as in out of place. This is an Imperial military world-base; would anyone really be so dumb as to try hustling here? He's tall, with dark, slightly greasy hair, and a few days growth of beard on his face. He has a long grubby coat, and a blood-red silk scarf around his throat. You commit his face and dress to memory, just in case you see him again.

Continue with your adventure

522

Looking hard, you realise the man in the doorway isn't the fake ID salesman, just another hustler selling third-division black market comlink equipment. What a dump this city is. You might just as well go back out to the spaceport and see what' s happening.

Go to 199

523

On duty at the Checkpoint is the Captain and 3 security guards for you to deal with. The Captain has Combat Skill 2 with his Blaster, and because he wears body armour, you must score an 8 to hit him. The other guards each have Combat Skill 1 with a Blaster, and no body armour. The combat starts At Range.

If you are still alive after five Rounds, go to 531

524

You are being pursued by 2 Imperial scouts on speeder bikes. On their speeder bikes, the scouts have Combat Skill 3 with their Laser Cannon. To hit them, you must score a 10 (because they are so fast, and they wear body armour). The combat starts **At Range**. Good luck!

If you can get them off the bikes, for example by fighting them upstairs in the Office Building, the Scouts each have Combat Skill 2 with their Blasters, and to pierce their body armour you must score an 8. If you have already started the battle, but you want to try your luck inside the building, fight two rounds of Combat outside first (you can't shoot back), then go to **162**.

Go to **601** to see how to deal with combat.

525

Facet's note reads:

Address: 525 Market Street

Time 23.00

See you there!

Facet

If you kill some time where you are, and then go to this address, go to 230

Otherwise, continue with your adventure

526

Now you're cooking! You have taken possession of an Aratech 74-Z Military speeder bike, a single-seat fast reconnaissance vehicle. It runs off powerful batteries, giving it a range of about 600 kilometres on a full charge, and it can reach up to about 300kph with the throttle wide open. It is partially armoured, and comes equipped with a small laser cannon.

When you ride the bike, use your Technical Skill, not your Combat Skill, when you get into a fight. Because of the speed you're travelling, your opponents have to score a 9 to hit you! This means no-one with a Combat Skill of less than 3 gets a look-in!

Unfortunately, you can't just ride this machine round whenever you like. For one, the battery isn't going to last forever (it has about 300 kilometres range left when you get hold of it, and it's 50 kilometres back to the spaceport district). That means you need a garage to charge the battery. Second, it's a dead give-away being caught in possession of a military bike, and on Toprawa you can't expect to ride it around and not be seen.

Still, it'd be worth finding some way of hiding the bike. Who knows when it might come in useful?

Continue with your adventure

527

Now that your back in the spaceport district, you need to find a place to stash the Aratech. You attract quite a bit of attention in the short time you're on the streets.

Fortunately, there are quite a few vacant lots and derelict buildings about, and you manage to steer the bike into one of the latter (close to the Imperial Research Station, just to be cheeky) without anyone around to notice. Even better news, there are some pieces of steel-weave sheeting covering some long-abandoned machinery, so you cover the bike with one of those.

Providing no-one comes looking for scrap metal in the next few days, the bike should be here waiting for you, with a couple of hundred kilometres left in the battery. If you need to make a quick getaway, this could be it.

Continue with your adventure

528

One of your most treasured possessions is "Arf", the small K9-series droid your grand-father left for you. "Arf" runs on batteries, and moves smoothly on small repulsorlifts. He's about 40 centimetres long, and has a box-like body. His head is filled with micro-processors allowing him to "think". He is voice-activated, obeying only your commands. He has a sound recorder in his ears, and can play-back at your command. He has a short video record function, using his eye-cameras, which you can play-back onto a blank surface (like a wall).

His body is hollow, with a small access hatch hidden cunningly in the belly. A small panel on his back contains a DNA-sample reader, so that if you press your finger to it, the hatch pops open. This is how you first discovered your lightsabre, which grand-father had hidden in the droid's body. The droid's structure is cunningly formulated so that – in place – the lightsabre looks like part of its internal workings, which defeats all sensor scans or inspections.

You carry "Arf" round in the large pocket of your coat. He is light, and you wouldn't go anywhere without him.

Continue with your adventure

529

You are carrying your lightsabre, the weapon of a Jedi. Even though you are frightened of your Jedi heritage, and have promised yourself not to use your Jedi powers in case you are uncovered, you cannot bring yourself to get rid of the weapon your grandfather left for you.

In the hands of a properly-trained Jedi, the lightsabre is a powerful weapon. You have had to train yourself, but you think you know how to handle the weapon correctly.

The question is, dare you? Although the Jedi are rumoured to be extinct (something you know isn't quite true), there are plenty of people round with long memories of what they were like, and what the significance of a lightsabre is. With it hidden in Arf's belly-hatch you are safe from detection. However, you can't get it it straight-away if there's a fight. On your belt, there is no way you can disguise it, but you can use it immediately if you get into trouble.

In Combat, if you use your lightsabre, add the dice roll to your lightsabre skill. You must be Close-Up. You must first draw your

weapon from Arf's secret compartment, so you may not fight back for one round

Add 1 to all attacking dice rolls when you use a lightsabre in Combat

If you wish to change the location of the weapon, change the box you have ticked on your Character Sheet, and check box 508

Continue with your adventure

530

Carmine's business card has a standard Toprawa 10-digit code, followed by a 3-digit access code – number 546.

If you're using communications equipment, and you want to call the number on the card, read 546

Continue with your adventure

531

Your battle at the road block is taking too long. The surviving security guards have been joined by an Imperial stormtrooper and 2 scouts. The stormtrooper has Combat Skill 3 with his Blaster Rifle, and because of his body armour, you must score 9 to hit him. The scouts each have Combat Skill 2 with their Blasters, and to pierce their body armour you must score 8.

Continue the battle

532

You are armed with a blaster, which you keep in your bag. It is a standard BlasTech DL-18, a civilian issue side-arm. It isn't going to do much harm to any armoured stormtroopers, but it's perfectly effective otherwise. Although it is legal to carry a weapon, you really need a license on Toprawa, which is a sensitive military base.

You could keep your blaster ready in a holster under your arm, where it is easy to get hold of.

In Combat, if you use your blaster, add the dice roll to your blaster skill. **You must be At Range. Before you can use your blaster, you must first draw your weapon from your bag. This means you may not fight back for one round**

If you wish to change the location of the weapon, change the box you have ticked on your Character Sheet, and check box 507

Continue with your adventure

533

Well, that was pretty easy, right? Did you keep a note of where you came from before you read this paragraph? OK, that's where you're going back to now.

Continue with your adventure

534

You are being approached by 2 Imperial scouts. They each have Combat Skill 2 with their Blasters, and to pierce their body armour you must score an 8. The Combat starts **At Range**. Because of your ambush, you get a free shot at them; they can't fire back for one round.

Go back to 162 when the Combat is over

535

You have been discovered by 2 Imperial scouts. They each have Combat Skill 2 with their Blasters, and to pierce their body armour you must score an 8. The Combat starts **Up Close**.

Go back to 178 when the Combat is over

536

Hobbling on an injured ankle, you are being hunted by 2 Imperial scouts on speeder bikes. The Scouts have Combat Skill 3 using the bikes' Laser Cannon. To hit them, you must score a 10 (because they are so fast, and they wear body armour). The combat starts **At**

Range, and because of their speed and your injury, you cannot get to **Up Close** combat.

Go back to 172

537

You are facing 2 Imperial scouts. One is seated on his speeder bike. He has Combat Skill 3. To hit him, you must score a 10 (because the bike is so fast, and he wears body armour). He starts **At Range**, and because of his speed, you cannot get to **Up Close** combat with him. The other Scout has a Blaster, with Combat Skill 2 and you need to score 8 to hit him. He starts **Up Close**. If you do not deal with him first, he gets on his bike (which means he'll have the same attributes as his mate).

Go back to 183

538

It may not be the best meal you ever tasted, but it restores your strength. If you have spent any Jedi Power Points, you may recover one point now.

Return to your adventure

539

All things considered, that was a pretty good meal. If you have spent any Jedi Power Points, you may recover two points now.

Return to your adventure

540

The drink is very refreshing. It isn't a Star Racer, but it'll do. If you have spent any Jedi Power Points, you may recover two points now.

Return to your adventure

541

The card Facet gave you has her name – Facet Anamor – and confirms that she is the Executive Personnel Officer at the Imperial Research Station. Some job for a woman barely older than you! You can bet she doesn't have to wonder if she can afford a Star Racer! The address is on a street you noticed when you were looking around, out near the spaceport.

If you want to call the number on the card – 876 877 5555 541 – you need to find a public comm booth. You should then read paragraph 545

Return to your adventure

542

You have no idea what this Rebellion is that Vermilion was talking about, but he has got you thinking. For the first time, you have met someone who didn't seem afraid of your Jedi powers, but *admired* them. If you meet up with him again, perhaps you might listen to what he has to say?

Return to your adventure

543

Your mysterious assailant fires at you with Blaster Skill 4. The Combat starts **At Range**.

If you are both unhurt after the first round, go to 164

Otherwise, return to your adventure at paragraph 120

544

So, just who was your mysterious assailant? The man in the turban? Someone helping him pursue the girl? Someone guarding the girl? It'd be nice to have some answers to all this, sure enough.

Continue with your adventure

545

Plucking Facet's business card from your pocket, you key her number at the Imperial Research Station. She isn't there, but someone in her department says if you give them a number, she'll call right back. You give them the number of the comlink you have borrowed (offering the owner your apologies), and wait a few minutes.

The comms unit rings, and a familiar voice come son the line. You tell Facet what has happened. "I'm sorry, Havet, I really am. Look, why don't you come straight here to the IRS, and I'll see what I can do. Take the Monorail to the end of the line, or you can walk from the main highway out to the spaceport."

If you take Facet's advice, go to 160

If not, return to your adventure

546

You call the number Carmine gave you. Moments later, his slightly mocking voice is on the line. "Hey, Havet, how're you doing?" You tell him. "Well, I'm sorry to hear that, Havet. Listen, if this means you're ready to join us, go to 182 Riverside in an hour. If not, well, I'd like to help you son, but my hands are tied."

If you go to meet Carmine, go to 182

If not, return to your adventure

547

The weapon you took from Vermilion is a Merr-Sonn Quick 6 Sporting Blaster, a lighter version of the standard blaster. It can slip into the pocket of your coat, or into the holster you wear under your arm, where it is easy to get hold of. It isn't going to do much harm to any armoured stormtroopers, but it's perfectly effective normally. Although it is legal to carry a weapon, you really need a license on Toprawa, which is a sensitive military base.

You could keep your blaster stashed in a bag, where it is less likely to be found.

If you wish to change the location of the weapon, change the box you have ticked on your Character Sheet, and check box 548

In Combat, if you use your blaster, add the dice roll to your blaster skill. You must be At Range

Continue with your adventure

548

In your bag you have a Merr-Sonn Quick 6 Sporting Blaster, a lighter version of the standard blaster. Not a weapon to do much harm to armoured stormtroopers, but it's perfectly effective normally. Although it is legal to carry a weapon, you really need a license on Toprawa, which is a sensitive military base.

You could keep your blaster ready in a holster under your arm, or in a pocket of your coat, where it is easy to get hold of.

In Combat, if you use your blaster, add the dice roll to your blaster skill. You must be At Range. Before you can use this blaster, you must first draw it from your bag. This means you may not fight back for one round

If you wish to change the location of the weapon, change the box you have ticked on your Character Sheet, and check box 547

Continue with your adventure

549

All your weapons are removed from you at the Security Gate.

Don't bother changing the information in your Equipment Box. Just remember that you're unarmed and behave yourself! After all, would you really want to get into a shoot-out in here?

Continue with your adventure

550

You have your application forms for work at the Imperial Research Station. Paperwork... on real paper! What a waste of time!

Continue with your adventure

551

You've told Facet everything you know about this Vermilion character. It has definitely got her on your side!

Continue with your adventure

552

It isn't going to be easy to forget that you are wearing the explosive bracelet Diamond gave you. It feels slightly warm on your wrist anyway, and every time you bang it accidentally, it seems to heat up, as if to remind you that things could get a lot warmer!

If you want to operate the transmitter, read 562. Don't forget to keep a record of the paragraph number you left to come here!

Otherwise, continue with your adventure

553

You have a metallic green card. This is a part of the security system at the IRS. You listen to an explanation of how it works. The Station is divided into three different zones for Security purposes – Green, Blue and Red. Sensors monitor all personnel and visitors throughout the complex. Only those wearing a badge are permitted within the complex at all. Only those with blue or red badges can enter the Blue Zone, and only those with Red badges can enter the most secure areas, the Red Zones. All the primary research and test areas, along with the Communications Centre, are badged Red.

Your green card permits you access to the Reception Building, certain low-grade office areas and part of the accommodation block.

Continue with your adventure

554

You have a metallic blue card. This is a part of the security system at the IRS. You listen to an explanation of how it works. The Station is divided into three different zones for Security purposes – Green, Blue and Red. Sensors monitor all personnel and visitors throughout the complex. Only those wearing a badge are permitted within the complex at all. Only those with blue or red badges can enter the Blue Zone, and only those with Red badges can enter the most secure areas, the Red Zones. All the primary research and test areas, along with the Communications Centre, are badged Red.

Your blue card permits you access to the administration and storage areas, and restricted parts of the accommodation block.

Continue with your adventure

555

The password bypass patch which Ta'al Pierc placed on the Research Station computer can be activated from any networked terminal in the IRS building. Not every terminal gives you access to all programs, however.

Continue with your adventure

556

You've never had a present from a girl before; it's a nice feeling. Of course, you can't forget that the bracelet Facet gave you is a transmitter, designed to call for help once you have found Vermilion. Even so, it means she trusts you!

If you operate the transmitter, read 567. Don't forget to keep a record of the paragraph number you left to come here!

Otherwise, continue with your adventure

557

Scarlett sticks in your mind, and you can't quite figure out why. He's a biggish man, with dark hair, light brown eyes, and a full beard. His slightly unusual dress sense – sober, boring business suit with a flamboyant red belt made from animal hide – isn't that striking that you should remember him. It's almost as if you have met him before!

Continue with your adventure

558

You are facing Boba Fett! He has Combat Skill 4 with his Blaster Rifle, which he will use if the Combat is At Range. If the Combat is Up Close, he uses his wrist lasers. He has Combat Skill 3 with those. Because of his powerful armour, you must score a 10 to hit him.

Continue with your adventure

559

You are facing Boba Fett! The Combat begins At Range. He has Combat Skill 4 with his Blaster Rifle, which he uses while the Combat is At Range. Because of all the cover provided by the walls and furnishings of the cantina, he needs to score 8 to hit you while the Combat is At Range. His armour is very powerful, and you need to score 11 to hit him.

If the Combat gets Up Close, he uses his wrist lasers. He has Combat Skill 3 with those. He needs a 7 to hit Up Close, and because of his powerful armour, you must score a 10 to hit him.

Continue with your adventure

560

Arf has been badly damaged. Until you can make some repairs, he is inoperative.

Continue with your adventure

561

You are facing Boba Fett! The Combat begins At Range. He has Combat Skill 4 with his Blaster Rifle, which he uses while the Combat is At Range. His armour is very powerful, and you need to score 10 to hit him.

If the Combat gets Close-Up, he uses his wrist lasers. He has Combat Skill 3 with those.

Continue with your adventure

562

You activate Diamond's bracelet, pressing the white stud as she instructed. Acting as calmly as you can, you wait for her to arrive.

Go to 37

563

You wounded Boba Fett in your first battle. Although his injuries aren't so severe that he can't quickly recover, you figure he shouldn't bother you again for a while.

Continue with your adventure

564

Fortunately, you don't have to fight the combat on your own. Even as some of the crowd sweep in, screaming with hate and aiming vibro-shivs in your direction, others enter the fight on your side. The Wookiee has seen heard everything, and he has no reason to side with Boba Fett, who has killed so many of his race. A tall, hammer-headed creature also weighs in on your side, as does a monkey-like humanoid, and a human who was standing behind a pillar on the far side of the room. Others remain neutral.

So, all you have to face are:

A cruel-faced lizard creature, wielding a vibro-shiv. He has Combat Skill 2

A grim demi-human with a mouth filled with teeth. He has Combat Skill 3 with his knife.

A stupid, wild, chattering creature, which rushes swiftly in and out of the combat. It has only Combat Skill 1 with its weapon, a serrated sword it has pulled from a sheath on its back. You need an 8 to hit it however, because of its great speed.

Go back to your adventure at paragraph 170

565

So, now you know who the black-haired woman is. Diamond; Head of Security at the Imperial Research Station. The sort of Imperial servant other Imperial servants jump to obey. A cold-hearted killer who knows you saw her murdering the little fat man. Just the kind of enemy you *don't* need.

Continue with your adventure

566

The agony in your arm is unbearable! You'll have to ease the pain, or you'll not be able to use your arm for weeks!

Spend 2 Jedi Power Points. If you have no Jedi Power Points, or you choose not to spend any, then you must reduce your Blaster Skill and your Lightsabre Skill by 2 points each until you choose to fix the arm. Put a ring round the skill boxes to remind you.

Continue with your adventure

567

You activate Facet's bracelet, pressing the white stud as she instructed. Now all you have to do is wait…

Go to 37

568

Of course, being able to get in through the front door is one thing. Getting out might be something different altogether.

Return to 187

569

The memory chills you to the bone. You may not know exactly what happened, but one's thing for sure – a murder took place in that alley, and you are the only witness!

Continue with your adventure

570

Using the patch Ta'al Pierc created, you break into the security badge program. It isn't that sophisticated, and you soon work out how the badges are activated. Popping yours into the slot on the console, you soon change the status of your badge, so that it is active, and shows you to be a genuine Imperial officer on the sensors.

Check 604

Continue with your adventure

571

You are in combat with Diamond! She has Combat Skill 4 with her Blaster, and she wears discrete body armour, which means you must score a 9 to hit her.

Since you don't have a weapon aimed at her, while she has you covered, in this combat Diamond goes first.

Continue with your adventure

572

Can't remember why you checked this box? Well, you're not supposed to. If you're lucky, all will become clear later.

Continue with your adventure

573

The weapon you took from Diamond is a specialised hold-out blaster, a SoroSuub Redemptor. Strictly Imperial service only, it is a weapon small enough to hide in the palm (although it can be equipped with an extending barrel, as this one is). It is almost silent in operation, its energy concentration being so pure, and so intense. It can be charged for a maximum of six shots. Diamond used one on Pierc, and how many on you? Make a note of how many shots the Redemptor has left.

You slip it behind your belt. It would take a full search to find it there.

The Redemptor's power is so great that you need only score 6 to hit an opponent. With a blaster like this, a near miss is often enough!

If you want to conceal the weapon in your bag, check 576.

Continue with your adventure

574

The metallic red badge will clearly the wearer automatically through the security sensors of some high-tech establishment – which has to mean the Imperial Research Station. Nice. Of course, something like this is strictly a limited edition, and if you get caught waving it around, you'll be fried Jullie-meat.

Continue with your adventure

575

The transmitter has no markings, and no obvious function. There's just one control, a small red button covered by a safety bar. Now, what do you suppose happens if you press it?

If you press the button, and you have checked 552 or 556, go to 37

If you press the button, but you haven't checked either of these, read 577

Otherwise, continue with your adventure

576

You have Diamond's Redemptor blaster hidden in your bag.

If you want to carry it on you, ready for action, check 573.

Continue with your adventure

577

How dull. Nothing happened. Maybe you could try again later.

Continue with your adventure

578

You are facing Boba Fett! The Combat starts Close-Up. Fett uses his wrist lasers; he has Combat Skill 3. Because of his powerful armour, you must score a 10 to hit him.

The good news is that you have an ally! The Wookiee takes his turn after Fett. He fights with his bare hands, and has Combat Skill 4 (which means he needs a 6 to hit Fett). Fett needs to score 7 to hit him (which means rolling a 4).

Fett will aim for the Wookiee first, then you.

Continue with your adventure

579

You are facing Boba Fett! The Combat starts At Range. Fett uses his Blaster Rifle; he has Combat Skill 4. He has the drop on you, so Fett takes his turn before yours. Because of his powerful armour, you must score a 10 to hit him.

If you can bring the Combat to Up Close, Fett uses his Wrist Lasers. He has Combat Skill 3 with these.

Continue with your adventure

580

The vehicle which came crashing down pretty much wrecked the cantina, what with the fire and all. Wonder if Al the Alchemist was insured? A pity, though. It was a fun place to frequent, if you like breathing solids and meeting up with homicidal maniacs, that is.

Continue with your adventure

581

You have a BlasTech DL-44 nestling snugly in your shoulder holster. This is just about the heaviest hand blaster you can get. The Empire had better watch out!

Continue with your adventure

582

If you have any injury which has reduced your Strength, Speed or either of your Combat Skills, the Rebel medical team put it right. Restore your attribute to its original score.

Continue with your adventure

583

You are facing an Imperial Officer. He has a blaster in his holster; he has Combat Skill 2 with that. He doesn't have this weapon in hand, so if you choose to start the Combat **At Range**, he can't fire back in the first round (while he draws his blaster). If you start **Up Close**, he fights with his fists – and he has Combat Skill 1.

Continue with your adventure

584

Boba Fett is waiting around near Facet's apartment. You don't know what he has planned, but knowing Boba Fett it can't be good news.

Continue with your adventure

585

Have you checked 563? If you have, read 587, then come back here. If not, read on

You opened fire on Boba Fett. Hey, it was your choice, Havet! The Combat starts At Range. Fett uses his Blaster Rifle; he has Combat Skill 4. Because of his powerful armour, you must score a 10 to hit him. If you can bring the Combat to Up Close, Fett uses his wrist lasers at Combat Skill 3.

You fire (or move) first. If you miss with your first two shots, and Fett misses with his first shot, this Combat ends there. Of course, there might be more to come…

Continue with your adventure

586

You have acquired a landspeeder, a small repulsorlift vehicle capable of good speed. This one is an Imperial TX-3; smart, functional, but not a patch on Boba Fett's SoroSuub XP-38.

Continue with your adventure

587

You are in combat with Boba Fett. You'd better hope that the beating you gave him last time has slowed him down.

Fett uses his Blaster Rifle at Combat Skill 3 (reduced because of his wounds). If you bring the Combat to Up Close, Fett uses his Wrist Lasers. He has Combat Skill 2 with these (again, reduced because he is injured).

Continue with this Combat

588

Have you checked 563? If you have, read 587. If not, read on

Boba Fett opens fire on you. The Combat starts At Range and he gets to fire first. Fett uses his Blaster Rifle; he has Combat Skill 4. Because of his powerful armour, you must score a 10 to hit him.

If you bring the Combat to Up Close, Fett uses his Wrist Lasers. He has Combat Skill 3 with these.

After Fett has fired his second shot, this part of the combat ends.

Continue with your adventure

589

You have the bracelet you were forced to wear, now safely removed, except for the remote detonator mechanism. That means it is still dangerous. You can get rid of it at any time; just remove this check before the book asks for it

Continue with your adventure

590

You have the sleeping draft given to you by the Rebel leader. He reckoned it would put someone to sleep for a good few hours, if you could trick them into drinking it.

Continue with your adventure

591

You and Boba Fett are in a scrap. In this first moment, only one shot is fired. The Combat starts At Range. If Fett fires first, he uses his Blaster Rifle; he has Combat Skill 4. He must score an 8 (ie, he has to roll 4 or better) to hit you because of the extreme range. If you fire first, you have to score 11!

Just deal with the first shot fired. Things are about to get much more complicated!

Return to your adventure

592

You have been wounded. You must spend 3 Jedi Power Points at once, or reduce your Speed, Strength and Lightsabre scores by 1 each.

Return to your adventure

593

Boba Fett takes on Diamond! The Combat starts At Range and Diamond goes first. If Diamond misses with her first shot, she uses her second turn to move in to Up Close. She has a Stun Gun for fighting At Range; she has Combat Skill 4 with this weapon, and needs to score 10 to overcome Fett's armour. Up Close, she uses martial arts. She has Combat Skill 6 at this!

Fett, of course has Combat Skill 4 At Range with his blaster rifle, and Combat Skill 3 Up Close with his wrist lasers. He needs to score an 8 to hit Diamond.

Have you checked 563? If so, read 587 before you start the fight

You can use your Jedi Power Points to help (or hinder) either Fett or Diamond. Got any preference?

Return to your adventure

594

You're up against Diamond! The Combat starts Up Close and you go first. Diamond uses martial arts. She has Combat Skill 6 at this! You needs to score an 8 to hit Diamond.

Return to your adventure

595

Heavy weapons open fire in the distance. The Rebel attack on the IRS has started. You have about 30 minutes left to fulfil your mission!

Return to your adventure

596

What a fight! You, Boba Fett *and* Diamond! The Combat starts At Range, and stays At Range while all three of you are on your feet. Diamond goes first, then Fett, then you.

Diamond has a Stun Gun for fighting At Range; she has Combat

Skill 4 with this weapon, and needs to score 10 to overcome Fett's armour. She fires at Fett.

Fett, of course has Combat Skill 4 At Range with his blaster rifle. He needs to score an 8 to hit Diamond. When it's his turn, use a dice or a card to decide who he fires at (1, 2, 3 or Red card means he fires at you; 4, 5, 6 or black means he fires at Diamond).

Last, but not (you hope) least, there's you. You need 10 to hit Fett, 8 to hit Diamond. Good luck!

Have you checked 563? If so, read 587 before you start the fight

You can use your Jedi Power Points to help (or hinder) either Fett or Diamond, as well as to alter your own scores

This phase of the combat ends when one of you is hit. Return to your adventure

597

With Diamond gone, you and Boba Fett fight it out to the finish! The Combat starts At Range. Fett moves first.

Fett, of course has Combat Skill 4 At Range with his blaster rifle, and Combat Skill 3 Up Close with his wrist lasers. You need to score a 10 to hit him.

Have you checked 563? If so, read 587 before you continue the fight

This is a fight to the finish. Return to your adventure

598

Diamond has injured your arm! You must spend three Jedi Power Points to limit the damage, or subtract 1 point from both your Strength and Lightsabre scores.

Return to your adventure

599

It's a shame you have failed to achieve your part of the Rebels' plan. Someone on the inside at the IRS would have been useful. Still, at least Diamond is out of the way.

Return to your adventure

600

The Rebels have armed you with a Merr-Sonn G8 blaster rifle. It has more hitting power than your regular blaster. If you come across a circumstance in which you would suffer a penalty in trying to hit something because it is armoured, using the G8 reduces the penalty by one. So, you still need to score 7 to hit an unarmoured security guard, but only 8 (instead of 9) to hit a stormtrooper.

Return to your adventure

601

You are in a big firefight inside the IRS Reception Building. On your side, there's you, and two other Rebels armed with blaster rifles. They both have Combat Skill 2; they need to score 7 to hit the Officers or 8 to hit the stormtrooper. Use the dice or cards to decide who they shoot at – on a 1 or 2, it's the stormtrooper; any other result means they fire at an Officer.

On the Imperial team there are two Imperial Officers, armed with blasters – they have Combat Skill 2, and need to score 7 to hit any of you. The stormtrooper has Combat Skill 3; he needs the same score. Again, use dice or cards to decide who they shoot at – on a 1 or 2, you're the target; any other result means they fire at one of the other Rebels.

The combat starts At Range.

Return to your adventure

602

You have fired at Diamond. The combat starts At Range. In this first moment, you have just one action – you can move Up Close or fire. Because of the distance and the armour Diamond is wearing, you must score 9 to hit her.

Just deal with this first action first. Things are about to get much more complicated!

Return to your adventure

603

You left Facet on the couch, sleeping quietly.

Return to your adventure

604

You have activated your metallic security badge.

Return to your adventure

605

You watched Facet open the door into the Blue Zone with the code 320.

Return to your adventure

606

You have the elevator key from Druth Anamor's room.

Return to your adventure

607

You are faced with two security guards, armed with blasters. They have Combat Skill 1. You may decide whether the Combat starts At Range or Up Close, and you fire first. You need a 7 to hit them.

If the Combat is still going after two rounds, go to 392. Otherwise, return to your adventure

608

You have the plans for the death star's super laser. This is the clincher as far as the Rebels' plans go. Now all you have to do is to get them to the Communications Centre, and have Vermilion transmit them up to Princess Leia.

Continue your adventure

609

You have acquired a stormtrooper's blaster rifle. It has more hitting power than your regular blaster. If you come across a circumstance in which you would suffer a penalty in trying to hit something because it is armoured, using the rifle reduces the penalty by one. So, you still need to score 7 to hit an unarmoured security guard, but only 8 (instead of 9) to hit a stormtrooper.

Return to your adventure

610

You must fight Druth Anamor. The combat starts Up Close. He is a poor fighter, with a Combat Skill of just 1. However, you need to score 11 to hit him, because of the tremendous speed and power the exoskeleton gives him.

Return to your adventure

611

You must fight the guard. The combat starts Up Close; you move first. He has a Combat Skill of 2, and you need to score 7 to hit him. If you win, you can take his blue security badge before you even have to step into the Blue Zone, and the alarms won't be triggered. After all, the Imperials are busy with other things...

Return to your adventure

612

You are in a fight outside the Research labs. The combat starts At

Range; you move first. There are two stormtroopers, each with a Combat Skill of 3, armed with blaster rifles. You need to score 9 to hit them (8 with a blaster rifle). Three technicians armed with pistols join in from the third round onward. They have Combat Skill 1; you need only a 7 to hit them.

Return to your adventure

613

You must fight Diamond. The combat starts At Range; you move first. She has Combat Skill 3 with her blaster, but if the fight becomes Up Close, she has Combat Skill 6 at martial arts! You need to score 8 to hit her (7 with a blaster rifle).

Return to your adventure

614

You are well rid of the bracelet Facet/Diamond gave you. Anything that madwoman has handled is poison!

Remove the check on 589

Return to your adventure

615

The original two security guards (if they are both still alive) are joined by two Imperial Army soldiers armed with blaster rifles. They have Combat Skill 2 and you need a 7 to hit them.

Continue the combat from where you left off, then return to your adventure

616

After your visit to Riverside, you know what the Rebels are after. Now, can you deliver?

Return to your adventure

617

The Officer reminds you that it is an offence to carry an unregistered blaster around with you. He recommends you pay a visit to the Imperial Command Building in Toprawa City immediately. "If you get searched on the street with that thing, son, you'll be in big trouble."

Return to your adventure

618

Hmmm. Was lying really the answer, Havet?

Return to your adventure. Or, if things are going badly, this might be a good time to start again

619

"By the way, Havet," Vermilion adds shortly afterwards. "Do you still have my Quick 6?" Ah. Yes. You took the blaster off him before, when you thought he was following Facet. Well, he *was* following Facet, but at least you know why now. "Sorry about that," you tell him. "Just as well I didn't hurt you too bad, right?" Vermilion grins. "Lucky for both of us," he replies.

Return to 106

Havet Storm

Strength ☐
Speed ☐
Blaster ☐
Lightsabre ☐
Tech Skills ☐

Jedi Power Points _____

Don't spend more than 6 points on any Attribute or increase any Attribute past 6 when using JPPs

---

Equipment

Arf [528]
Lightsabre [belt] [508]
DL25 Blaster [holster] [507]

ID [520]
[Arf] [529]
[bag] [532]

_____ ☐   _____ ☐
_____ ☐   _____ ☐
_____ ☐   _____ ☐
_____ ☐   _____ ☐

Data Bank

503	504	509	510	511	513	514	515	516	517	518
521	525	526	527	530	533	541	542	544	550	551
552	553	554	555	556	557	560	562	563	565	568
569	572	574	580	584	586	589	590	599	603	604
605	606	608	614	618						

Time track ☐ ☐ ☐ ☐ ☐ [Read 595] ☐ ☐ [Read 56]

253

Havet Storm

Strength ☐

Speed ☐

Blaster ☐

Lightsabre ☐

Tech Skills ☐

Jedi Power Points _____

Don't spend more than 6 points on any Attribute or increase any Attribute past 6 when using JPPs

---

Equipment

Arf [528]

Lightsabre [belt] [508]

DL25 Blaster [holster] [507]

ID [520]

[Arf] [529]

[bag] [532]

_____ ☐   _____ ☐

_____ ☐   _____ ☐

_____ ☐   _____ ☐

_____ ☐   _____ ☐

Data Bank

503	504	509	510	511	513	514	515	516	517	518
521	525	526	527	530	533	541	542	544	550	551
552	553	554	555	556	557	560	562	563	565	568
569	572	574	580	584	586	589	590	599	603	604
605	606	608	614	618						

Time track ☐ ☐ ☐ ☐ ☐ Read 595 ☐ ☐ Read 56

254

Havet Storm

Strength ☐

Speed ☐

Blaster ☐

Lightsabre ☐

Tech Skills ☐

Jedi Power Points _____

Don't spend more than 6 points on any Attribute or increase any Attribute past 6 when using JPPs

---

Equipment

Arf [528]   ID [520]

Lightsabre [belt] [508]   [Arf] [529]

DL25 Blaster [holster] [507]   [bag] [532]

_____ ☐   _____ ☐

_____ ☐   _____ ☐

_____ ☐   _____ ☐

_____ ☐   _____ ☐

Data Bank

[503]	[504]	[509]	[510]	[511]	[513]	[514]	[515]	[516]	[517]	[518]
[521]	[525]	[526]	[527]	[530]	[533]	[541]	[542]	[544]	[550]	[551]
[552]	[553]	[554]	[555]	[556]	[557]	[560]	[562]	[563]	[565]	[568]
[569]	[572]	[574]	[580]	[584]	[586]	[589]	[590]	[599]	[603]	[604]
[605]	[606]	[608]	[614]	[618]	☐	☐	☐	☐	☐	☐

Time track ☐ ☐ ☐ ☐ ☐ Read 595 ☐ ☐ Read 56

Havet Storm

Strength ☐

Speed ☐

Blaster ☐

Lightsabre ☐

Tech Skills ☐

Jedi Power Points _____

Don't spend more than 6 points on any Attribute or increase any Attribute past 6 when using JPPs

Equipment

Arf [528]

Lightsabre [belt] [508]

DL25 Blaster [holster] [507]

ID [520]

[Arf] [529]

[bag] [532]

_____ ☐   _____ ☐

_____ ☐   _____ ☐

_____ ☐   _____ ☐

_____ ☐   _____ ☐

Data Bank

[503]	[504]	[509]	[510]	[511]	[513]	[514]	[515]	[516]	[517]	[518]
[521]	[525]	[526]	[527]	[530]	[533]	[541]	[542]	[544]	[550]	[551]
[552]	[553]	[554]	[555]	[556]	[557]	[560]	[562]	[563]	[565]	[568]
[569]	[572]	[574]	[580]	[584]	[586]	[589]	[590]	[599]	[603]	[604]
[605]	[606]	[608]	[614]	[618]						

Time track ☐ ☐ ☐ ☐ ☐ Read 595 ☐ ☐ Read 56

256

LOST JEDI ADVENTURE GAME BOOKS

THE BOUNTY HUNTER

PAUL COCKBURN

B⬡XTREE

If you have already played Jedi Dawn...

If you have already played Jedi Dawn, Havet can continue his adventures from where you left off. Transfer all the data from your character sheet to the new one in this book. You should make the following adjustments:

• Keep all the weapons you had at the end of Jedi Dawn, but dispose of the rest of the Equipment. The new check numbers for Arf, your lightsabre and any other weapons are as follows:

Arf – **501** (if Arf was damaged in your first adventure and not repaired, check **502**);

Your lightsabre – **503** (if you want to start the game carrying it) or **504** (in Arf);

BlasTech DL-18 blaster – **505**

Merr-Sonn Quick 6 blaster – **506**

SoroSuub Redemptor – **507**

Merr-Sonn G8 blaster rifle – **508**

Imperial stormtrooper's blaster – **509**

I'm afraid you don't get to keep the speeder bike.

• Add 1 point to any of the following attributes – Strength, Speed, Combat (Blaster), Combat (Lightsabre), Tech Skills.

• Add 2 points to your Jedi Power Points' Starting Level. You start your new adventure with this score, regardless of how many JPPs you spent during Jedi Dawn.

• Check **510** – Boba Fett knows exactly who you are.

• If you injured Boba Fett in a fight during Jedi Dawn, check **511**.

• Check **512** – You're a wanted man on Toprawa now.

Darth Vader fixes his stare on the other man. Both are masked so you can't see their eyes. "Your situation could be to my advantage, bounty hunter," rasps Vader. The other man bows slightly. "Precisely, my Lord," he says. "It is vital that I take Han Solo back to Jabba the Hutt as soon as possible."

"Then continue your search," Vader reasons. "If Solo falls into my hands, I shall release him to you. But anything about the location of the new Rebel base is to be communicated to me instantly."

"Of course!" The other man hitches his weapons, preparing to leave. You are struck again by the strangeness of his armour plundered from all over the galaxy, battered and scarred in a hundred conflicts; weapons in his hands, on his arms, in the bulky pack on his shoulders. Boba Fett, the bounty hunter.

Two evil men together. One, the embodiment of the Empire, clad in seamless black; the other a misfit, with no loyalty that hasn't been paid for. Darth Vader and Boba Fett – the two most dangerous men in the galaxy. You listen for a moment longer, hoping for some clue as to Fett's plans. "Do not cross me," continues Vader. "It would displease me to hear that you had abused our arrangement."

"There is no danger of that, Lord Vader. I shall find Solo, return him to Jabba, and take my pay. I do have another quarry, though. He has caused me much inconvenience, and for that must die. His name is Havet Storm."

Vader's hand reaches out to Fett's shoulder, the movement a blur. The bounty hunter is startled. "Storm?! There was once a Jedi Knight by that name!" Fett steps back, so that Vader's hand falls. "It is not the same man. This is just a youth, a young man with the luck of the devil. If he were a Jedi –"

Vader interrupts. "If he were a Jedi, I would have sensed it. All who possess the power of the Force are known to me. If Storm were a Jedi, then you would worry about him no more. I would hunt him down as I did all his kind, as I did the other Storm, the old Knight."

The cold voice freezes your bones. Locked in your past, is a secret – your grandfather was a Jedi, and he passed on both his power and his lightsabre to you. All your life, you have believed that the Jedi were a force for evil. You hid your talent. Now, you realise the truth at last. Darth Vader, who has cloaked the galaxy in fear, killed your grandfather. Now, you fear more than just the bounty hunter – you have just become the enemy of Darth Vader, Dark Lord of the Sith!

The action in **The Bounty Hunter** takes place 2 years after the events of **Jedi Dawn** and the original *Star Wars* movie, and about 1 year before the events depicted in *The Empire Strikes Back*.

There is only one successful conclusion to **The Bounty Hunter**. Some of the game's endings represent alternate realities which did not really happen in the Star Wars universe.

1

Did you play JEDI DAWN?

If you did, go to 17

If not, go to 27

2

You are inside the HQ building of the Toprawan Rebels. It's early morning and all is quiet. The Rebels have suffered some heavy defeats in the last few weeks – it looks like the end is close.

You have just returned from an overnight scouting mission. You're tired and miserable. There are a few faces around the place, but most of your fellow Rebels haven't even begun to stir.

Is this the first time you have been here? If so, look at the Time Track on your Character Sheet. Tick all the boxes except the last three (use pencil; you may have to use the Time Track again!). Ignore this instruction if you have already started your Time Track

If you enter the Rebel Commander's Office, go to 28

If you enter the Armoury, go to 13

If you visit the Workshop, go to 38

If you look for some breakfast, go to 48

If you leave the HQ building, go to 58

3

You crash through a side door into the Commander's Office. General Halmain is dead, and three wounded Rebels are all that remain of the defenders in here. One, a guy you know as Windward, is clutching a small transit canister, the kind of thing you use to carry data disks.

There are Imperial soldiers in here. Read 517, and use the combat rules from the beginning of the book. Record this paragraph number so you can find your way back

If you defeat the Imperial soldiers, check 514 (unless you have already done so), then go to 37

If you are hit, go to 30

4

You pull Arf from the deep side pocket in your coat and hand him to Kalkett. The engineer smiles as he takes the droid, and fusses over him for a few moments. "Actually, the damage isn't half as bad as it seems. His motor circuits are burned through, and there's some damage to the camera, but I can fix those." He disappears behind a mountain of boxes and crates, a chaotic jumble of spare parts, returning after a few minutes with the equipment he needs. Opening Arf up, he replaces the ruined camera with a new one, and wires in the replacement circuits. He tackles some other damage, then sets Arf on his feet.

"Switch him on," he instructs. You activate Arf, placing your hand on the DNA scanner on the toy dog's back. Arf comes to life, yapping loudly. "Be quiet," you tell him, and the droid stops barking and whimpers an apology. "He could do with a paint job and a thorough overhaul, but he's basically OK. You want to leave him here for me to do the rest now?" You shake your head. "Say thanks to Kalkett, Arf." The dog yaps loudly, then you deactivate him, and slip him into the huge pocket on the side of your coat.

"Aren't you a little old to be running round with one of those?" asks Kalkett. "He still has his uses," you reply, making your way out.

Remove check 502

Tick the next box on your Time Track

Have you now ticked them all? If you have, read 526 and go to 37

If you haven't, go to 2

5

The entrance hall is filled with the dead and injured. A gratifying number of these are Imperial troops, but it chills your heart to think of the price the Rebellion is paying. Just now, there is a lull in the fighting here at the front of the building. Two Rebels are helping a wounded colleague through a hole in the wall. Perhaps you should follow them.

A voice calls you. It's Durvenna, General Halmain's aide. "Havet! Come quickly! They've captured our plans for the new base! We have to get them back!"

You follow Durvenna. Two Imperial troopers are running towards the exit. One clutches a small case, the kind of thing you carry data disks around in. You recognise it well; it's Halmain's personal records case. You've never seen it this far from his side before.

You must defeat the Imperial soldiers to recover the plans. Read 521, and use the combat rules from the beginning of the book. Record this paragraph number so you can find your way back

If you defeat the Imperial soldiers, check 514 and go to 18

If you are hit, go to 30

6

Following alleys and back streets, you reach the apartment block where Kalkett lives. His wife, Robinn, lets you in. With the door locked tight, she throws her arms round you and gives you a big hug. "Thanks," she whispers, holding back the tears. "He told me what happened." You can feel yourself blushing down to your roots. "Aw, Robinn, it wasn't any big deal, honest..."

She ushers you into the sitting room. Kalkett is lying on a portable bed, with a tray on his lap, eating a heap of food. He smiles when he sees you. "Hey, Havet! Hungry?" Is a star hot? "Sit, eat! Hey, Robinn, bring Havet some food." You take a seat, and relax. Kalkett looks pretty good, all things considered. His legs will heal quickly, and you can't imagine that he'll get anything other than the best of care from Robinn. She feeds you enough to last a week!

You know you can't stay long, but you make the most of the good food and the better company until it's time to leave. "Keep out of trouble," you tell Kalkett. "You know it!" he replies. Robinn opens the door to let you out. "This may be a good time for you guys to consider moving to a quieter planet," you tell her. "If only we could, but the spaceport is locked up tighter than the Emperor's bank balance." You laugh. She's right, though. There's no way off Toprawa.

"He'll think of something. Keep him out of trouble for a few weeks. I have a feeling the Empire will throttle back on Toprawa soon; there aren't enough of us left to justify all this security." She asks: "What will you do?" Good question. First off, find whatever's left of the Rebel command. Then, who knows? Maybe you should take your own advice and get off this rock.

Robinn must be the best cook on Toprawa. Add 4 Jedi Power Points to your current total

Go to 53

7

Sometime later, you catch up with Surna. She smiles brightly, though you catch the brittle fear behind the good humour. "Thanks for saving me, Havet. I don't know what I would have done if…" Along with everyone else, you know Surna was captured and tortured once before; she has always said she would fight to the death rather than be captured again. "Don't mention it. Just be glad I hadn't already had breakfast." She laughs, and makes room for you to sit down. "You're always hungry, Havet!" You share some of her rations; nothing much, but better than nothing.

"Surna, is it true your brother is a pilot?" you ask. She confirms what you were told. "How do you feel about getting off Toprawa? Would he help us?"

"He would, but I don't think he can. His ship has been impounded. Jabba the Hutt – you ever heard of him?" Who hasn't. Jabba is behind just about every semi-legal and downright illegal activity in this part of the galaxy. "Jabba loaned Tann the money to buy the ship through one of his front companies. Tann kept up with the payments fine at first. Then the Empire started strangling trade around Toprawa, and he got a little behind. After the attack on the Imperial Research Station, the Empire shut down the civilian part of the spaceport altogether. He hasn't earned a credit in ten months, but the interest just keeps building. The ship is out at the spaceport, but Jabba's agent, a Gamorrean called T'blisk, has it locked up tight. Tann's been gambling, trying to raise the money, but it's just making things worse."

"So, what you're saying is that if we want to get off Toprawa, we have to find your brother, we have to get his ship away from this T'blisk character, and then we have to blast a way through the Imperial blockade. Does that about cover it?" Surna dips her head in defeat. "Can't see where we have a problem, then…" you tell her. All round the campfire, other heads turn to listen to your plan. You do have a plan, don't you Havet?

It's a thin meal, but the best on offer. Add 1 Jedi Power Point to your current total _____

If you arrange to meet T'blisk, go to 32

If you go off in search of Tann (you could try Al the Alchemist's), go to 43

8

The jail where Surna is being held is a lock-up over on Market Street, a converted safety deposit vault, deep underground, and heavily guarded. There are some disturbing rumours about what they use the open ground behind the building's street level entrance for.

You scout the place out. There are only two ways in. A direct, frontal assault, or through an underground route, maybe using the sewers to get close and explosive to blow a way through the wall. Trouble with the second option, you have no idea where the prisoners are held. If they are close to where you set off the explosives, you could kill the very people you want to save.

On the other hand, you can't imagine a more desperate option than a frontal assault. You'd be outnumbered and in clear sight all the way across that open ground. There are bound to be all kinds of alarms and sensors... It's a tough nut to crack, make no mistake.

If you have checked 528, tick another box on the Time Track

If you assault the jail, go to 34

If you blow your way in from underground, go to 45

9

While you're here, you decide to take advantage of your time inside the spaceport perimeter, and to check out how well guarded Tann's ship is. T'blisk seems to think you pose no threat; OK, let's see if his confidence is well-founded. Just to be on the safe side, you send Surna back to the Rebel camp. "I'll meet you there later," you tell her. Using a service terminal, you discover that Tann's ship is in Docking Bay 35. You follow the signs, walking the link-ways with the confident air of someone who belongs here. No-one halts you, or asks for ID, not at first. And the Empire thinks it has this place sewn up tight! Ha!

"Halt!" Ooops. Where did he come from? An Imperial navy officer is walking over, scanning a data pad. "Are you the pilot for the ore freighter?" Good question...

If you attack the officer, go to 35

If you talk to him, go to 46

10

You pull Arf from your pocket, and set him on the ground. After all, there's no point getting him locked up too. And besides, you've just had an idea… You give Arf some orders, and put him into Stand-by mode. Stepping away from the alley, you walk boldly towards the lock-up.

Check 529

Go to 68

11

You pull back from your suicidal attack on the lock-up. The Imperials had too much of a firepower advantage. You can hear alarms ringing, and you know reinforcements are on their way. It's time you were well away from here, Havet!

By the time you get back to the Rebel encampment, you feel pretty low. A Rebel officer comes up, his face flushed with anger. "What was that all about, Havet? We don't have the manpower for frontal assaults on Imperial buildings! Just how many people did you lose?"

If you have checked 528, tick 2 more boxes on your Time Track. If you have reached the end of the track, go to 530

If none of the Rebels with you were hit, go to 40

If one or two Rebels were hit, go to 52

If all three were cut down, go to 67

12

You recognise your sworn enemy, Boba Fett, at once. Weapons at the ready, he wheels round, and sees you sheltering beneath his ship. "You!" he cries. Nice to be remembered, isn't it?

If you have checked 511, go to 41

If you haven't checked 511, go to 56

13

You step into the Rebel armoury. Majerrit, the part-cyborged armourer is polishing an E-Web, glowing with pride at having repaired such an important weapon. You cast an admiring eye over the heavy blaster; it will give the Rebels some much-needed support firepower.

"What do you think, Havet? Isn't it beautiful?" Majerrit has a strangely disjointed attitude towards killing machines. You once heard him describe an Imperial AT-AT as a "pussy-cat". You run your hand along the barrel. "Nice job, Maj. You tried it out yet?" He grimaces, and polishes the spot where your hand touched the weapon. "Not very likely, Havet. After all, the Imperials might just catch wind of us letting loose with an E-Web in the middle of the city, don't you think?" True. "What do you want anyway?"

You wander over to the racks of blaster rifles. "I wondered if you had any spare artillery you were keeping back. Thermal detonators, chain guns, that kind of thing." Majerrit snorts. "What's the matter, Havet? Need a bit more of an edge?" Always. You lift a BlasTech A280 rifle from the rack, and test it for balance. Majerrit rushes over to take it away from you. "Forget it. I don't have the authority. You need something, take it up with the general."

"You're all heart," you smile. Majerrit goes back to his beloved E-Web. "Keep that thing ready, Maj. You never know when we might need it."

Tick the next box on your Time Track

Have you now ticked them all? If you have read 526 then, go to 37

If you haven't, go to 2

14

You dodge into the Rebel armoury through a side door, hoping to find some heavier weaponry. Majerrit is nowhere to be seen – perhaps he has fled. There are Merr-Sonn G8 blaster rifles spilled on the floor.

Four Imperial soldiers are over by the main door, having just blasted their way in. They catch sight of you, and swing their weapons over to cut you down.

If you take a blaster rifle, add it to your Equipment list and check 508

You must defeat the Imperial soldiers. Read 531, and use the combat rules from the beginning of the book. Record this paragraph number so you can find your way back

If you defeat the Imperial soldiers, go to 60

If you flee before they are all defeated, go to 37

If you are hit, go to 30

15

You don't have a good reason to go see him, but Kalkett, the Rebels' best Technical Officer, is a close friend. It's pleasant enough just passing the time of day with him. "You'll have to come over," he says. "Robinn would love to see you again." Hmmm. Kalkett's wife is a pretty good cook, as you remember. That sounds like an invitation you can't refuse. You leave Kalkett working on some piece of heavy machinery, and head back outside his workshop into the hall.

Tick the next box on your Time Track

Have you now ticked them all? If you have, read 526, then go to 37

If you haven't, go to 2

16

The entrance hall is filled with the dead and injured. A gratifying number of these are Imperial troops, but it chills your heart to think of the price the Rebellion is paying. Just now, there is a lull in the fighting here at the front of the building. Two Rebels are helping a wounded colleague through a hole in the wall. Perhaps you should follow them.

A voice calls you. It's Prosser, one of the guys who helps Kalkett out in his workshop. "Havet! Kalkett's trapped under some machinery in the workshop! We have to get him out!"

You follow Prosser into the workshop. As he told you, a heavy machine tool Kalkett was using has been thrown over by the blast with which the Imperials blew open the main doors. Kalkett's legs are trapped beneath it. He's conscious, but in great pain.

"It's OK!" you shout. "We'll get it off you!" But before you can even attempt to lift the equipment, there is a shot, and Prosser falls. Three Imperial soldiers have followed you into the workshop.

You must defeat the Imperial soldiers before you can rescue Kalkett. Read 520, and use the combat rules from the beginning of the book. Record this paragraph number so you can find your way back

If you defeat the Imperial soldiers, go to 49

If you are hit, go to 30

17

Two years have passed since the events of Jedi Dawn, and the attack on the Imperial Research Station. They have been two extremely difficult and dangerous years. But then, when has your life ever been easy, Havet?

Certainly not since you discovered the secret of your family's heritage, the night your mother lay in hospital, and you discovered a large trunk in her closet. Inside, you found a K9-series droid, and your long-dead grandfather's recorded voice. He told you that he was a Jedi Knight, and that this was your destiny too. As the voice faded, a small, hidden hatch in the droid's belly popped open, and a cylinder popped out. It had a small control at the base, and a continuous energy lens guarded by a flared disk. That aside, the cylinder was almost featureless – until you activated the control set in its side.

At once, a blade of pure energy, glowing orange-white, sprang from the lens. It slashed through pieces of metal furniture as if they were cloth. It was a lightsabre, the legendary Jedi weapon.

You learned still more, about how your grandfather was killed, and your father's spaceship sabotaged and plunged into a star as part of a campaign to eliminate all the Jedi, along with those who might carry their blood. And you heard a name, 'Vader', the name of the man who had killed them both, and who would slay you too if your secret was ever discovered.

So, you travelled the byways of the galaxy, one step ahead of discovery and exposure, until you came to Toprawa. Here, in just the first few days, you met a girl, the lovely Facet Anamor; you made an enemy, the renowned and dreaded bounty hunter, Boba Fett; and you joined the Rebels in their quest to topple the corrupt reign of the Emperor.

The climax came when the Rebels captured the plans to the Death Star, a deadly and powerful weapon which the Emperor intended to use to destroy the Rebellion once and for all. You were part of the attack on the Communications Centre of the Imperial Research Station, which resulted in the plans being transmitted to Princess Leia of Alderaan. The word is that those plans played a major part in the destruction of the Death Star, and the Rebel victory at the battle of Yavin. All the glory may have gone to the pilot who made the killing shot, somebody called Luke Skywalker, but you know that it was the sacrifice of the rebels on Toprawa which made the victory possible.

You also learned that innocent Facet Anamor was really Diamond, the Head of Security at the Station. You defeated her, but at a terrible cost – the life of Vermilion, the charismatic Rebel leader. Diamond's body was never discovered. In your heart, you know that she must resurface one day.

Since the battle, life has been brutal. The Empire launched a major drive to uncover, punish and destroy the Toprawan Rebels. They have almost succeeded. The population are starving, your forces have been whittled down to a handful. The end cannot be long distant for the survivors.

So, here you are, Havet Storm. Eighteen years old, and one of the last fifty or so Rebels on Toprawa. Last night, as on most nights, you led a team out on patrol, looking for ways to strike back at the Empire. Last night, as too often lately, one of the team was lost and you achieved nothing. As you return to headquarters, you look up at the stars. Perhaps it's time you were moving on again.

Go to 2

18

Your fight with the Imperial soldiers has carried you out to the street. Behind you, the battle at the HQ building seems to be reaching its last stage, and the Empire's minions are winning, inevitably. Another defeat… maybe the worst of them all. What next?

If you return to the battle, go to 37

If you leave the battle behind, go to 31

19

Following alleys and back streets, you reach the apartment block where Kalkett lives. Your heart feels heavy – you know that the news you must give his wife Robinn will break her heart. Better she should hear it from you than from a stranger, or from an Imperial stormtrooper come to arrest her.

Robinn opens the door, surprised to see you. "Havet! What a surprise! I thought you were Kalkett – he's always forgetting his keys." She stops chattering, realising from the look on your face that Kalkett isn't coming home. "You'd better come in," she says, solemnly.

"It might not be as bad as you think. He got trapped; I expect they captured him, rather than..." Robinn cuts you off. "If he's been captured, that's worse than if he were dead. You know what the Empire's capable of." She looks around the apartment. "I'd better leave; they could be here for me any moment." You tell her that she can come with you up to the Rebel camp.

"I'll pack," she says, leaving the room. "There's food in the oven. Don't let it go to waste." You fetch the meal and consume it in silence. Robinn has a reputation for being the finest cook on Toprawa, but knowing that this was supposed to be Kalkett's dinner makes it taste like ashes in your mouth. Robinn returns with a small case.

"I know you did all you could, Havet." she says, abruptly. You give her the message Kalkett asked you to tell her. She blinks back the tears. "We'd better go," she says, and leaves the apartment without once looking back.

Even covered in guilt, Robinn's food is a welcome change from your recent diet. Add 2 Jedi Power Points to your current total

Go to 53

20

"The problem is," Foester continues, "that Surna was captured in the battle at HQ." The Rebels all look at you. What, is it your fault? "Then we'll have to break her out," you reply.

With three other Rebel fighters, you make your way back to Toprawa the following morning, following a secret trail past the checkpoints and patrols. Once in the city, you make your way to a lock-up the Imperials have established on Market Street. "She's in there?" you ask, checking it out from the safety of a nearby alley. Phew! The place is a converted safety deposit bank, with thick walls, barred windows and a heavy door. It's crawling with Security guards. You could attack, but the odds look grim. Maybe you could get inside some other way?

If you plan an attack, go to 8

If you look for a way to get a man on the inside, go to 33

21

Straining your arms, you try to lift the heavy machinery which is pinning Kalkett to the ground. It doesn't budge a millimetre. Your pal grunts with pain. "You're a wimp, Havet, you know that?" You'd have to agree. "Look, you're wasting your time here. Get out while you can." You draw a deep breath, and insist you'll try again. "OK," he groans. "But be careful." You put your shoulder under the equipment once again, and heave. It lifts a fraction. Maybe, just maybe –

A blaster shot crashes into the machine near your hand, burning your fingers. Without thinking, you drop the machine the centimetre or so that you had lifted it. Kalkett shrieks with agony. The Imperial soldier in the doorway advances as you scrabble for your weapon. Somehow, and you don't like to think how, Kalkett manages to close his hand around a blaster and drops him.

By the time the smoke clears and you turn around, Kalkett is dead, the shock and loss of blood having been too much. He saved your life with the last of his strength. It feels like a lead weight attached to your soul.

Lose 1 Jedi Power Point from your Starting Score (which is also the max you can ever have)

Go to 37

21-24

Straining every muscle in your body, you try to lift the heavy machinery which is pinning Kalkett to the ground. It barely moves, and your pal grunts with pain. "Give it up, Havet! You'll kill me before you can get it off." What then? "Get out while you can."

"I can't just leave you here," you insist. "You must," insists the Technician, his face ashen with pain. "You have to warn Robinn, let her know that she can't stay in the apartment anymore. When they find me, they'll come looking for her next. Promise me you'll go and get her, Havet; take her to the Rebel camp." You promise. "Tell her I love her." You promise that too.

"OK, now get out of here," he whispers, "I have to get some rest…" Kalkett's head drops back to the floor. You hold his hand for a moment, then – wiping a tear from your eye – you grab your weapons and leave the wrecked workshop.

Check 515

Go to 37

25-26

Straining muscles you never knew you had, you heave up the heavy machinery, and drag Kalkett from underneath. "Stars, Havet! What vitamins do you take?" he asks. "I'm really Mighty-Man in disguise," your reply, hauling him to the side door. You find a couple of Rebel medics and place Kalkett in their care. He lives nearby; they can take him home. "What are you going to do?" asks Kalkett. Gunfire continues to rock the building. "I'm sure I can find something to keep myself amused," you reply.

Check 516

Go to 37

27

Let's start with an introduction. Your name is Havet Storm. You were born on a well-populated planet on the outer edge of Imperial space almost eighteen standard years ago. Your mother and father are dead – as far as you know you have no close living relatives anywhere in the universe.

Nothing unusual in that. The Empire is filled with orphans scraping a living at the edge of society. Many are recruited into the mincing-machines of the Imperial Army or the Fleet. That was never an option for you, because you have a secret, one which you have kept hidden for the last three years.

Life had been normal up to then, or fairly normal, anyway. Your mother had brought you up alone, after your father's death in a space accident. Just about the only really unusual thing about your life was the way your mother kept you on the move, hopping from planet to planet, always obscuring your tracks. It meant that you were always poor, and always alone, but you grew up used to that, and it made you strong.

Finally, though, illness and exhaustion caught up with your mother, and she was taken into hospital. She never recovered. Alone in the house on that first night, looking for some things to take into the hospital for her, you found a large box in her closet. It was locked, but you found the key hidden in your mother's purse. There were a few letters, souvenirs from family holidays, that kind of thing. No still-slides, no tapes of the family – no visual records at all, in fact – but, otherwise, the kind of junk you collect as a family.

Except... there was also a toy dog, a K9-series droid, the kind of thing fond parents give their children as a companion. And, when you touched a small panel on its back, the droid came to life, and a voice spoke through its mouth, a deep, resonant and vaguely familiar voice.

"Havet, you don't know me, but this is your grandfather speaking – Morvet Storm. I don't know how much your parents have told you about me, but I am a Jedi Knight, one of the last of our breed. I am old and I am tired, and my enemies are closing in around me. I shall probably not see you again, but I am sending you this small toy, so that you will remember me, and what I stood for. Who knows, one day you may come to stand for the same things.

"I have a gift for you, Havet. When your father was born, I hoped I would one day pass this gift to him, but he was unlucky, and so I never had the opportunity. So, instead, I pass it to you."

As the voice faded, a small, hidden hatch in the droid's belly popped open, and a cylinder popped out. It had a small control at the base, and a continuous energy lens guarded by a flared disk. That aside, the cylinder was almost featureless – until you activated the control set in its side.

At once, a blade of pure energy, glowing orange-white, sprang from the lens. It slashed through pieces of metal furniture as if they were cloth. The shock made you drop the cylinder, at which point the energy beam shut off. As if on cue, your grandfather's recorded voice continued.

"This is a lightsabre, Havet, the weapon of a Jedi. It is powerful enough to cut through any material yet known in the universe. Properly trained, a Jedi can wield his lightsabre to block blaster fire! Sadly, unless I am very much mistaken, that training will be denied you.

"Havet, the Jedi are not like ordinary beings. Each has a special power, an ability to tap the mysterious power-source known as the Force. Like a beacon, the Force exists to provide a light for our journey through life. However, some Jedi turn aside from the light –"

At this point, with a harsh crackle, the recording broke up, as if the storage medium had been corrupted. You looked for control filters on Arf to counter the noise, but found none. Then you realised, what you had thought was static was in fact blaster fire!

There were snatches of your grandfather's voice then, challenging his attackers. Finally, you heard him cry "Vader! Has it come to this?" and there was an abrupt silence. The recording was still running, and you waited, breathless, for the end. Your grandfather's voice came again, spluttering, agonised.

"Havet... the Dark Side... the death of all Jedi. Never reveal... never..."

That was the last of the recording, though you listened to the silence for some while. Arf offered a few whimpering noises, picking up on your sorrow. The air around you felt as solid as glass.

That night, you listened to the words of another on her deathbed. Your mother confirmed the story; amplified it. Your grandfather had been hunted down, executed as a traitor to the Empire, as were all Jedi. You father, who might have followed in Morvet's footsteps, suffered a debilitating accident as a child, and never underwent Jedi training. Even so, the same agents who caused your grandfather's death, arranged for the navigational computer aboard your father'sfreighter to malfunction, spinning him into a star's raging heart.

Your mother apologised for never having spoken of this before. "I always feared it would be you next." She moved you from planet to planet, hiding, running, always fleeing in front of the unseen shadow of grandfather's killers. You stayed with her all the next day. At dusk, she died.

All through that night, as you sat alone in an unfamiliar house, you put the pieces together. Your grandfather, a Jedi Knight, killed because of what he was; your father, a humble man, crippled in his youth, but still carrying the Jedi inheritance inside him, also slain; your mother, who had constantly kept you on the move from planet to planet, never settling in any one place for more than a few months, sheltering you from the people who would have done the same to you.

Come morning, you packed your few possessions, including your new found companion, Arf, and the powerful lightsabre. For the next year, you kept on the moving, trying to stay ahead of the mysterious power which murdered your family. Inside, you felt the growing power of the Force, the curse your grand-father had warned you of. You learned how to use it, experimenting during the many lonely hours you spent in hiding. You learned that many people throughout the Empire feared the Jedi, feared the unseen power of the Force. On some worlds, you slipped up and allowed people to catch a glimpse of your secret power. Each time, they recoiled from you, and you had to escape yet again.

Two years ago, you came to Toprawa. A battle occurred here between the might of the Empire and a small band of revolutionaries, the Rebel Alliance. The Toprawan Rebels stole the plans for the Empire's master-project, the Death Star, and passed those plans to Princess Leia of Alderaan. According to the news that has trickled back, Leia and the Rebel Alliance were able to use the plans to defeat the Death Star in a battle at Yavin.

More by luck than choice, you ended up with the Alliance soon after that. You have seen a lot of action over the two years since then. The Empire has been hunting down the Toprawan Rebels, gradually grinding them into the dust. Only a few of you remain, in hiding. You're one of the few. Frankly, soon there won't be any left at all.

Go to 2

28

Knocking on the door, you enter General Halmain's office. Halmain is the guy who took over from the guy who took over from the woman who took over from the Calamarian... You're not sure you can remember them all. Since Vermilion was killed, the Toprawan Rebels have had a hard time holding onto their leaders.

You hand in your report. It's the usual thing. Your patrol swept the perimeter of the spaceport. No movement visible; heavy guards. You were spotted by a patrol, and Lens was killed. Just another page in the Toprawan Rebellion.

"Thank you, Havet," the General acknowledges, though he barely listened to your report. He seems more concerned with packing some data disks into his personal records case. "You'd better get some rest. We think the Imperials are preparing an attack. We're moving everyone out into the forest; we have the camps, the supplies and the route all worked out. So, gather all your gear and be ready to move out tonight."

"I'm carrying everything I own," you explain. The General takes a look at your grimy, floor-length cloak, with its many pockets. "You've probably got room for some of my stuff too," he grins, and goes back to his packing.

"General," you interrupt. "Why don't we face the facts? The Imperials have won here on Toprawa. We could go to another world, join up with some of the Rebels who are doing some real fighting." He looks up at you. "Where do you suggest?" Where else? "Yavin, sir. That's where the action is; that's where we could do the most good."

"We haven't heard anything out of Yavin in months," he explains. "We may have beaten the Death Star there, thanks to Luke Skywalker –" There's that name again! – "but we couldn't hope to hold the planet long against a new Imperial assault. High Command must have abandoned Yavin and gone to look elsewhere for a secure base. I have no idea where." Hmmm. OK, but you could still – "And besides, Havet," he continues. "How are we going to get off Toprawa? The spaceport is locked up tight, and there are still Imperial warships in orbit. How would you get us all off; in fact, who would you take? Just the fighters? Their families? Our other supporters? How many would you leave behind to face the Imperials alone?"

Point taken. People like the General can't go. But you could. "I can't make you stay if you want to leave, Havet," he says, almost reading your mind. "But I hope you do stay. Meantime, I have a job for you – carry these plans out, will you? Be careful; they show the location of the new camp. Don't let them fall into Imperial hands."

You take the case, and head for the door. Halmain's given you a lot to think about.

Tick the next box on your Time Track

Have you now ticked them all? If you have, read 526, then go to 37

If you haven't, go to 2

29

You fight your way towards the dining hall. There's been a rare fight in the hallway outside; bodies are scattered everywhere. Two Imperial soldiers are battering on the dining room door; it looks like some of the Rebels have barricaded themselves inside.

You must defeat the Imperial soldiers. Read 518, and use the combat rules from the beginning of the book. Record this paragraph number so you can find your way back

If you defeat the Imperial soldiers, check 519 and go to 37. You can also take one of the fallen soldiers' blaster rifles if you wish. Add the blaster to your Equipment (check 509)

If you flee before they are all defeated (you can do this at any time instead of taking your normal move), go to 370

If they defeat you, go to 30

30

As the fighting intensifies, you are suddenly knocked off your feet by a stray blast. The wound isn't too bad, but you can't move freely. A Rebel medic appears, and gives you a shot to kill the pain. "We'll have to get you out of here," he says.

If you have checked 522, go to 70

If you haven't checked 522, check it now

31

The battle is dying down. There doesn't seem to be anything more you can do here.

If you have checked 516, go to 6

If you haven't checked 516, but you have checked 515, go to 19

If you haven't checked either of these paragraphs, go to 42

32

Arrangements are made for you to meet T'blisk, the Gamorrean who represents Jabba the Hutt's interests on Toprawa. In great secrecy, you and Surna are smuggled into the spaceport. T'blisk meets you in a ready room, smugly confident, grunting and snorting. Like all Gamorreans, T'blisk has the manners of a pig (which is, you notice, pretty much what he is). He also doesn't speak Basic. A protocol droid stands close by, to offer a translation. "You have the money?" asks the droid, without introductions. "No," replies Surna. You're glad you agreed beforehand that she should do all the talking. You feel like serving T'blisk up with an apple in his mouth.

T'blisk offers a few more grunts. "Has Tann sent his sister to make excuses? Nothing changes – except the size of the debt owed to our illustrious master, Jabba. 65,000 credits." T'blisk picks something that was once food off the end of one of his heavy, brutal tusks. Then eats it. Yeccch! "But T'blisk," Surna continues. "How can Tann earn any credits while his ship is impounded?"

The Gamorrean isn't interested. "We'll get the money," you break in, which causes a flutter of interest all round. "Can we see the ship?" T'blisk waves his hand. The droid interprets this as: "You can look. And when you bring 65,000 credits, you can fly it away." T'blisk titters stupidly. Perhaps it sounded funnier in Gamorrean. You know as well as he does that the Imperial blockade means even if you get the ship back from T'blisk, you aren't going anywhere.

If you check out Tann's ship, go to 9

If you leave the spaceport, go to 55

33

Having checked out the lock-up from all sides, you can see an attack isn't going to work. You need someone on the inside, but there is a conspicuous lack of volunteers. "OK, I'll go." You hand over your blasters to Michels. "How are you going to get out again?" he asks. "I'll think of something," you mutter, trying to come up with a plan at the same time. Even by your own, high standards, this is a dumb thing to try.

Arf's weight against your leg reminds you that you need to decide what you will do with the droid and your weapons. Decisions, decisions.

Don't remove all your blasters from your Equipment list, just remember that you have left them with Michels and the others.

What will you do with your lightsabre? Keep it on your belt, or stash it in Arf? Check 503 or 504 in your Equipment Box according to which choice you make.

Finally, what will you do with Arf? If you keep him with you, go to 47

If you leave him behind, go to 10

34

You decide on a frontal attack, and position your small force as close to the lock-up as you dare. "We'll hit them hard and fast!" The other Rebels glance quickly at each other, as if they were expecting more of a plan. None of them voice their fears out loud. "We can do it!" you say by way of encouragement. "Are you ready to follow me?"

The lock-up looks very imposing from this close. If this crazy scheme is going to work, you'd better hope the Imperials don't have too many men inside!

Read 524 and use the combat rules from the beginning of the book. Record this paragraph number so you can find your way back.

If you are hit, go to 44

If you defeat the lock-up's defenders, go to 59

35

For once, you don't have a clever come-back to help you talk your way out of trouble. So you whack the guy. Sometimes, it can be almost as effective.

Read 525 and use the combat rules from the beginning of the book. Follow the instructions in 525 for your next choice

36

"Surna!" you yell loudly, breaking free of the guards escorting you to a cell. She jolts upright, alarmed. "You traitor!" you continue. "Did you tell them about our plans? Or did you just tell them that I knew everything?" Surna's eyes are wide open. She hasn't any idea what your plan is, but to her it sounds like a fast way to become Number One on the interrogation shortlist.

The guards exchange words. You can hear the strain it is causing them to have to think this hard. They turn round, and throw you into the cell next to Surna's. Three other Rebels who were in there already are taken out and housed elsewhere. The gate crashes shut. "You coward!" you continue, getting into the role. "Are you so afraid of a bit of torture that you would tell them everything?" Surna looks into your eyes, pleading. "Havet, I..." she begins. "Shut up!!" *Please,* shut up. "You don't know anything about the plans, do you? Thought they wouldn't believe you. So you told them I knew every-thing, is that it?" You rant on like this for a while longer. Surna clutches the bars, trying to halt your tirade, pleading with you... You don't stop, but you try to touch her hand, to reassure her somehow. She jerks back, terrified.

"Listen," you whisper. "The attack on the fuel dump takes place tonight. You don't have to hold out that long!"

One of the guards leaps from his seat in a boxed-off room on the other side of the vault, rushing for the stairs. The dumb ox hasn't even removed his headset. "They were listening?" whimpers Surna. "You bet," you tell her. "The cells must be wired for sound. Terrible invasion of privacy, isn't it?" You wink at her, and settle down for the night. Come morning, you'll explain everything to her – if you both live that long.

If you have checked 529, go to 51

If you haven't checked 529, go to 77

37

You are in the main hallway of the Rebel HQ on Toprawa.

If you look for hardware in the Armoury, go to 14

If you check out the CO's office, go to 3

If you see if your pal in the workshop is OK, go to 49

If you look in the dining area, go to 29

If you leave the HQ building, go to 39

38

You enter the workshop. Kalkett, the senior technician amongst the rebels, runs things in here. You never know what you might find him working on. And does he love to talk!

Have you checked 502? If you have, go to 4

If you haven't checked 502, go to 15

39

Though you can still hear firing in distant parts of the building, it's pretty clear that the Imperial attack has succeeded in over-running the Rebel HQ. If you stay, you'll just add your name to the Rebel casualty lists. Time to go!

If you have *not* checked 514, go to 5

If you have checked 514, but you haven't checked either 515 or 516, go to 16

If you have checked both 514 and 515/516, go to 31

40

Fortunately, you didn't lose anyone. "Then you were lucky!" the Officer exclaims. "What did you expect to achieve, Havet? I know you and Surna are close friends, but to launch a suicidal attack on an Imperial building..." You don't tell him your reason – he's angry enough with you already. Think how much worse things would look if he thought that the only reason you were so desperate to rescue Surna was that you wanted her brother to fly you off Toprawa in his ship. "I won't make the same mistake again, sir," you promise, a promise you intend to keep (you can't attack the lock-up again if you're on another planet, can you?).

"What about Surna?" you ask. The Officer thinks for a moment. "I don't mind you trying to rescue her, Havet, but don't try anything so dumb as a head-on attack, OK?"

If you make another rescue attempt, perhaps trying to sneak someone inside the jail, go to 33

If you go back to the lock-up with some explosives to blast through the walls, go to 45

If you give up trying to rescue Surna, choosing to rest for a while, go to 43

41

"I took it too easy on you last time," says Boba Fett. "This time, it'll be different."

Read 533 and use the combat rules from the beginning of the book. Record this paragraph number so you can find your way back.

If you defeat Boba Fett, go to 89

If he defeats you, go to 100

42

Moving quickly, you put distance between yourself and the one-sided battle at the Rebel HQ. The firing dies down, though whether because of the gap you open up or because the Imperials have crushed the defenders, you can't say.

Before the attack, the Rebels were in the process of moving their base out of Toprawa City, and into the forests beyond. You decide to link up with them. After climbing through abandoned buildings for a while, you meet up with some stragglers who have had the same idea. Several of them are wounded. They don't seem that pleased to see you.

"Well, Storm," spits a tall, hulk-like woman with blue skin and a lizard's tongue, "I see you managed to save your own skin." Hmmm, hostile. "What's your problem, Piekna?" you ask. She tells you. "In your hurry to be first out of the building, you left Kalkett trapped in the workshop. Remember Kalkett? Your *friend*? The best technician we had?" Right on all three counts. "That was a no-win fight, Piekna. I'm not proud of leaving Kalkett behind, but he wasn't going to get out of there alive. You know it, and I know it." Maybe that's true, but she isn't ready to admit defeat in the argument. "Live to fight another day? Is that what you're trying to sell us, Havet? But everyone knows you're planning to get off this rock first chance you get. Were you afraid Kalkett would slow you down?"

The others in the group aren't as aggressive as Piekna, but they clearly feel the same. You don't exactly have a lot of friends left on Toprawa. Maybe it's time you were somewhere else – even if it just proves that what they are saying is true.

For now, though, you keep silent. You hand over your medical pack so that one of the wounded can be looked after. When you offer to help carry someone, your offer is ignored. After an hour or so, the group moves off. You follow them at a distance, moving deeper into the forest. It gets darker with every step you take.

Go to 53

43

After everything you've been through, there's only one place to restore your spirits – Al the Alchemist's newly re-opened cantina, the Drop-In Crash Pad.

You and Al have become as thick as thieves over the last two years. Just before the attack on the Imperial Research Station, Al's old cantina was razed to the ground by a crashing shuttle craft. The Rebels had attacked a convoy in orbit above Toprawa, capturing the Death Star plans. Al's place just happened to end up wrecked as a result. Since then, he has been fighting the odds to get the place rebuilt. Trying to make a living on Toprawa is pretty hopeless these days, but if there's one thing even the most depressed people in the world can't live without, it's a place to drown their sorrows, and when Al runs a cantina, you can hold your sorrows under for a *long* time. So, with a little help from his friends (you included), he managed to get the place up and running once more.

As you walk in, you see the place is humming as usual. Al keeps his prices low and his atmosphere seedy, just the way people round here like it. The food is diabolical, but it's the only place on the planet which serves ice-cold Star Racer, your favourite low-calorie, no-additives spice drink. If Al has found a way to water tubes of Star Racer down, you haven't seen through it yet.

If you have checked 562, go to 125

If you haven't, go to 141

44

A searing pain lances through your body. You've been hit! It feels like a bad one – your enemies close in as you collapse, knowing that they have you.

A ghostly image appears – your grandfather! "The Force teaches us that direct aggression is a window into the dark side. To attack blindly, bluntly, is to invite disaster. Always look for a path that avoids senseless confrontation."

The image fades, and so do you. Start a new adventure from paragraph 1

45

You find your way into the sewer system, following the pipes and drains towards the lock-up. After a few hours of hit and miss, you find a duct which runs along the outer wall of the safety deposit vault inside the lock-up. One of your fellow rebels produces some ceramic explosive, a powerful shaped charge which should throw its full force inward at the wall. If you get lucky, you should be able to res-cue all the prisoners.

"Where do we place this?" she asks. Good question. If the prisoners are directly behind the wall at the point at which you place the explo-sive, the force will kill them. How can you tell where they are – unless the Force can guide you. Reaching deep inside yourself for the power, you seek out Surna's aura behind the heavy obstacle.

Decide how many Jedi Power Points you will spend. Add this number to 80; this is the number of the next paragraph you should read. So, if you spend 3 JPPs, you will read paragraph 83

46

The Imperial Officer looks up, impatient for your reply. You can feel that he is starting to realise you can't be who he thought you were. You need to act quickly!

Decide how many Jedi Power Points you will spend. Add this number to 60; this is the number of the next paragraph you should read (so, if you spend 2 JPPs, you would next read paragraph 62)

47

You can't leave Arf behind. After all, the Imperials aren't going to suspect a toy dog, are they? Stepping out of the alley, you walk boldly towards the lock-up.

Go to 68

48

Hmmm. Breakfast. You catch the smell of eggs and ham, and it draws you towards the dining room. The door opens on a largely empty room – it's still pretty early in the day. Among those few early risers you can see in here, you recognise Surna, who you have been friends with since the assault on the Imperial Research Station a couple of years ago. She beckons you over to sit with her. You do her the honour of sharing her breakfast.

"Anything happening over at the spaceport?" she asks, watching her food disappear. "Why? Are you booked on a flight out of here?" She laughs. "I'm not in the same hurry you are, Havet. When I leave Toprawa, it won't be because the Empire has run me off the planet. I'm just interested in what they're doing at the port, that's all." You wipe her plate clean with some bread. "You'll have to tell me what's so interesting about the spaceport later," you tell her. "I have stuff to do. Meet you here for lunch?" She laughs again. "What's that; about twenty minutes from now?" You grin back at her as you leave the room.

Tick the next box on your Time Track

Have you now ticked them all? If you have, read 526 then go to 37

If you haven't, go to 2

49

The workshop is clear of enemy forces. Which leaves you free to look around.

The news could hardly be worse. Kalkett is trapped under a heavy lathe, which was thrown over by the blast which blew in the main doors. His legs aren't crushed, but they are pinned. You'll have to get the lathe off him. Bending down, you brace your legs solidly, and curl your fingers under the metallic mass. "You have to be kidding!" murmurs Kalkett. "Don't make me laugh, now," you warn him. "I might drop it again." With a last shift of position, you get ready to lift.

Find your Strength score on your Character Sheet. You may spend Jedi Power Points to increase this total temporarily. Add this score to 20. This is the number of the next paragraph you should read. So, if your Strength is 3 and you spend 2 JPPs, you would next read 25.

50

The guards lead you past Surna's cell. They throw you into a cage already occupied by a badly wounded Rebel, who has been left on the cot without treatment. They turn their backs on you just as completely. For the rest of that day and into the evening you are left alone, then the guards return to remove some of the prisoners from their cells, Surna included. You start to protest, and get a warning tap from a blaster rifle butt for your pains. By the time your head stops spinning, Surna and the others are gone.

Your scheme to rescue Surna has come to nothing. Now you must find a way to rescue yourself.

If you have checked 529, go to 51

If you haven't checked 529, go to 77

51

The hours pass by slowly. The other prisoners fall asleep one by one, and the guards gradually relax. Several go off-duty; a small number remain on watch.

A soft whirring sound reaches your ear; so soft that you only hear it because you have been listening for that particular noise. You move to the door of your cell. From there you can see that Arf is at the door to the room. He is waiting patiently, half-hidden in the shadows. So far our programming has worked well. Arf has followed you into the vault, slipping silently past the guards, running fractionally off the floor on his repulsorlifts. You instructed him to avoid contact with anyone, so he has picked his way forward in the gaps between the comings and goings of the security guards. Having reached the vault, he has stopped – the presence of so many strangers means he will come no further without fresh orders. So, what's next?

If you left the lightsabre in Arf (you have checked 504), go to 80

If you brought it into the lock-up with you (checked 503), go to 91

52

You confess that one of the Rebels who joined you in the attack was killed. The Officer grimaces. "What did you think you were doing, Havet? I know Surna is a friend, but to launch a *suicide* attack like that…" You reflect on your motives. Would you have tried to rescue Surna if her brother didn't own a ship? Did the Rebel who was killed die because of your hunger to get off Toprawa? "We can't afford to lose anyone, Havet – not even you!" the Officer continues. "This kind of stupidity just makes the Empire's job that much easier!" You can see that several other Rebels are listening. They all seem to be in agreement with the Officer. Even after two years, you still aren't one of them. It's as if they have always known that you are different…

The Officer isn't happy that you haven't been paying attention, and he turns up his anger a notch. "Get out of my sight, Storm! Maybe I was wrong, maybe we can afford to do without you! If you can't follow orders, you're no use to the Rebellion!" Right. Well, maybe there is an order you can obey. If he wants you out of his sight, you have it in mind to find a place where no-one can find you.

Go to 43

53

The new Rebel HQ is a camp in a narrow forest clearing, about five kilometres from the outskirts of Toprawa City. It's fairly inaccessible – a pair of easily-defended trails provide the only routes in and out –

and there's a stream providing fresh water. On the negative side, the place is very poorly equipped. Most of the heavy gear was left behind.

You are allocated a tent, and your duties are mapped out. There's a hastily-prepared meal of soup and bread. Sitting with some of the others round the fire, you find the conversations is very subdued. Everyone is depressed after the latest defeat. "We'll have to organise hunting parties," mutters one of the others. You realise it is Collit Hegerra, probably the next commander of the Rebels on Toprawa. It's not a job you envy him. "We'll make some plans tomorrow." An older man with grey whiskers nods his agreement. Hegerra looks at him, looks at one or two of the others, then carries on thinking out loud. "We have to stay out of any major fights. Build up our strength. Maybe move back into the mountains." You wince. The mountains? They're 300 kilometres away!

"You have a problem with that, Storm?" asks Hegerra. You've never been one to avoid speaking your mind. "We should leave," you say. "It's all over for the Rebellion here. Let's find a ship, and blast our way out of here. After all this time, the crews on those Imperial ships aren't going to expect a break-out. We could be through them before they knew what hit them. After that, who knows? We could maybe join up with –"

"How many could we take, Havet?" Hegerra interrupts. "What happens to the rest? They'd be defenceless." You consider reminding him that if the Rebels keep up the fight much longer, the whole population of Toprawa is at risk anyway. And what good will it do the Rebellion if you are all massacred? You hold back. You know what Hegerra's feelings are. He has a big family, with cousins scattered all over the planet. He won't abandon them. "Besides," he says. "Where would we get a ship?" Ah, yes. The big hole in your logic.

"Surna's brother has a ship." Who said that? You see that it's Foester, a big, slow-thinking man you have been on patrol with a few times. Good old Foester. He's just given you the means to get off this planet forever.

If you *haven't* checked 514, read 528 (keep a record of this paragraph number so you can come back here afterwards)

Then, if you have checked 519, go to 7

If you haven't checked 519, go to 20

54

The new arrival aims a squat bulk weapon at the approaching port security guards. He squeezes the trigger, and they collapse in a heap. A neural stunner. Very neat.

He checks the damage caused to his ship by the brief fracas. "Don't tell me why they were chasing you, I don't want to know." His head is encased in a battered helmet with a T-shaped visor. You can't see his face. "Do you know who I am?" he growls. "My name is Boba Fett." Ah! The most feared bounty hunter in the galaxy, and just about the only man who could zap Imperial personnel and get away with it. "Remember that name. I'm doing you a big favour." Huh? He's letting you go? Well, don't argue about it, Havet – head for the nearest exit!

Check 532

Go to 55

55

You leave the spaceport the same way you came in. You doubt very much that T'blisk will leave the secret entrance unguarded now that you know where it is. Still, it's nice to know that security around the spaceport isn't airtight. You make the same point to Surna when you meet her outside. "Very helpful of them," she agrees. "So, what's next?" Well, you need two things if you're going to get off this planet – a ship and a pilot. "Tann can fly anything you put in front of him," insists Surna, "but the *Rust Bucket* is the best ship for what we want. Tann's ship is called the *Rust Bucket*? "Family joke," explains Surna. Oh. Ha, ha.

"So where's Tann?" you ask. Surna thinks it over. "At a guess, he'll be in the big card game at Al's cantina." OK. So, what comes first? The pilot or the ship?

If you search for Tann, go to 87

If you work out how to get the *Rust Bucket* out of T'blisk's clutches, go to 98

56

"I beat you easily last time," sneers Boba Fett. "This time, it'll be different," you insist. Fett laughs, and turns to the security guards. "Keep out of this, he's mine!" As he turns back, he raises his weapon. "Step away from the ship, Storm." You ready your own weapon. "Make me," you reply.

Read 537, and use the combat rules from the beginning of the book. Record this paragraph number so you can find your way back

If you defeat Boba Fett, go to 89

If he defeats you, go to 100

57

The Officer goes down without sounding the alarm. You look for somewhere to stash him, and see that a nearby ship has its access hatch open. You pull the body up the ramp, and into what would be the cargo bay on any normal ship. On this baby, however, the hold has been fitted out with cages, like old-fashioned jail cells. You realise what it means – this must be Boba Fett's ship, the *Slave I!* Those cages are where he keeps his prisoners – you can almost hear the echoes of people pleading for their very lives...

You consider a little sabotage, but then an even wilder plan comes to mind. There's no way the Imperials would impound this ship – Boba Fett must be free to come and go as he pleases. If you could just stay hidden, perhaps you could sneak off Toprawa as a stowaway! What a stunt that would be! You decide to try it. There's no point hiding now – you need food and other supplies – but you make up your mind that this is the way to escape Toprawa. You pull Arf from your pocket and activate him, plugging him into the door mechanism. "Pull off the access codes, Arf." The droid does just that.

Alright! Time to get out of here, get the stuff you need, and then come back. You find another hiding place to hide the Imperial Officer. Moments later, you're heading for the exit.

Check 538

Go to 55

58

You're so tired, you leave the HQ building at once, slipping out the main door and trotting up the street so that no-one interrupts you. You look up for the first time as you reach the first corner. Hey – what was that? It looked like an Imperial troop carrier, ducking back into an alleyway about a block further on. What is *that* doing here? Have the Imperials discovered the location of the Rebel HQ? Are they about to launch an attack?

You drop down the steps into the basement of the building beside you, and take a look around. Now that you know what you're looking for, you see signs of other Imperial personnel preparing an assault. Armed soldiers glimpsed through windows facing the HQ building; a squad of infantry moving stealthily towards their jump-off point; back-up specialists in armoured vehicles – all signs of a major attack. Then you catch sight of a heavy blaster being moved into position, more or less opposite the Rebel building's front entrance. Man! They really mean business. You have to do something!

It's too late for you to make it back before the attack. How can you warn the Rebels from where you are hiding? Perhaps you could take some action, and make the numbers a bit more even, providing the defenders with a warning at the same time… Or perhaps it would be suicide to intervene. What should you do next?

If you wait for the attack to start, and then get well clear of the danger, go to 42

If you look for a way to help, go to 92

59

Against impossible odds, you defeat the Imperials guarding the lock-up, bursting through the doors and scything through their ranks. You get them all – all bar one. The guy has been wounded, but he hauls himself to a terminal while you're trying to find a way into the vault. And while you're still halfway down the ramp, still trying to find the prisoners, he keys the command that floods the building with poison gas…

There was no victory to be gained on this route, Havet. Start again (and try a little less force and a little more Force!)

60

You defeat the Imperials attacking the Armoury. You take a moment to consider whether if you could carry the E-Web out with you, but it is too bulky. Well, if you can't have it, nor can the Empire. You pull the detonator pin from a thermal grenade, and toss it towards a box of ammunition. As you slip out through the side door, you catch a glimpse of three Imperial soldiers coming in the other way. Man, are they in for a surprise!

Go to 37

61-62

The Officer has a weak will, and falls under your influence easily. "You knew I would be coming here this morning," you tell him. "I'm supposed to fly out the ore freighter."

The suggestion lodges firmly in his mind. "I thought I recognised you," he says, a little indecisively, but unable to shake off your control. "You're in the wrong place, though, you want Docking Bay 84b." You apologise for the mistake. "Is this the ship the Gamorrean has impounded? Looks a good tub." The man actually laughs out loud. "You don't recognise that ship? How long have you been flying this sector? That's *Slave I* – Boba Fett's ship. You've heard of Boba Fett, haven't you?" He laughs again. "Ha, ha! Of course. How silly of me," you respond. He looks at you, a shadow of suspicion reappearing on his face. "Bay 84b?" you ask. He jabs his thumb back along the connecting passage. You leave at once.

So Boba Fett's ship is here… While you can't pretend to be happy about that, it does give you another option, if you can't rescue Tann's. Thinking over what you have learned, you head out of the spaceport.

Go to 55

63-64

The Officer has a very weak will, and submits completely to your influence. "You knew I would be coming here this morning," you tell him. "I'm supposed to fly out the *Rust Bucket*. You were going to arrange clearance."

He hesitates, but you can feel his mind yield to your suggestion. "I recognise you now," he says. "You're flying the *Rust Bucket* out of here." He taps the keys on his data pad. "I'll arrange clearance – what time do you want to start preflight?" You haven't made up your mind, so you tell him to hold on that information. "OK. Do you have a flight plan logged with the fleet?"

"Not yet; I'll do that now." He nods and taps his data pad. "OK, you're cleared for take off. Don't forget to file that Flight Plan." He moves off, and you lift your influence from him gently. With luck, he'll not check that entry again, and have doubts why an impounded ship has been cleared for flight. Because if he does…

Still, ground clearance is the least of your worries. Right now, you figure you'd better get out of the spaceport, before anyone else intercepts you. Stepping away from the ship you had been passing, you head back to the secret route T'blisk's people brought you in through.

Check 540

Go to 55

65-66

The Officer has the willpower of a fish, and caves in under the pressure of your Jedi power. "You knew I would be coming here this morning," you tell him. "I'm inspecting all the ships impounded here, to see which ones can be flown out and used elsewhere."

He snaps out a salute. "Of course, I remember now," he says. "Where would you like to start?" You point at the vessel behind you. "Who does this ship belong to?" He hesitates, and you step up your control. "That's *Slave I* – Boba Fett's ship," he replies. What? This is too good an opportunity to miss! There's no way the Imperials would impound the bounty hunter's ship, which means Fett must be free to come and go as he pleases. If someone could hide themselves on board, it would be the perfect way to get off Toprawa once and for all. "Wait here," you command the Officer, climbing onto the ship's entrance ramp.

You board *Slave I*. Instead of a standard cargo bay, Boba Fett's ship has an area fitted with cages, rather like jail cells. These must be where he keeps his prisoners before he hands them over for the bounty. Though the ship is empty, it reeks of fear. You can imagine the echoes of people pleading for their lives in this very place…

You explore a little further, nervous in case he comes back on board or you trigger an alarm. *Slave I* is a three-crew vessel; fast, well armed and fuelled for take-off. The flight deck and Boba Fett's quarters are locked, but no matter. You could, of course, just hide yourself in one of the darkened cell areas now, but that wouldn't be smart. You have no food, and no way of telling if Fett might need those cells for prisoners from Toprawa. Besides, you have to offer this chance to Surna and the others. Running away without saying anything really would be cowardly.

You head back towards the ramp. You activate Arf, and plug his remote cable into the door mechanism. "Pull off the access codes, Arf!" you whisper. The droid offers some happy puffing noises while it completes the task. Moments later, you're heading down the ramp.

"Nice ship," you comment to the nervous Officer. "Much better than the *Rust Bucket* I'm supposed to take. Where is that, exactly?" He leads you to a small Corellian light freighter, an old design, not a patch on the later YT-1300. "Is it cleared for take-off?" you ask. The Officer checks on his data pad. "No…" he replies. "And there's no flight plan either. It's registered as being privately impounded by Jabba the Hutt's emissary –"

"T'blisk. Yes, yes, I know that. I'll deal with T'blisk and the flight plan. You just get my ground clearance, OK?" He salutes again, and taps some entries in on the data pad while you check that there is enough fuel and that the hyperdrive hasn't been disabled. All is well, as far as you can tell. "I'll be back later," you tell the Officer. He nods, and turns away.

So long as he doesn't check that entry again, and have doubts why an impounded ship has been cleared for flight, you'll be fine. Meanwhile, ground clearance is the least of your worries. Right now, you figure you'd better get out of the spaceport, before anyone else intercepts you. Stepping away from the ship you had been passing, you head back to the secret route T'blisk's people brought you in through.

Check 540 & 538

Go to 55

67

With a heavy heart, you confess just how great a disaster the attack on the lock-up was. The Rebel Officer swallows hard, his face clouded with rage. "What did you think you were doing, Havet? I know you and Surna are close, but to launch a suicidal attack…" You don't tell him your reason; if he knew you wanted to rescue Surna because you hoped her brother would fly you away off Toprawa, it wouldn't look good.

"We can't afford to lose anyone, Havet – but I'm going to make an exception with you. Get out of my sight. You're no good to the Rebellion." Two Rebel soldiers are detailed to remove you from the camp. With a heavy heart, you make your way back towards Toprawa City.

If you have a blaster rifle, the Rebel Officer takes it off you. Remove it from your Equipment Box

Go to 43

68

The guards at the front door of the lock-up watch closely as you stroll past. You remove some gum from your mouth, and flick it at the entrance. As you figured, they're bored enough to consider this a mortal insult. "Hey, you! Hold it right there!!" You stop, turning with your hands held high. The two guards approach, blaster rifles levelled. The younger one leans into your face. "What did you mean by that?" You shrug your shoulders. "By what?" you ask. The older guard jumps in, sticking to tried and tested tactics. "ID!" he demands. "Don't have any," you reply, which gets him pretty flustered too. Seconds later, they frog-march you into the lock-up.

The Duty Officer looks harassed enough as you come up. On a scale of one-to-ten, he rates about 1.1 in the Imperial hierarchy, which means he gets to sit at a desk, trying to keep on top of the red tape. "Who's this?" he asks, resignedly. "We don't know; he doesn't have any ID." The Officer scowls. "Check him against the imager." You've seen this drill before; they line you up in front of a camera, which builds up a 3-D portrait of you from images taken from the front and sides. They then compare the image with records on a central database. You know full well what they're going to find when the match is made on your face…

Sure enough, the Officer leaps up with excitement when the match is made. The two guards recover from their surprise and level their weapons at you. "Do you know who you have caught? This is Havet Storm! One of the last of the Toprawan rebels! Good work, lads." The two guards look at each other. You can see there is no way they're going to admit you just walked up and asked to be arrested. With luck, no-one will see anything at all suspicious in what has happened so far.

You are searched, and taken downstairs into what was the safety deposit vault, but which now serves as a holding pen for the Empire's enemies. Cages have been built to house a dozen prisoners. Surna sits in the corner of the nearest, looking very unhappy and frightened. The guards lead you towards a cell on the far side of the room. It suddenly occurs to you that it would be better if you were near Surna – but what can you do about it?

If you brought your lightsabre with you (checked 503?), the search finds it. You can't use your lightsabre, and you didn't bring a blaster, so check 541

The search will also find Arf if you brought him along

If you create a disturbance, go to 36

If you behave yourself, go to 50

69

You manage to escape. The guards are caught flat-footed by your bold action, and with the aid of the other Rebels you steal some weapons, and bust your way out. You remember to recover your equipment – Arf included – on the way. The other escapees are heading towards the Rebel camp in the forest. You give them the slip. After what happened to Surna, you feel disappointed and angry. There's only one place to go when you're feeling this low.

Go to 43

70

No-one can fault your courage, but the battle finally becomes too frantic for your luck to hold out. A second shot strikes you, and you feel the strength leave your broken body. You have saved a few Rebel lives this day, but at the cost of your own.

Courage never dies. Try starting again from paragraph 1

Well, it was a good plan, but you don't seem to have quite pulled it off. You had hoped to be able to use your telekinetic power to retrieve your lightsabre and bust out, but the weapon stubbornly refuses to move.

If you spend 3 more JPPs on another attempt, go to 73

Otherwise, go to 544

73-76

Concentrating hard, you use the Force to bring the lightsabre to your side. It flies from Arf's hatchway into your hands. The gloom of night is dispelled as you ignite the weapon, and slash through the bars on your cell. With more quick hacks to left and right, you open more of the cell doors before the guards have had a chance to react. Finally, they start to fight back, but you can feel other Rebels joining in the attack.

Go to 545

77

You can't sleep. Your mind keeps trying to work out a plan to rescue the imprisoned Rebels – including yourself now, of course. Nothing comes to mind.

Go to 544

78

You try to run away, but Boba Fett cuts you off. You realise now that he was hoping you would move away from his spaceship, so that he could use his heavier weapons. Caught in an open landing bay, you wait to see what he has in store for you.

Read 546

If you defeat Boba Fett, go to 89

If he defeats you, go to 95

79

"Boba Fett?" you groan. Al smiles. "He remembers you too. In fact, he was in here the other evening saying that the only thing preventing him leaving Toprawa is the fact that he hasn't killed you yet." That's the worst excuse you've ever heard anyone give for being late for take off. "So, you don't think he'd give me a lift off-planet, then?" you ask. Al chuckles, and you join in. A small grey-furred Mannovan sitting close by cackles as well, without knowing what the joke is, until you silence him/her/it with a glare.

"I didn't think so. That means I'm going to have to be sneaky and devious." Al shakes his head. "I'm going to miss you, Havet," he says, sadly. You lean back. "You think I'll make it off Toprawa, then?" Al shakes his head. "No, I think you'll get killed. I've seen you trying to be sneaky, remember."

If you have checked 557, go to 122

If not, go to 137

80

You have one trick left up your sleeve. You call to the nearest guard. "Hey, when do we get something to eat? My belly is empty." The guard snarls back at you – "You can wait, Rebel scum. We do breakfast every morning – except when we don't!" Very funny. You can see that the guys down at the barracks must crack up with this guy.

The reason for your outburst was that Arf was programmed to open the hatch on the lightsabre compartment when he heard the word "belly". You look across to the darkened doorway, and see that Arf has obeyed your instruction. The lightsabre has slipped forward on the hatch. Of course, it is still about 6 or 7 metres away, but there is one aspect of your Jedi power you know you can try. By drawing on the Force, you can pull the lightsabre towards you.

Decide how many Jedi Power Points you will spend (no more than 6). Add this number to 70; this is the number of the next paragraph you should read (so, if you spend 1 JPP, you will read paragraph 71).

81

You search along the wall, trying to let your senses reach out through the polymer of the duct wall, the intervening earth and stone, and through the metallic walls of the vault itself. Long minutes pass by; your fellow Rebels become nervous and impatient. Eventually, you give up. You can feel nothing which reveals where Surna might be.

If you plant the explosive at the west end of the duct, go to 94

If you plant the explosive at the east end of the duct, go to 119

If you plant the explosive in the centre, go to 105

If you abandon the attempt, and prepare a frontal assault, go to 34

If you try getting someone on the inside, go to 33

If you abandon all efforts to rescue Surna, go to 43

82

You search along the wall, trying to let your senses reach out through the polymer of the duct wall, the intervening earth and stone, and through the metallic walls of the vault itself. You know Surna's life-aura quite well, and feel it registering in your mind.

Read 542

If you plant the explosive at the west end of the duct, go to 94

If you plant the explosive at the east end of the duct, go to 119

If you plant the explosive in the centre, go to 105

If you abandon the attempt, and prepare a frontal assault, go to 34

If you try getting someone on the inside, go to 33

If you abandon all efforts to rescue Surna, go to 43

83

You search along the wall, trying to let your senses reach out through the polymer of the duct wall, the intervening earth and stone, and through the metallic walls of the vault itself. You know Surna's life-

aura quite well, and feel it registering in your mind. At the end of
your search, you can at least feel confident that you can eliminate
one of the options.

Read 547

If you plant the explosive at the west end of the duct, go to 94

If you plant the explosive at the east end of the duct, go to 119

If you plant the explosive in the centre, go to 105

**If you abandon the attempt, and prepare a frontal assault, go to
34**

If you try getting someone on the inside, go to 33

If you abandon all efforts to rescue Surna, go to 43

84

You search along the wall, trying to let your senses reach out through
the polymer of the duct wall, the intervening earth and stone, and
through the metallic walls of the vault itself. You know Surna's life-
aura quite well, and feel it registering in your mind. At the end of
your search, you can at least feel confident that you can eliminate
one of the options.

Read 552

If you plant the explosive at the west end of the duct, go to 94

If you plant the explosive at the east end of the duct, go to 119

If you plant the explosive in the centre, go to 105

**If you abandon the attempt, and prepare a frontal assault, go to
34**

If you try getting someone on the inside, go to 33

If you abandon all efforts to rescue Surna, go to 43

85

You search along the wall, reaching out with your senses through the
polymer of the duct wall, the intervening earth and stone, and the
metallic walls of the vault itself. You know Surna's life-aura well,

and feel it register in your mind. You are confident you know where she is.

Read 556

If you plant the explosive at the west end of the duct, go to 94

If you plant the explosive at the east end of the duct, go to 119

If you plant the explosive in the centre, go to 105

If you abandon the attempt, and prepare a frontal assault, go to 34

If you try getting someone on the inside, go to 33

If you abandon all efforts to rescue Surna, go to 43

86

You search along the wall, reaching out with your senses through the polymer of the duct wall, the intervening earth and stone, and the metallic walls of the vault. You know Surna's life-aura well, and feel it register in your mind. At the end of your search, you know what to do.

Read 560

If you plant the explosive at the west end of the duct, go to 94

If you plant the explosive at the east end of the duct, go to 119

If you plant the explosive in the centre, go to 105

If you abandon the attempt, and prepare a frontal assault, go to 34

If you try getting someone on the inside, go to 33

If you abandon all efforts to rescue Surna, go to 43

87

Right next door to Al the Alchemist's newly reopened cantina, there is a small building. Al uses it to house a nightly high stakes game of seven-card Comet. Some of the few remaining high rollers on Toprawa meet there to play the greatest 'take no prisoners' card game; lesser citizens come to watch. If Tann is involved with these people, he must be pretty desperate.

You're tempted to visit the cantina first, but Surna insists you check out the game instead. As she predicted, Tann is sitting at one of the three tables. He has a depressingly small pile of chips in front of him. Even as you watch, he loses another hand. He leans back, catches sight of his sister across the room, and comes over. Under normal circumstances, he's an ordinary-looking guy, with a strong body, reasonable good looks and a mop of wild, red hair. Tonight, he looks wasted. He has several day's growth of beard, and his eyes are hollow and dark-ringed. He even seems to have lost a few pounds in weight. "Surna!" he smiles, weakly. "What brings you here? Who's your friend?"

"This is Havet. He's here to help. We're trying to find a way of getting you out of debt to Jabba the Hutt." Tann laughs, dryly, without humour. "Me too. Trouble is, I'm getting further away." He shows you the credits he has left. "I think the guy in the green shirt is cheating, but I haven't managed to find out how."

"Then why keep playing?" shrieks Surna, attracting a lot of attention. You've never seen her this angry before. "We went to see T'blisk. He says you owe him 65,000 credits." Tann shakes his head. "More like 70,000, after tonight's fiasco." Surna almost screams with frustration. "OK! 70,000! Havet thinks he can find you the money." Tann turns his pale, tired eyes in your direction. You try to radiate the confidence of a man with a plan. You see a flicker of hope in his face, but then he quickly lapses back into despair. "What's the point? Even if I get the ship back from T'blisk, the Imperials won't let me leave Toprawa."

"We have a plan for that too," says Surna. Tann's eyes open wide. "Yeah? What do you want me to do?"

"Go home!" says Surna. "Get some sleep. I'd prefer a pilot who can stay awake beyond preflight. I'll call you later." Tann turns to go. "And you can give me that money. That way I can be sure you won't find a game somewhere else." Tann turns over the 400 credits, and leaves the room. Surna turns to you, and whispers: "Didn't I say I'd find you a pilot? Now, all you have to do is get his ship back!" Ah yes! It's time for this famous plan of yours. Perhaps you'd better think of one, Havet!

If you want to check out the game, go to 109

If you leave in search of another fund-raising idea, go to 98

If you wander into the cantina next door, go to 43

88

You leave the spaceport the same way you came in. You doubt very much that T'blisk will leave that secret entrance unwatched now you know where it is. Still, if he has found a way to get in and out without the Imperials noticing, maybe you can find a way you can do the same.

Surna is waiting outside. "What next?" she asks. You tell her about Boba Fett's ship. She listens, but you can tell from her face she doesn't like what she hears. "Are you crazy? Boba *Fett's* ship? You think we can just hide in those cages and escape whenever we want to? What if he finds us? And even if he doesn't, where's he heading for? It's a stupid idea, Havet!"

"Surna, even if we can get your brother's ship back from T'blisk, we don't have much chance of getting past the Imperial blockade. With this plan, we don't have to worry about either. As for Boba Fett, he's only one man – we could overpower him once we were in deep space, and take the ship wherever we wanted." Surna's anger boils over. "But how many people could we get out like that? Two, three? I thought you were prepared to take anyone who would come with us. We have to use the *Rust Bucket*!" Tann's ship is called the *Rust Bucket?* "Family joke," says Surna. Ha, ha.

"And just where is Tann?" you ask. "My guess is that he'll be at Al's cantina. Are you going to come and help me find him, or are you going to chase after this stupid idea of yours?"

Check 539

If you press on with your scheme to steal Boba Fett's ship, go to 101

If you search for Tann, go to 87

If you look for ways to get the *Rust Bucket* out of T'blisk's clutches, go to 98

89

Boba Fett keeps very low, out of your direct line of fire, gradually getting closer as he stalks you across the landing field. No alarms have gone off yet, but it is only a matter of time before the place is swarming with stormtroopers and other undesirable types. You have to take Fett out of the game, and escape, before it's too late!

He passes a storage area, above which you can see some industrial lubricant, stacked in drums on a tall rack. "Hey, Fett!" you yell, and you see him freeze. "I think you need an oil change!" Immediately, you pop three shots into the rack, splitting open the cans like ripe fruit. The non-flammable (more's the pity) lube gushes out, and Fett gets caught in the downpour. You see him fall, struggle to his knees, then slip again. He's covered in the thick, viscous green goo. Even his helmet is smeared.

"You want me to wipe your windshield too?" you laugh loudly. Fett howls with frustration, firing blindly at the source of your voice. You've already darted away however. You could go in and finish him off, but with the Imperials lurking in the background, and Fett still fully armed, you don't think it's wise. Leaving him floundering in the pool of lubricant, you make tracks for the spaceport perimeter.

Check 549

Go to 55

90

"Boba Fett? *The* Boba Fett? The bounty hunter?" Al smiles. "You've heard of him, then?" he says. "Who hasn't?" you reply. "From what you know of him, Al, do you think he'd give me a lift off-planet?" Al chuckles, and you join in. A small grey-furred Mannovan sitting close by cackles as well, without knowing what the joke is, until you silence him/her/it with a glare.

"I didn't think so. That means I'm going to have to be sneaky and devious." Al shakes his head. "I'm going to miss you, Havet," he says, sadly. You lean back and enjoy the moment. "You think I'll make it off Toprawa, then?" He shakes his head. "No, I think you'll get killed. I've seen you trying to be sneaky, remember."

If you have checked 557, go to 122

If not, go to 137

91

You could almost bang your head against the wall in frustration. Arf has made it all the way down here to the vault – but he doesn't have the lightsabre! You brought it with you into the lock-up, and it was taken from you when you were searched. Fortunately, these low-rank

Imperial guards didn't recognise what it was, or you would have been in even more trouble than you are now, but even though it is just a few metres away, it is locked up in a cabinet where you can't get at it!

Go to 102

92

There's one thing you can do to help. You jump out of the basement, and work your way across to the side street alley in which you saw the troop carrier. Peering round the corner, you see that the troops have not yet disembarked. A solitary soldier is standing with his back to you, apparently with his eyes on the far end of the alley, which would come out almost opposite the Rebel HQ.

You crack him over the head, and then use your lightsabre to fuse both the electronic and manual locks on the door of the troop compartment. This squad, at least, will take no part in the fighting.

You can do no more to hinder the attack, however. Moments later, you hear a massive roar as a heavy blaster takes out the main doors. Blaster fire echoes down the alley from the distant fight.

If you return to the HQ building to help your comrades, go to 118

If you escape to fight another day, go to 103

93

Your desperate attempt to break out of the lock-up has ended in failure.

If you are ready to start a new adventure, go to paragraph 1

94

You set off the explosives at the western end of the duct. You take cover as the timer winds down, and cover your face as the charge fills the sewers with thunder, dust and smoke. Rushing forward, you reach the gap the shaped charge has blown in the wall – and realise that the explosive force has ripped through the cells beyond. Although the guards are stunned, they are unharmed, while the prisoners...

You have made a terrible mistake. Fleeing from the carnage you have inflicted on your own people, you realise that you can never face the other Rebels again.

Check 543

Reduce your starting Jedi Power Point score by 2. This is now the maximum you may have.

Go to 43

95

Faced with the overwhelming firepower carried by Boba Fett, you are quickly defeated.

Perhaps you should create a new character – and increase his Blaster skill – if you're going to get involved in battles like this!

96

You sit in on the first hand. In 7 Card Comet, the aim is to build up powerful hands on each of six separate parts of the table. The dealer nominates which part of the table you play on. Coming in late like this, all you have are the first seven cards you are dealt. You make two hands of three; one on the Star table, and one on the Asteroid. Vain dealt the first hand, and calls Star. It looks like he's decided to check you out right away.

In any hand, every winning line you have counts as a point. Whoever has the most winning lines wins the hand. Each card has three numbers or symbols on it; Ace-10, like a conventional card deck, plus Senators, Princesses, and Emperors. Each run of three or three of a kind you can make out of the cards you hold is a winning line.

You placed a 9-9-10, a 6-8-10,and a 5-9-12. So, you have 3 nines, and six 8-9-10s – seven winning lines. Call it beginners' luck, or call it Vain setting you up, but you win 200 credits from the Trinovate. Over the next few hands, you win another few hundred, but all your winnings are sucked onto the Comet's Tail, where Vain and the Trinovate have a lot of cards. The three-eyed player has a fortune on the Tail; Vain has been setting him up for a big fall.

You have about 50 credits you could walk away with by the time your deal comes round. You win again, and see that your stake on the Tail increases to 1,500 credits. The Trinovate has over 20,000 there, and Vain just 5,000. Both of them have a lot of cards in play on the Tail, so you'll have to play a long-term strategy to build up your strength. However, even playing defensively you do OK; on his deal, you hit the T'sarki for over 900 credits. After four more hands, you have 2,000 credits in front of you, another 6,000 on the Tail. It's Vain's deal. The Trinovate is in big trouble. All his money has gravitated onto the Tail; he either has to play it on his next deal, or walk away from the game. Either way, one of the next two hands is going to be very expensive.

If you play the next hand, go to 107

If you leave the table, go to 120

97

As cheats go, Vain is a master. When he shuffled the cards, he must have sorted them so that you had a modestly good hand. That way, he hoped you'd gamble the ship.

Will you?

If you're going to expose Vain as a cheat, you must do so now. Go to 104

Otherwise, you must see who wins this final hand. First, decide if you will bet the ship or not. Then roll the dice for each player (Vain first, then Groomert the T'sarki, you, and finally Pilliask the Trinovate). Add two to your score, to represent the good cards Vain dealt you. If you checked 554, add 3 to Vain's score. If you have checked 555, add 1 to Vain's score.

Whichever player scores the highest wins the hand. If there is a tie, roll again for each player in the tie

So, who won?

If it was Vain, go to 108

If it was Groomert, go to 124

If it was Pilliask, go to 150

If you won, go to 139

98

"The way I see it," you explain, "we can beg, borrow or steal the money for Tann's ship." Surna turns her eyes up. You can see her wondering how on Toprawa you could ever beg or borrow 65,000 credits. Only, under Havet Storm's rules, that means we steal, steal or steal."

"We can either crash one of the big-money gambling tables, and out-cheat the experts; or we can use some Rebellion muscle to hit the black-market money-lenders for a 'loan'; or we can just plain steal the credits we need from the Empire." You can see Surna has grave doubts about your sanity. "Forget the middle one," she says. "Stealing from one of Jabba the Hutt's money-sharks to pay back another of Jabba the Hutt's money-sharks doesn't ring quite right." OK, what about the first option. "Havet, have you ever played a big money game before?" You confess that you haven't. "They'll eat you alive."

"So, if those two are stupid ideas, what about stealing the money from the Empire?" you ask. Surna sighs. "That's a *real* stupid idea..."

If you join a big money game, go to 110

If you steal the money from Jabba the Hutt's people, go to 121

If you steal the money from the Empire, go to 138

99

Once all the firing has stopped, Groomert lies dead. Vain rushes to the body and searches him. "As I thought! A cop! Must have been looking for counterfeit money or something. Well, that's his bad luck." He makes a rapid division of the large pile of credits on Groomert's side of the table, and looks up at Pilliask, who is still standing with the blaster in his hand.

"You'd better get out of here. I'll say it was self-defence, but you know what the cops are like. We'll split this money three ways – me and the boy will keep quiet, won't we son?" He gives you a conspiratorial wink. Pilliask hesitates, then grabs the money and runs. Vain isn't long in following him. "There's 15,000 credits left for you. Think about it. Keep your mouth shut, and who need ever know what really happened?"

He leaves. The room vacates rapidly as word spreads that a police-man has been killed. You decide it's time you saw Al, and made arrangements to get off Toprawa. Behind you, you hear Surna ask: "Should we take the money, Havet?"

If you take the money, check 559 and go to 43

If you take just what you had before the last hand, check 553 and go to 43

100

As you change position, Boba Fett scores a hit on your leg. It doesn't look too bad, but the pain is excruciating. You draw on the Force in an effort to fight it.

You limp away from the smoke-filled landing bay. Boba Fett doesn't pursue. How come? He must know he has hit you, and that you are easy prey now. Perhaps he's worried that, like a wounded animal, you'll fight even harder if cornered. Perhaps he thinks this beating squares things up for the 'insult' you did him before. Maybe. More likely, he has just lost sight of you for a moment. Make the most of it! You struggle along the walkway towards the perimeter fence, where T'blisk's secret entrance is waiting for you. There is no-one behind you.

Check 548

Go to 55

101

"Look, Surna. Most of the others don't even want to leave Toprawa. Why bother making life difficult for ourselves stealing a ship we may not be able to fly? If things get any worse, and the other Rebels want to leave, Tann's ship will still be here, right? This is a once-in-a-lifetime chance with Boba Fett's ship. We have to take it!" Surna has disappointment etched deeply on her face. "I misjudged you, Havet," she says, coldly. "I thought you were one of us. I see now that you have been looking out for Number One all along. Go; take Fett's ship; run away if you can. I'm staying here. Leaving Toprawa is one thing; running away and abandoning your comrades is anoth-er." She turns to go, and then throws one last stinging rebuke back at you. "I don't ever want to see you again, Havet." With that, she slips away, leaving you alone to wonder whether you have done the right thing. You decide it will be easier to think away from here, and set off towards Al the Alchemist's cantina.

Check 551

Go to 43

102

You try to sleep, but the mistake you made keeps playing around in your mind. Man! You were so close! If you had just left your lightsabre in Arf... In the middle of the night, you are awakened from a fitful doze as the guards open your cell. They are moving some of the prisoners out, you and Surna amongst them. Even though you are unarmed, this may be your last chance to rescue Surna – and yourself!

If you win the battle and escape, go to 106

If you are hit, go to 93

If Surna is hit, check 543 and go to 69

103

Leaving the battle behind, you make your way out of the City. There was talk of moving the Rebels' HQ out of Toprawa City, and into the deep forests, to frustrate the Imperial victory a little longer. At first, you think the search could take a long time, but you stumble across some fugitives from the battle making their way out of town through a part-filled water culvert. As you guessed, the HQ building fell easily. The Commander has been killed, along with many others. "What about Kalkett?" you ask, wondering what happened to your mate, the Rebel's best technician. "He was trapped under some machinery in the initial blast," replies Foester, a useful fighter who leads the small group. "I guess they captured him. Surna too," he adds, knowing how fond you were of the fiery demolitions expert.

You feel bad about leaving the battle, even though you did at least put one Imperial squad out of action. Knowing that Kalkett and Surna have been lost makes it even worse. Weary, and sick at heart at having abandoned your comrades, you know that you have been a bit of a coward. It's a mess, and it's made you even more determined to leave Toprawa, and to take as many of the others with you as you can persuade to leave. For now, though, you fall in with Foester's bruised and battered band, and make your way into the forest.

Remove 2 Jedi Power Points from your current total

Go to 53

104

You look at your cards. It looks like you might even have a winning hand. Unfortunately, you're just too honest to take advantage of it. This Jedi thing can be a real pain, sometimes! You spill your cards, face-up, on the table.

"Listen, guys," you announce. "I hate to spoil a fun game, but I have to tell you that Vain is cheating. This hand he's dealt me is a good one, but I bet if you take a peek, you'll find he has a better one…" Groomert and Pilliask whirl to face Vain. The cheat's face has screwed up with hate, and his skin has gone the same colour as his shirt. He leaps up, and you realise there is a blaster in his hand, aimed at you. "Hey!" you yell, throwing yourself clear. "Nothing personal!"

Read 558, and use the combat rules from the beginning of this book. Record this paragraph number, so you can find your way back here.

This combat starts At Range with just you and Vain. Vain goes first, and you need to draw your blaster in the first round. After two rounds, Groomert and Pilliask join in, both firing at Vain (they draw their weapons in the second round, and fire in the third). Pick Vain's targets randomly.

If you are hit, go to 123

Otherwise, if Groomert is the first to be killed, go to 99

If Pilliask is the first to fall, go to 157

If Vain is the first casualty, go to 140

105

You set off the explosives against the wall in the centre of the duct. You take cover as the timer winds down, and cover your face as the charge fills the sewers with thunder, dust and smoke. Rushing forward, you reach the gap the shaped charge has blown in the wall – and realise your plan has worked perfectly. The guards took the full brunt of the explosion – there is no-one in the vault to resist your attack. The prisoners have been spared the worst effects of the blast. A couple are wounded, but not seriously.

They're delighted to see you. You funnel them out into the duct, and the other Rebels lead them on the beginning of their journey to safety while you cover the rear. As Surna goes past, she plants a kiss on your cheek. "We owe you one, Havet," she smiles.

You keep the Imperials at bay with a few shots from your blaster. They don't seem that eager to chase you. After all, you have just taken out half their strength in the explosion. You still face a difficult and dangerous journey back to the rebel camp, but you feel confident that you'll make it.

If you have checked 528, tick another box on your Time Track. If you have reached the end of the track, go to 530.

Add 1 Jedi Power Point to your current total

Check 519

Go to 7

106

The battle in the jail is short and savage. At the end of it, the Imperial soldiers have been defeated, and the Rebel prisoners set free. You scoop up Arf and kiss him on the end of his nose. "You did well!" you tell the droid, and he chuffs away happily.

Now you have to get out of here. Making contact with the Rebels you left outside the lock-up, you direct your fellow escapees out into the street, and into a honeycomb of rat-runs and tunnels the Rebels have established through some nearby ruins. You stay back to cover the rear. As Surna goes past, she plants a kiss on your cheek. "We owe you one, Havet," she smiles.

You keep an Imperial patrol (alerted by an alarm at the lock-up) at bay with a few shots from your blaster. They don't seem that eager to chase you. After all, you have just taken out six of their comrades. You still face a difficult and dangerous journey back to the rebel camp, but you feel confident that you'll make it.

If you have checked 528, tick another box on your Time Track. If you have reached the end of the track, go to 530.

Add 1 Jedi Power Point to your current total

Check 519

Go to 7

107

What makes 7 Card Comet the fastest money-changer in the galaxy is the Tail. Each hand, a proportion of all losses goes into the Comet's Tail. Any player can call for their deal to be a Tail game at any time, for a fixed fee. Vain has decided that moment is now. "We'll play for the Tail this hand," he smiles. You wince. Most of your winnings are in the Tail; if you lose, you'll be back where you started. The Trinovate is philosophical; he had to call the same on his next deal anyway, seeing as he had so little cash left. Groomert doesn't have much to lose, so he's OK. Vain, though, is very pleased with himself. What you and he know, of course, is that he has two cards stashed in the sleeves of his lurid green shirt, with which he expects to win this vital hand.

You could just take your punishment, but it occurs to you that you could sting Vain pretty hard. Since he's so sure this is a winning hand, perhaps he'll up the stakes?

"Vain, neither you or I have much to lose on this hand," you say, offering the challenge. "Care for a side bet to make it interesting?" Vain smiles his false grin. "I don't see how we can 'make it interesting'. You have just a couple of thousand in front of you. There's 40,000 in the Tail."

"Maybe, but this lady here is the sister of Tann, the owner of the *Rust Bucket*. Once we've seen our cards, she'll put the 'Bucket' on the line for 10,000 credits." Everyone gasps. The whole room is focussed on you – just the way you wanted it. Vain sneers. "Tann's ship is impounded. It isn't worth 10, let alone 10,000"

"Ah yes," you continue. "But with the beating the Rebels took recently, the Empire must be getting ready to lift the blockade. After all, there are still many minerals and other precious materials on Toprawa, and they need them. So, I figure it's a bargain." Actually, it isn't, since there would still be the problem of T'blisk and Jabba the Hutt to sort out, but you figure Vain is that confident about winning that he'll jump at the offer. Which is just what happens. "Is that how you feel?" he asks Surna. She looks a little grey-skinned, but she nods her head, and says "Let's do it!" at which point everyone, Vain included, is looking at her. And that's the moment when you dig deep into the Force and concentrate on the cards up Vain's sleeve.

You are going to use the Force to try and dislodge the cards up Vain's sleeve. Decide how many Jedi Power Points you will spend (from 1-6), and add this number to 110. The total gives you the number of the paragraph you should read next (so, if you spend 4 JPPs, you would read 114).

108

As the cards are revealed, you realise that Vain has won. You consider revealing that he was cheating, but you have no proof. You'll just have to live with your defeat. Pilliask, on the other hand, isn't feeling so charitable. Having dropped 30,000 credits tonight, something inside him just snaps. You see it happen before anyone else. His three eyes fill with hate, and his skin colour mottles. As he stands up, there's a blaster in his hand.

Read 558, and use the combat rules from the beginning of this book. Record this paragraph number, so you can find your way back here.

This combat starts At Range between Pilliask and Vain. Pilliask goes first.

If you choose to get involved and are hit, go to 123

Otherwise, if Vain is killed, go to 140

If Pilliask is killed, go to 157

109

You watch the card game for a while. 7 Card Comet is game of skill and bluff, in which money can change hands at an appallingly fast rate. You've never played for anything higher than meal tokens before. In this game, thousands of credits are riding on each hand.

There are three players. A human in a green shirt, who has an impressive stack of credits in front of him, and who smiles with all the charm of a dead Marshfang; a very dull T'sarki, who only plays the low-stake hands; and a Trinovate, who loses steadily to green-shirt while you watch. The game is hopelessly mismatched. The T'sarki wins his fair share of hands, but only on the smaller games. Green-shirt and the Trinovate play the big games; the three-eyed Trinovate is losing two in every three, and is being forced to place more and more money in the Comet's Tail to stay in the game.

Through your Jedi senses, you realise green-shirt is cheating. He's good, but he hasn't learned to shield his thoughts as efficiently as he shields the cards he has palmed. He has a triple-Ace and a triple-Emperor up his sleeve. That means any hand he has a Princess, he can make eight winning lines. He must be saving this up for when he takes the Trinovate onto the Comet's Tail.

"How much money have we got?" you whisper to Surna. "I've got the 400 we took off Tann; maybe another 250 of my own... why?" You count out money from your own pockets. 35 credits. Ah,well. You take Surna's money and approach the table. "Mind if I sit in?" you ask. The players look at you, checking you over. You smile, trying to look like just another mug. "Sit," says green-shirt. He makes rapid introductions – "Vain, Groomert, Pilliask" – pointing in turn at himself, the T'sarki and the Trinovate. "Havet Storm," you reply. "Shall we play?"

To play the first hand, go to 96

110

"Don't worry!" you reassure Surna. "I can take these guys blindfold-ed. And if they won't wear blindfolds, we'll try some other way. How much money do you have?" Surna counts about 250 credits from her wallet. You add 35. "See? We're only looking for a 10,000% increase."

The only game in the universe where you can make that kind of money is 7 Card Comet. You've heard that Al the Alchemist has a gameroom adjacent to his new cantina. This is the place to try.

You arrive at the game, and look it over. There are three players. A human in a green shirt, who has an impressive stack of credits in front of him,and who smiles with all the charm of a dead Marshfang; a small T'sarki, who sits perfectly still and looks only at his cards; and a Trinovate, who laughs loudly and drinks furiously. The game is hopelessly mismatched. The T'sarki wins his fair share of hands, but only on the smaller games. Green-shirt and the Trinovate are playing the big games, and the three-eyes Trinovate is losing two in every three, and is being forced.to place more and more money in the

Comet's Tail to stay in the game.

Through your Jedi senses, you realise green-shirt is cheating. He's good, but he hasn't learned to shield his thoughts as efficiently as he shields the cards he has palmed. He has a triple-Ace and a triple-Emperor up his sleeve. That means any hand he has a Princess, he can make at least eight winning lines. He must be saving this up for when he takes the Trinovate onto the Comet's Tail. You approach the table and ask "Mind if I sit in?" The three players look at you, checking you over. You smile, trying to look like just another mug. "Sit," says green-shirt. He makes rapid introductions – "Vain, Groomert, Pilliask" – pointing in turn at himself, the T'sarki and the Trinovate. "Havet Storm," you reply. "Shall we play?"

To play the first hand, go to 96

111

You don't put enough effort into your attempt, and the cards stay firmly in place. Vain deals the hand. You watch him palm two cards, and switch them for the two from his shirt. He selects the three cards with which he'll play the hand, and places them face down.

"So, Havet Storm," he says. "You've seen your cards. Are we playing for the ship or not?"

Check 554

Go to 97

112-114

You concentrate your telekinetic powers on the cards, and dislodge one of them from Vain's sleeve. It gives you great satisfaction to see his face as he feels the card flutter away, unseen, to the floor. Biting his lip, Vain deals the hand. He palms a card, and switches it for the remaining card from his shirt. He selects the three cards with which he'll play the hand, and places them face down, his confidence dented, but not destroyed.

"So, Vain," you say once you have seen your cards. "Are we playing for the ship or not?"

Check 555

Go to 97

115-116

You focus all your telekinetic powers on the cards, and dislodge both of them from Vain's sleeve. It gives you great satisfaction to see the look of horror on his face as he feels the cards flutter away, unseen, to the floor. Trembling a little, Vain deals the hand. He selects the three cards with which he'll play the hand, and places them face down, his confidence shaken.

"Well, Vain," you say once you have seen your cards. "I think we'll play for the ship, don't you?"

Go to 97

117

You try to flee, even though you know that the odds are poor. To your amazement, Boba Fett doesn't follow. He fires a few shots to hurry you along, but he doesn't hunt you down. "You're not worth my time," he calls as you scamper out of the landing bay. "I could beat you with both hands tied behind my back." Yes, well, considering he has a rocket launcher strapped there, he probably could.

You feel humiliated, but at least you're alive. Maybe you'll get your chance to have revenge one day.

Go to 55

118

You'd have to be simple to go back into a battle you have already escaped, right? Well, you'd take simple over difficult every time. Checking your weapons, and bracing yourself for the worst, you run towards the HQ building. You surprise the heavy blaster crew, and destroy the weapon. Moments later, you burst back in through the main doors, to see if there is anything you can do to help your comrades-in-arms.

Go to 37

119

You set off the explosives at the eastern end of the duct. You take cover as the timer winds down, and cover your face as the charge fills the sewers with thunder, dust and smoke. Rushing forward, you reach the gap the shaped charge has blown in the wall – and realise that the explosive force has ripped a hole not into the main vault, but into an adjacent area. The prisoners are safe, but so are the guards, and they have been protected from the shock.

Your plan has achieved nothing, except to alert the Imperials to your determination to spring the prisoners. They won't give you a second chance. You leave the drainage duct, and head back out onto the street, filled with a sense of bitter disappointment. What next?

Check 543

Go to 43

120

You cash in your chips, much to the annoyance of the other players, particularly Vain. You guess he was using you to pull the Trinovate further and further into trouble. Groomert buys your stake in the Tail for 800 credits – a pretty poor rate of return, but the best you're going to get. You walk away with that plus the 2,000 you had in front of you.

"Why did you quit?" asks Surna, completely confused. "You left over 5,000 in the Tail!"

"Didn't you see? Vain was cheating. He has cards up his sleeve which would probably win the Tail on their own, but which need just a Princess in the deal to become virtually unbeatable. One of the next two games would have been an all-or-nothing hand for the Tail, and I didn't have the credits to buy my way out of it. We would have lost everything."

As you predicted, Vain calls the Tail on his next deal. He lays down the Triple-Ace, the Triple-Emperor and a 7-8-Princess. Eight winning lines. The Trinovate had a lucky, hope-raising six lines. Vain has crushed him, financially and morally. Surna whistles. "Lucky you got out when you did." Lucky indeed.

"Let's take what we've got, and see if T'blisk will take it as a down payment," you propose. Surna agrees, and you make your way over to the main room of Al's cantina to make the arrangements.

Check 553

Go to 43

121

Rather desperately, you decide to get the money you need for Tann's ship from the money-lenders Jabba the Hutt has established on Toprawa. It's suspiciously easy. You track down their base of operations, which is in a building marked with a large, fluorescent sign reading ZIGGY'S LOANS, MEDICAL INSURANCE & PREVENTATIVE COST MANAGEMENT. That night, you break in. The hired muscle surrenders without a fight, caught completely by surprise, and you scoop up 40,000 credits.

As you leave, one of Jabba's henchthings asks: "Let me give you some advice. Spend that money real quick. When the glorious Jabba gets to hear about this, he'll hire Boba Fett to hunt you down. And Boba Fett isn't an enemy you want to have." So, what else is new?

Check 561

Go to 43

122

You decide you might as well let Al in on your little secret. "Forget Boba Fett," you whisper (interesting rhyme, that...). "I have a ship. You know Tann?" Of course he does. "It's his ship, the *Rust Bucket*. All I have to do is get into the spaceport and pick it up. You got any ideas?" Al leans forward conspiratorially. "What's in it for me?" he asks. You're shocked. "I'm shocked, Al. After all the time I've spent in this place, don't you owe me a favour?" Now he looks shocked. "I'm not after credits or anything, Havet! I want to get off Toprawa too! You have any idea what it's like getting supplies here? And who's going to cook while you're on your way to who-knows-where? And who's going to bring all the Star Racers you can drink?"

"OK, OK! I'm convinced already! You're in! Now, can you help us get into port or not?" He beams with pride. "Of course! It just so happens that the Port Commandant is one of my best customers; I keep him supplied with Tantooine brandy, 50 years old. You just can't get it any more! I make regular runs to the port bars and rest rooms. We could all get in together while I was making a delivery. Once we're inside, things will be much easier, right?"

You hate to tell him the rest of the problems you face. Why ruin his day? Instead, you thank him for the excellent plan. "We have a deal, right?" he asks. "We have a deal." You clap him on the shoulder. "What about me?" chips in the furry Mannovan. You feel a sudden dread – could he have overheard you? Mannovans are renowned for sticking their beaks into everything. Then you remember that they are also supposed to have really bad hearing. "You want a free beer as well?" you ask. "Sure!" says the Mannovan. Al sighs, and pours the diminutive humanoid his ale, while you look round to see if you can find where Surna and Tann are lurking.

If you have checked 569, go to 162

Otherwise, go to 144

123

After all you have been through, to meet disaster in a stupid gambling brawl is a miserable way to die. Perhaps you would have done better to have never got mixed up with these people in the first place.

Start again – return to paragraph 1

124

As the cards are revealed, you realise that Groomert has won. Well, doesn't that beat all? The little T'sarki hasn't played a big hand all night, but now he's won the big pay-off, including Tann's ship. Oh, well. That's the way the Krumbli cooks.

Suddenly, you realise Pilliask isn't feeling so philosophical. Having dropped 30,000 credits tonight, something inside him just snaps. You see it happen before anyone else. His three eyes fill with hate, and his skin colour mottles. As he stands up, there's a blaster in his hand, aimed at Groomert.

Read 558, and use the combat rules from the beginning of this book. Record this paragraph number, so you can find your way back here.

This combat starts with just Pilliask and Groomert. Pilliask goes

first. **After two rounds, Vain joins in, firing at Groomert (he draws his blaster in the second round, fires in the third)**

If you choose to get involved and are hit, go to 123

Otherwise, if Groomert is the first to be killed, go to 99

If Pilliask is the first to fall, go to 157

If Vain is the first casualty, go to 140

125

Al waves to you across the crowded cantina as you enter. You walk over, and find an empty stool at the bar. "Have you seen a white-haired humanoid?" he asks urgently. "Little guy?" You're surprised – he hasn't even offered you an Engineers' Safety Valve. "Is this a gag?" you ask. *"Have you seen him?"* Al repeats. You think back – does he mean the Mannovan you were talking to the last time you were here? "No, another guy – least ways, I think he was a guy." Ah! Now you remember. What about him?

"He works for Boba Fett," Al says, reaching into the cooler. He sets a tube of Star Racer on the bar, and breaks the seal. "I think you might have a problem." Maybe, but it can wait. You take a long, refreshing pull from the tube.

Add 1 Jedi Power Point to your current total

If you have checked 528, tick 1 more box on your Time Track. If you have reached the end of the track, go to 530

If you have checked 510 or 532, go to 145

If not, go to 160

126

The second battle ends as abruptly as the first. Groomert is the first to reach Vain's body. "Dead," he announces. He stands, and flashes an ID. "OK, everyone, stay where you are. I'm a cop!" You look around. Only you and Surna are left in the room with him (if you don't count the two bodies, that is). Funny that – a couple of blaster fights, and everyone else has lit out of here. Groomert thinks for a moment. "We're kind of short in the witness department," he says. "That will look messy on my report." He was, of course, chasing

Vain. "He's wanted for fraud, confidence scams and card sharking on Kalishik. Shame it had to end this way, though."

"What happens now?" asks Surna. Groomert smiles. "I'll explain what happened to the local authorities. What should the official report say? There was a dispute over the last hand, a fight broke out, we all exchanged shots. Vain killed the Trinovate; I shot Vain. That OK with you?" You agree rapidly. Groomert sits down at the table, pulls out a data pad, and records his report, surrounded by all the money. He has you and Surna add voice-print and manual signatures.

"So," announces the T'sarki cop. "That's that. Ooops! There's all this money – I nearly forgot." You hadn't. "Well, Vain doesn't have any next of kin, so why don't you take it? As a reward, I mean." He scoops his own money off the table (plus a healthy 'bonus'), leaving about 120,000 credits – Vain's stake plus the Comet's Tail. "There's almost enough there to buy Tann's ship twice over!!" says Surna. You quell her joy by reminding her that it represents two lost lives. Still, it's as honest as dirty money ever gets. And with 120,000 credits you could find T'blisk's contact, and arrange the pay-off on Tann's ship.

How much will you take?

If you take just what you won before the last hand, check 553 and go to 43

If you take just enough to pay off on Tann's ship, check 561 and go to 43

If you take it all, check 565 and go to 43

127

The final battle is over. Other than Surna, who's over by the doorway, you are the only one left standing. Vain gasps his last breath as you approach. "You... little hustler..." he groans. "You've... got it all now. You're... you're no better... than me..." He slumps to one side.

"What happens now?" asks Surna. Her voice is very loud in the deadly still of the room. "The place will be crawling with Imperial Security guards soon. But they won't bother us, I guess. It's just another card-game brawl. They'll find plenty of witnesses to explain that someone said someone was cheating someone else..."

"Should we go?" She sounds worried. "We're as safe in Al's place as anywhere," you reply. "We'll mingle with the crowds. Besides, if we find T'blisk's contact, we can buy back Tann's ship." You indicate the money on the table. "You're right!," she says. "There must be 120,000 there! Almost enough there to buy Tann's ship twice over!!" You quell her joy by reminding her that it represents three wasted lives. Still, it's as honest as dirty money ever gets.

How much will you take?

If you take just what you won before the last hand, check 553 and go to 43

If you take just enough to pay off on Tann's ship, check 561 and go to 43

If you take it all, check 565 and go to 43

128

You don't have the manpower to cover all three routes, so you decide to concentrate on just one. But which one?

Select one of the three routes – Market Street, the Highway or the Hill route. Now roll a die. If you roll a 1-2, you guess right – the convoy comes your way.

If you are watching Market Street, go to 143

If your attack takes place on the Highway, go to 169

If you attack the convoy in the Hills, go to 158

If you roll a 3-6, you guess wrong. If you have checked 528, tick another three boxes on your Time Track. If that means you reach the end of the track, read 530

If you try again, go back to the beginning of this paragraph

If you want to reconsider your fund-raising plans, go to 98

129

The guard gets lucky – and you don't.

Better luck next time, Havet. Perhaps a different character might help?

130

The convoy guards subdued, you approach the armoured speeder. The troop compartment stands open and empty, but the strong-box is sealed by an electronic lock. You go to work on it at once.

Find your Tech Skills score on your Character Sheet. Decide how many Jedi Power Points you will spend to temporarily increase it. Then, add the total to 150, and that is the number of the next paragraph you should read. So, if your Tech Skills score is 2, and you spend 2 JPPs, you would read 154.

131-133

There's a moment, when both you and the patrolman freeze, neither quite able to believe in the other. You hear Surna's strangled cry – "Havet!" – and it jerks to you into movement, but the patrolman has shaken himself free even quicker, and races towards an alarm pad on the wall. You chase him across the landing apron, but you were too slow getting started, and you never quite run him down. With a final lunge, he smashes the heel of his hand against the pad. The alarm bursts into life. Seconds later you crash into him, crushing him against the wall, and driving the breath from both your bodies.

Check 568

Go to 146

134-136

The patrolman freezes, unable to believe what he has seen. You hear Surna's strangled cry – "Havet!" – but you are already leaping towards the patrolman. Too late, he turns towards an alarm pad on the wall, but you chase him across the landing apron, and crash into him before he can reach it. You roll over, placing yourself between him and the alarm. He lifts his head, fear in his eyes, and reaches towards the holster on his hip.

Go to 146

137

"Do you have some kind of plan?" asks Al, with more than usual curiosity. Fat chance, you think. "Sure," you reply.

If you have checked either 536 or 543, go to 172

If you have checked 519, go to 447

If neither of these apply, go to 161

138

Checking with the Rebel Intelligence Officer, you are told that an armoured speeder regularly makes the run from the Spaceport into Toprawa City – supposedly carrying valuable minerals to exchange for artwork and artifacts from the galleries and museums. The civilian government of Toprawa is selling the family silver to line its own pockets while the planet falls to pieces. Well, that's three good reasons for hitting the convoy. It'll get you the money you need, it strikes a blow at the Empire and it preserves a little of Toprawa's heritage. "There's only one good reason why you shouldn't hit the convoy," the Intelligence Officer announces. Which is? "It's suicide. Three scout outriders sweep ahead of the convoy on separate routes. They keep in constant contact with the main convoy, warning them of anything which looks remotely unsafe. The armoured speeder can only be opened by an electronic master key. It has three stormtroopers aboard, and there are at least twelve in another vehicle two minutes behind."

Whew! It's a tough problem, sure enough. And who can you rely on for help? Surna, Tann, two or three Rebels. "Can we get any support from you guys?" you ask. "To help you steal money, Havet? Money you'll use to get a spaceship and fly out of here? Why should we?" You think about that one for a moment. "If – *if* – I get out off Toprawa, I'll find the Rebel HQ. That means I can deliver any message you want. Maybe they'll send help." The Intelligence Officer smiles; you can see he'd thought of this himself, but he has a more practical suggestion in mind. "I'll tell you what, Havet. I'll give you some help, and I'll accept your offer to contact the Rebel HQ. But I also want half the money." What?! "We need food, weapons, medical equipment. I can get them, but I need cash. An Imperial donation could come in quite handy."

If you agree to the offer, and plan the attack, go to 149

If you want to take another look at the plan to steal the money from Jabba's money-lenders, go to 121

Or, if you join one of the big-money card games, go to 110

139

Well, surprise, surprise! You won! Vain looks as if he has been smacked between the eyes with a force pike, but what can he do, except watch you scoop up your winnings. "Nice game," you say, smiling sweetly at him. He tenses for a moment, but then relaxes. You see his eyes flicker to one side... Glancing over, you realise Pilliask isn't feeling so philosophical. Having dropped 30,000 credits tonight, something inside him just snaps. His three eyes are filled with hate, and his skin colour mottles. As he stands up, there's a blaster in his hand, aimed right at you.

This combat starts with just Pilliask and you. Pilliask goes first, and he has his blaster drawn already, while you don't

After two rounds, Vain joins in, firing at you (he draws his blaster in the second round, fires in the third)

If you are hit, go to 123

If Pilliask is the first to fall, go to 157

If Vain is the first casualty, go to 140

140

As Vain staggers back, the firing halts. The card-cheat topples over, and crashes to the ground. Groomert is the first to reach him. "Dead," he announces. He stands, and flashes an ID. "OK, everyone, stay where you are. I'm a cop!" Oh, great. Is this what you need right now? "This man is a wanted con man and card shark. You're all witnesses to what happened here; so nobody move." You're too close to do anything much, but you notice that most of the crowd melts away. Groomert doesn't seem that bothered. He's got you, he's got Vain and he's got you and Pilliask as witnesses. "I've tracked him all the way from Kalishik," Groomert says to no-one in particular. "Shame it had to end this way."

Pilliask looks shocked. He is sitting at the table once more. Vain's winnings and the pot in the Comet's Tail lie piled in front of him. "Who – who – who –" You've heard Trinovates lose their power of speech when distressed, so you help out. "Who actually shot him?" Groomert smiles. "Didn't you see? I did. You two saw that, right, for the official report? There was a dispute over the last hand, a fight broke out, we all exchanged shots, but I shot Vain. That OK with you guys?" You answer for both of you. Groomert sits down, pulls out a data pad, and records his report. He has you and Pilliask add voice-print and manual signatures.

"So," announces the T'sarki cop. "That's that. Ooops! I nearly forgot – there's all this money." You have already done a rough count of the money Vain had in front of him. "Well, he doesn't have any next of kin, so why don't you boys take it? As a reward, I mean." He scoops his own money off the table (plus a small 'bonus'). There's about 140,000 credits left – Vain's stake plus the Comet's Tail. After a long look at the Trinovate, you take 65,000, and hand it to Surna. Groomert is heading for the door, dragging Vain along by his collar. "I'll be seeing you!" he chirps. You and Surna follow, leaving the Trinovate to deal with his problems himself.

"We've got everything we need!" says Surna. You quell her joy by reminding her that it cost a man's life. Still, it's as honest as dirty money ever gets, so you take Surna through into the main part of the cantina, to find T'blisk's contact, and arrange the pay-off on Tann's ship.

Check 563 and go to 43

141

Al calls you over when he sees you. "Havet! Sit down! Let me pour you an Engineers' Safety Valve." You chuckle wearily. You go through the same ritual most times you come here. "No thanks, just a Star Racer, Al. A cold one." Wearily, crossing the room, you collide with a small, white-haired humanoid, not much bigger than a human child. He (you'd guess it's a he) picks itself up, and rushes for the door, with wide eyes betraying fear. You walk over to the bar.

"You look like you could use one of these," Al says, reaching into the cooler. "Got a problem?" Nothing that being fifty light-years away wouldn't cure. "You leaving, Havet? Some pal you are; I just laid in an extra case of Racers just for you. You don't want to hear what they cost me."

Al pours drinks while you pour out a few of your problems. "You got itchy feet is all," he says, dispensing an instant diagnosis the way bartenders do. "You know as well as I do, there's no way off this rock. The Imperials control the spaceport, and they've impounded every ship on the planet. Nothing comes in or goes out without a thorough search, including Mass Parity checks, sensor sweeps, the works. Nothing, except…"

You see a ray of hope. Al wipes a glass with the cloth he has in his hand. The glass gets dirtier. He holds it up to the light; you're amazed that a single photon could get through. "Well, there's one ship they don't search." Which one? "The *Slave I*. The owner was in here earlier; says he's going to cut out of here within three standard days." Alright, so who's the owner?

"Boba Fett," says Al.

Check 562

If you have spent any Jedi Power Points, you may recover 1 point

If you have checked 528, tick 2 more boxes on your Time Track. If you have reached the end of the track, go to 530

If you have checked 510 or 532, go to 79

If not, go to 90

142

The second battle ends as abruptly as the first. Vain crosses the room to where Groomert lies in a twisted heap on the floor. "As I thought! A cop! Must have been looking for counterfeit money or something. Well, that's his bad luck." He starts gathering the money into one pile, and sweeping it into a bag. Almost as an afterthought, he looks up at you.

"It was self-defence, you saw that. If you go talking to the cops, it'll get us both into deep trouble." He splits off about 18,000 credits from the pile. "Take this. It must be over 20,000 credits." Ha! "Keep your mouth shut, and who need ever know what really happened?"

You hesitate, and a frown crosses his face. "There are two dead men in here already, Havet. We're not going to have to fight about this, are we?"

If you take just as much money as you had won before the last hand, check 553 and go to 43

If you take the money Vain offers, check 559 and go to 43

If you try to stop Vain, read 566, and use the combat rules from the beginning of this book. Record this paragraph number, so you can find your way back here

143

You lay your ambush on a deserted part of Market Street, and wait for the convoy. It's your lucky day. At the appointed hour, an Imperial Scout flashes by on a speeder bike. You have just a few moments to wait until the armoured speeder arrives.

There it is! You have mined the road and placed more charges in empty buildings close by. One of the Rebels now sets off the blasts, sealing the Armoured speeder inside a small pocket of rubble. It spins to a halt, clipping one pile of fallen masonry. Stormtroopers spill out of the troop compartment. You have about 2 minutes to take them out, break into the strongbox area, and get the goodies before reinforcements arrive!

Read 567, and use the combat rules from the beginning of this book. Record this paragraph number so you can find your way back here

If you win the battle, go to 130

If you are hit, go to 159

144

Al makes a call, and arranges the delivery. Within a few hours, you're on your way to the spaceport in a freight speeder Al borrows for jobs like this. Listening to him chatter as you make your way the short distance to the port gates, it appears he has quite a few 'contacts' with the Imperial forces, supplying them with little luxuries on what is a backwater planet.

"It doesn't bother you," asks Surna, "working for them?" Al scowls at the woman. You can see they are going to make great shipmates. "I notice you're not unhappy about using my contacts when it suits you," Al replies. Fortunately, you reach the gates before they can expand the fight.

The guards at the checkpoint perk up when they see Al. "You're not due for a few more days yet," says a junior Officer, who stares hard at you, Tann and Surna while he checks Al's papers. "Special delivery," Al replies, with a conspiratorial wink. The young Officer leans into the cab. "What are we talking here? A party?" Al shakes his head. "VIP visit, I'd say." The Officer's eyes open wide. You can see him flying off in his imagination to find his dress uniform and give it an extra coating of spit and polish.

"Park in the usual place," he orders, and Al steers the speeder across the port towards a pair of low buildings. "We'll park behind the Officer's Recreational area. From there, I know a door we can use to get into the landing area. We'll take the brandy with us; make it look like we're searching for my contact. Then we find Tann's ship, and it's up to you."

The plan works perfectly up to a point. You park the vehicle, unstack a few boxes while a security guard checks you out, then follow Al through a door, along a passage, and out into a cargo area. Slipping past the Imperial personnel there, you come out into the landing area. Tann steals a pilot's uniform from a ready room, and you swipe an engineer's data pad. You set off to find Tann's ship.

You're almost there when another Guard appears. His mouth drops open – clearly he was told no-one was supposed to be in this area. For a moment, you consider bluffing your way past him, but you can see he has already decided you are trouble. You have to silence him fast.

Look up your Speed Rating from your Character Sheet. You can spend Jedi Power Points to increase this temporarily. Add the total to 130, and this is the number of the next paragraph you should read. So, if your Speed score is 4, and you don't spend any JPPs, you would next read 134.

145

"I think you might have a problem too," says an almost-familiar voice. You whirl around, but there's no sign of anyone who looks like the bounty hunter, just an assortment of aliens, and an old man in the corner, shrouded in a heavy cloak… "That Boba Fett, he's a mean animal." The old guy sounds about a hundred and ninety. You push some nuts closer to his quivering hand, noting the discoloured skin and the thick knuckles. Make that two hundred and ninety.

"He's also a madman, pops," you tell your new 'friend'. "We had a run in some time ago, and he has been carrying a grudge ever since. The sooner I get off Toprawa, the sooner I get him off my back. And that can't come soon enough for me."

You turn away quickly. Out of the corner of your eye, you realise the old man was going to reach out and stop you, but you don't have time to talk to him now. You have work to do.

Check 569

If you have checked 557, go to 122

If not, go to 137

146

Having prevented him setting off the alarm, you now have to defeat the guard.

Read 570, and use the combat rules from the beginning of this book. Record this paragraph number so you can find your way back.

If you defeat the guard, go to 448

If you lose, go to 129

147

Even you can't outrun a slug from a gun, Havet.

Bad luck. Try again, starting from paragraph 1

148

Holrga is a Twi'lek, a tall, thin, pale-skinned humanoid, distinguished, like all of his race, by his bald, lumpy head, and the two long 'trunks' which grow from it, winding around his neck. He is watching a trashy holo-vid thriller, which is being projected down onto his table. You saw the film on the flight in to Toprawa, two years ago.

"The Gannymedan did it," you explain by way of introduction. Holrga snaps off the vid angrily, his snake-like appendages twisting with rage. "Tann," he spits, seeing who is beside you. "You have made some very unpleasant new friends." Tann tries hard not to laugh at the Twi'lek's injured pride. "This is Havet Storm. He's been helping me get the money to pay off on the *Rust Bucket*." Holrga twists the lumps above his eyes upwards. "Really? Has he succeeded?"

"We want to see T'blisk," you explain, forcefully. Holrga ignores you. "How much money have you brought me, Tann. Show me first, then I'll talk to T'blisk."

So, how much have you got?

If you have checked 565 (120,000 credits), go to 168

If you have checked 563 (65,000 credits), go to 167

If you have checked 561 (40,000 credits), go to 166

If you have checked 559 (20,000 credits), go to 165

If you have checked 553 (2,000 credits), go to 164

149

You agree the terms the Rebel Intelligence Officer demanded. He supplies you with four extra fighters. You leave the camp with Surna, and pick up her brother, Tann.

You check out the routes most frequently used by the convoy. There are three popular ones. The Highway, Market Street and the Hill route. The run takes place every three days. How can you be sure which route they'll take on any particular day? And how can you be sure they'll stick to it? If the scouts see anything suspicious, they'll divert the armoured speeder to another route...

How will you plan the attack? If you concentrate your small force at one point, go to 128

If you split into three teams, go to 158

150

As the cards are revealed, you realise that Pilliask has won. What a relief! He was so tight-wired during the play of that final hand, you wondered if he might not snap. Now he's won back all the money he had been forced to play on the Comet's Tail. Gathering it together, he announces that he has had enough for the night, and leaves the table.

Vain looks pretty angry, as well he might. He spent all evening setting the Trinovate up for this sting, and now it's been blown. He seems to think it's your fault. "You cost me a great deal, friend," he hisses through his teeth. A woman behind you screams. Vain is rising up, throwing back his chair, and pulling a blaster.

Read 558, and use the combat rules from the beginning of this book. Record this paragraph number, so you can find your way back here.

This combat starts with just you and Vain. Vain goes first. After two rounds, Groomert joins in, firing at Vain (he draws his blaster in the second round, fires in the third)

If you are hit, go to 123

Otherwise, if Groomert is the first to be killed, go to 99

If Vain is the first casualty, go to 140

151-155

Just as you'd suspect, the lock on the Imperial armoured speeder is too difficult for you to open in the limited time at your disposal. If only you had some micro-explosive, or a laser-lance. The others grow increasingly nervous as time passes. Reinforcements could be here at any moment. "Well, Havet?" urges Surna. "It's no good," you admit. "I can't beat it." You kick the speeder in frustration. "Let's go."

You disappear into the back streets. "What next?" asks Surna. "After that little incident, you can bet the Imperials will make one final effort to finish off the rebellion here on Toprawa. If we're going to escape, it has to be now." Surna spreads her hands in despair. "But how? We don't have the money for Tann's ship!"

"Then we'll have to find another way. Meanwhile, let's split up and get clear of this place. I'll meet you at Al's cantina."

Go to 43

156

Time passes slowly, but you know the feeling is deceptive. The others grow increasingly nervous as the seconds slip away. Imperial reinforcements could be here at any moment. "Well, Havet?" urges Surna. "Wait…" you hiss, your face streaked with sweat. You move an electronic probe a nanometre deeper, and there is a satisfying click. "That's it!" The speeder door flies open, and you look inside. There's a single strong-box. As you grab it, you feel its impressive weight. Tann grabs the other handle, and cocks an eyebrow at you. "Gold?" he wonders out loud. "Uranium? Preatorium?" You'd have preferred gold, old-fashioned, high-denomination credits. Still, you're rich – that's what counts. With the box slung between you, you disappear into the back streets.

You reach a safe house about twenty minutes later. Distant alarms and sirens are howling. "Let's see what we got," says a Rebel Officer who meets you there. He uses a small quantity of thermal explosive to blow the lid open. As one, you all look inside. It nearly breaks your heart.

"Copper?" wails Surna. "We risked our lives for copper?" Sure enough, the box is filled with thousands of small copper disks. Tann places his hand on her shoulder, and shakes his head in disbelief. "I don't get it. Why would the Imperials ship a few thousand credits' worth of copper around in an armoured vehicle?" The answer comes to you as he finishes the question. "A decoy. The real shipment must have gone another way."

"There's about 7,500 credits in copper here," says the Rebel Officer, sarcastically. "Where do you want your 50% delivered?" You shut the box. "You take it. Give us 2,000 cash, and the metal is all yours." He grins. "You've got a deal. You know, Havet, perhaps you should go into the scrap metal business full time."

"What next?" asks Surna, once the money has been handed over. "After that little incident, you can bet the Imperials will make one final effort to finish off the rebellion here on Toprawa. If we're going to escape, it has to be now." Surna spreads her hands in despair. "But how? We don't have enough money for Tann's ship!" Not even close, in fact. "I don't know. Maybe we can cut some kind of deal with T'blisk. Or maybe we can find another way off Toprawa. Meanwhile, let's split up and get clear of this place. I'll meet you at Al's cantina."

Check 553

Go to 43

157

As the hot-headed Trinovate goes down, the firing stops. Vain walks over to the body. "He's dead," he announces. "I hate bad losers."

"Me too, Vain," adds Groomert. You look across, and realise he has his blaster aimed at Vain! "I hate bad winners even more. I'm placing you under arrest." He flicks open an ID with his free hand – the little T'sarki is an off-planet cop! Vain shoots you a desperate glance! "It's a trick!" he howls, and then lifts his blaster in a blur of movement.

Read 564, and use the combat rules from the beginning of this book. Record this paragraph number, so you can find your way back here.

This combat starts At Range with just Vain and Groomert. Vain fires first. You can join in, use your Jedi powers to influence the outcome, or stay clear, whichever you choose. If one of the other combatants has a choice of targets at any time, use the dice to decide who he goes for

If you get hit, go to 123

Otherwise, if Vain is the first to be killed, go to 126

If Groomert is the first to fall, go to 142

158

You lay your ambush on the long road which winds its way through the hills south of Toprawa City, choosing a narrow cutting where the road passes through a man-made gully. You settle down to wait for the convoy.

It's your lucky day. At the appointed hour, an Imperial scout flashes by on a speeder bike. You have just a few moments to wait until the armoured speeder arrives. There it is! You have placed explosives in the rock on either side of the road; one of the Rebels now sets off the blasts, sealing the armoured speeder inside twin walls of rubble. It crashes heavily into one pile of fallen rock and halts. Three stormtroopers spill out of the troop compartment. You have about 2 minutes to take them out, break into the strongbox area, and get the goodies before the back-up vehicle arrives!

Read 567, and use the combat rules from the beginning of this book. Record this paragraph number so you can find your way

back here

If you win the battle, go to 130

If you are hit, go to 159

159

The odds were just too long. A blaster rifle brings you down. Maybe this wasn't the smart way to go about your plan after all.

When you're ready to start again, go to 1

160

"I think you might have a problem too," says a wavering voice. An old man in the corner, shrouded in a heavy cloak, taps a gnarled finger to his forehead. "I've heard of this Boba Fett," he says. "They say he's the deadliest man in the galaxy." The old guy sounds about a hundred and ninety. You push some nuts closer to his quivering hand, noting the discoloured skin and the thick knuckles. Make that two hundred and ninety. "I've heard the same stories, pop – and that's all they are... just stories. Besides, why would Boba Fett be after me?"

"Maybe he's heard you're trying to leave Toprawa," whispers Al. So? "Maybe the Empire has hired him... maybe..."

"Come on, Al. This is paranoia! You think the Empire is going to hire a psychotic madman for that, when they have a planet crawling with men? I don't think so. You'll have to come up with a better reason than that."

Check 569

If you have checked 557, go to 170

If not, go to 180

161

"Maybe I'll stowaway on one of those Imperial freighters," you say, thinking out loud. Al wrinkles his nose. "No chance. They'd find you and feed you to the stars. What you need is a ship of your own."

"You got one in mind, Al?" He studiously polishes the bar. When you see what damage some of his drinks do to the surfaces around here, makes you wonder why anyone touches them. "There's this guy. Tann. Comes in here now and again. He's got a ship at the port." Al looks around, making sure no-one is listening. "Impounded by Jabba the Hutt's Gamorrean representative, T'blisk." Aha! And? "Get Tann his ship back, and he could fly you out."

"Where do I find this Tann now?" Al thinks briefly. "You need to talk to his sister." You wait, but that's all he says. "Come on, Al! Where do I find his sister?!"

"You should know! She's with the Rebellion – one of your people." She is? "Get a grip, Havet. It's Surna. I've seen you in here with her." Surna?! She never mentioned having a brother who was a pilot (well of course she didn't – she knows as well as anyone that you're itching to get off Toprawa). "You do know where she is, don't you, Havet? The Imperials caught her – she's in the lock-up on Market Street." Right. So, you'll get her out. With thirty or forty men, you could blow the lock-up walls with explosives, race in... Except you don't have thirty or forty men, do you? With the way things are between you and the Rebels, they aren't likely to approve of any half-baked scheme you come up with. "Let me talk to them, Havet. I have some friends in the top ranks of the Rebellion. I think they'll listen to me. All you need is a plan." Ah. Well, you could either get someone on the inside, or you could assault the place from the out-side. "I love it when you're coming up with a scheme, Havet. Want another Star Racer?"

The Racer goes down easy, the plan is a little more difficult. Even so, the next thing you know, you're in a dark alleyway opposite the lock-up with a few of the remaining Rebels.

Add 1 Jedi Power Point to your current total

If your plan includes putting someone on the inside of the lock-up, go to 33

If you launch an attack, go to 8

162

"Time we were gone," you tell Al. "No," says the old guy at the bar. "Stay and have one last drink." You grimace – it'd be nice to do something sneaky and clandestine without an audience for once. "I promise you, it really will be your last drink..." Say again? What did he mean by that? And why did his voice sound so familiar all of a sudden.

The old man throws back his hood. A familiar helmet with a T-shape visor is revealed. If it could express a grin, that helmet would be cracking up right now. "Fett!" Boba Fett laughs in his old man voice; he thinks this is a grand joke. He removes the cloak, exposing his ancient, battered armour. The only unusual feature which remains is the fake second-skin old man's hand, a joke shop prop. He aims a snub-nosed slug thrower in your direction with the other hand.

"I hear you want to leave Toprawa," says Fett. "I'd like to persuade you to stay. Permanently. Below ground." Across the bar, Al whitters nervously. "Not in here," he whimpers. "Last time you guys got it on, the place was wrecked." Fett doesn't move a muscle. "I'll pay for any breakages, Alchemist. Not that I expect any. From here, I'd say I couldn't miss, wouldn't you?"

You would. Your life starts passing slowly in front of your eyes. It had better get a move on.

If you leap at Boba Fett, go to 147

If you wait, go to 184

163

It never rains but it pours. No sooner have you hidden the body than Al, who has been on watch, is hissing a warning. "Stormtroopers!" Three white-armoured soldiers are walking down the ramp from a security tower on the edge of this part of the apron. They are coming towards you. "OK, that's it!" hisses Surna. "If we stay here any longer, we're bound to be caught! Let's get spaceborne – now!" She skips away, into the shadows. You follow at once.

Check 571

Go to 174

164

You put the money in front of Holrga. His lip turns up in a sneer, and the appendages sag. He doesn't bother to count it.

"Is this a jest, Tann? Your debt to the incandescent Jabba the Hutt stands at –" pause for mental calculation "– 64,998-decimal-386 credits. This is a derisory amount."

A small fire burns inside you. You have known all along that this would be his attitude. After all, 2,000 credits represents just – pause for mental calculation – 3% of the total debt. The interest rate is probably nearer 30%. At this rate, Tann will owe more than the ship could ever be worth, even if it were encrusted in gems and it could skip across the galaxy in a day and a half... For a brief moment, the Force burns more brightly inside you. You lean across the table, reaching out with your mind, and say, in a clear, though soft voice: "Count it."

Add 2 Jedi Power Points to your current total

Read 573

165

Holrga counts the money. He does it very quickly, with just the faintest tremor of his lips.

"I'm impressed, Tann! Your debt to the incandescent Jabba the Hutt stands at –" pause for mental calculation "– 64,998-decimal-386 credits. This payment reduces the balance to a mere –" shorter pause; easier sum "– 46,376-decimal-386 credits. His illuminated majesty, the glorious Jabba was wise to give you additional time to pay. Another payment like this next month and –"

You slap your hand down on the table. A few coins scatter from the table (was that a 500-credit which just went rolling out of the booth?). "You don't understand," you growl. "This isn't a down-payment. This is it. All you're ever going to get. This is take it or leave it money." The Twi'lek's appendages lift apprehensively. "You don't mean –"

"I do," you continue. "Either you cancel the debt, and give Tann back his ship, or we walk from here with this money, and you can keep the *Rust Bucket* all for your very own." Tann starts to butt in, but Surna catches him in the stomach with her elbow, and he coughs and splutters instead. Holrga looks past you irritably, then fixes his attention back on your unmoving (you hope!) features. Finally, he reaches a decision. "I cannot authorise such a transaction. We must go to see T'blisk at once." Great. That's just what you hoped for. Holrga stands, and leads the way from the booth. You find you have to step round a furious fist-fight between a large apezoid and a female lizard. It appears to be over the ownership of a 500-credit coin.

Go to 179

166

Holrga's eyes light up a little as he counts the money you have placed in front of him. "Most impressive! How did you find such a sum so quickly?"

"Never mind. Do we get the ship back, or what?" Holrga grins, showing sharp, narrow teeth. "I am sure T'blisk will want to see you personally about that. Will you follow me?"

Go to 177

167

Holrga's prehensile appendages twist with pleasure as he calculates how much money you have brought. "My, my! The whole amount! You have been busy."

"That clears the debt, Holrga. I want my ship back," says Tann, in a slow, determined voice. "And you shall have it! I believe we should go at once to see T'blisk. Will you come with me?"

Check 563

Go to 179

168

Sorting through the large stack of money you have acquired, you hand just over half to Holrga. His eyes take on a glassy sheen, and his appendages grip his head tightly, in what you take to be an expression of delight. His greedy pleasure is so extreme, it makes you feel ashamed. After all, you have acquired the money in the most unfortunate way.

"Such a large amount of money! And so unexpected! The exalted Jabba was indeed right to be so very patient with you. And I see you still have a tidy sum left over! Perhaps there is some way I could help you invest it – perhaps finding you the right cargo, yes?"

You feel physically sick in Holrga's presence. Worse, you feel sick because you know that you're not that much better than him. You too felt that moment of glee when you realised you had all the money you needed – and more. Although you needed money to recover Tann's ship, you didn't need this much, and you didn't need it this badly.

Read 578

Go to 179

169

You lay your ambush on the main Highway from the port to Toprawa City. At the appointed hour, an Imperial scout flashes by on a speeder bike. A few moments later, the armoured speeder appears. It's your lucky day – you're in the right place!

Two large masts cross the Highway at this point, bearing overhead cables. You have placed explosives on both. Hitting the detonator, you topple the masts over, sealing the armoured landspeeder between two masses of twisted metal and high-voltage cable. The speeder ploughs clumsily into one of the fallen masts and stops. Three Imperial stormtroopers clamber out of the troop compartment, tripping over the shattered spars. You have about 2 minutes to take them out, break into the strongbox area, and get the goodies before the back-up vehicle arrives!

Read 567, and use the combat rules from the beginning of this book. Record this paragraph number so you can find your way back here

If you win the battle, go to 130

If you are hit, go to 159

170

Al leans across the bar. "Perhaps he's heard about the *Rust Bucket*. After all, he does do a lot of work for Jabba the Hutt." So, what's the problem there? "Al, we've sorted things out with T'blisk. Tann doesn't owe Jabba anything any more. So, Boba Fett can take a running jump as far as I'm concerned. It isn't any of his business."

Al leans even further forward. He's a big man, and you wonder if the bar can take the strain. "It isn't any of my business either, Havet, but when you go – will you take me with you?" Wow! Big surprise. "I'm surprised, Al. You want to leave Toprawa too?" Now he looks shocked. "Sure! You have any idea how hard it is to make a living on this rock anymore? I could cook for you. I could bring all the Star Racers you could ever want! And I can get you into the Port; I supply the mess once a month, and I slip the Commandant his favourite brandy as a bonus."

"OK. OK. You're in! But no cooking – OK? – I've eaten in this cantina for too long to have any illusions about your skills as a chef. Just pack the Racers; I'll go and find the others."

Go to 162

171

You decide you don't like the way things are shaping up, and reach into your coat, pulling your blaster from your pocket. Tann and Surna react, following your example. T'blisk gapes – completely surprised – as you open fire.

Read 576, and use the combat rules from the beginning of this book. Record this paragraph number so you can find your way back here.

If you're hit, go to 175

If you win, but Surna is hit, go to 176

If you win, but Tann is hit, go to 178

If you win, but they are both hit, go to 173

If you win, and all three of you are OK, go to 200

172

"Maybe I'll stowaway on one of those Imperial freighters," you say, thinking out loud. Al wrinkles his nose. "No chance. They'd find you and feed you to the stars. What you need is a ship of your own." You shake your head. There's no way you can manage that. Even if you could beg, borrow or steal a ship, you don't know how to fly one!

"I don't have any choice. Maybe they don't check as hard as you say. Maybe I'll get lucky. First, though, I have to get into the spaceport. You got any ideas about that, Al?"

Al looks into your eyes, his face touched with sadness. "You know, Havet. If you had a halfway decent plan for getting off Toprawa, I'd come with you. But this…" He shakes his head. "I don't even think I should be helping you get in – it's a suicide run!"

"You know a way, then?" you say, picking up on the positive part of what he said. "I guess. I deliver to the officers' mess; I could take you in with me. Once we were inside the port, though, you'd be on your own." That's fine by you. "Are you sure this is what you want to do, Havet?" You nod. "Then we'll go at once. I'd like to get this over with." Al steps back into a back room, leaving you to finish your drink and look around.

If you have checked 574, go to 185

If you haven't checked 574, go to 197

173

To your horror, once the fighting dies down, you're the only one left standing. Worse still, you have the distinct impression T'blisk wasn't going to do anything before you pulled your weapon. After that, there just wasn't time to stop.

You check Tann for any sign of life, but the pilot is completely still. Surna is badly injured. You find an electronic key in T'blisk's pocket. It looks like the kind of thing you use to disable the controls on a vehicle. This must be for the *Rust Bucket*. However, without a pilot, the ship is useless to you. Who else do you know? Nobody. Holrga, too, has survived this long, though he is fading fast. "Why… did you… open fire?" You've started asking yourself that.

"T'blisk was about to…" you start lamely. About to what? Holrga shakes his head, and you manage to feel a twinge of sympathy. "Why… should we risk… our lives? Boba Fett… already has contract… on your life. You'll never… leave Toprawa… alive." The strange appendages on his head shiver, and then the Twi'lek is silent and motionless.

You leave the room, slipping out through the heavy door into the alley. You use your comlink to call a Rebel unit to come and find Surna, aware that a deep chill has settled on your heart. Your mind is made up. You have to get off Toprawa right away. With that in mind, you go back into the cantina, to talk over your options with Al the Alchemist.

Go to 197

174

Ahead of you lies the landing bay where Tann's ship is berthed. There are no guards anywhere obvious. Another ship is parked close by, and an Imperial ore carrier is docked beyond that (it looks like it has been through a fight recently; perhaps the Rebels have been active in this Sector?). "So," whispers Tann. "What now?" You look around again. The area is very quiet. "I don't see anyone, but we better play this careful. I'll check out the ship for anyone skulking on board. When I signal, Tann, come running. You can check the on-board systems while we all keep watch. T'blisk may have put some alarms or self-destruct mechanisms on board; check carefully."

"I know my ship. If there's anything out of place, I'll find it." You hope so.

You rush quickly across the apron, and into the pit where the *Rust Bucket* lies waiting. All clear. You drop down onto the access ramp, and signal to the others. They run across from behind the other ship – wait a minute! There's four of them, not three! Who's the extra guy?

It's an Imperial dockyard technician. He came too close, so Surna grabbed him. The guy looks terrified; perhaps he can supply some useful information. "Check the ship, Tann," you order, and the pilot runs into the ship. "OK, friend. You have about thirty seconds to tell us all we need to know about getting this crate off the ground and past the blockade. Start talking." The guy is looking at you with his eyes out on stalks. You're not sure if he's terrified because Surna has a blaster in his ear, or because he can't believe what you just said. "You want to take off?" he asks. "We're overdue for an appointment. Twenty-five seconds."

Like all good servants of the Empire, he considers his duty for a moment. Then he decides not to bother. After all, if he doesn't do what you say, he's dead, right? Whereas, if he does tell you what you need to know, he can be fairly sure you'll be atomised by the fleet before anyone finds out. That's how you'd see it. He starts talking. "OK. Is this thing fuelled for flight? Has he done his preflight check?"

"Don't quote regulations! We're in a hurry!" He wises up. "I understand – tell your friend she needn't get nervous! So – if the ship is OK, first you need Ground Clearance." Why? "If you take off without clearance from the tower, the ground batteries will shoot you down before you can get 100 metres into the air."

If you have checked 540, go to 211

If you haven't checked 540, go to 222

175

Even though T'blisk's people seemed strangely hesitant, they were still more than fast enough to take you out.

Your adventure is at an end. Perhaps you would do better with a different character – or maybe there was another way to handle that encounter?

176

T'blisk and the rest of his bandits are taken completely by surprise, and you quickly mop them up. However, your reckless attack was not without loss – Surna has been injured. It's quite a bad wound, and needs treatment at once. Tann is beside himself with worry for his sister's well-being. "Why did you open fire?" he wails. "I didn't see any sign of trouble; I didn't think T'blisk was going to do anything before you pulled your weapon."

Were you too hasty? If you had delayed, T'blisk and his goons might have managed to kill all of you. What else were they going to do? Right now, there's no time to waste thinking about such things. You must draw on the Force to stabilise Surna's condition, and staunch the loss of blood from her wounds. Bending over your friend, you place your hands on either side of her head, and allow the Force to flow through your fingers.

You must spend 3 Jedi Power Points immediately to aid Surna resist the effects of her wounds. If you spend 3 JPPs, go to 189

If you don't have 3 JPPs left, or don't choose to spend them, go to 201

177

Holrga gathers up the money, and heads for the back door. Outside, in the secluded back alleyway, he hands it over to a very large apezoid character, who drops it into a landspeeder, and disappears. You wonder for a moment if you should allow this to happen, but you figure that if Holrga or T'blisk is going to rip you off, there are plenty of ways for them to do it. Besides, what are you going to do – ask for a receipt?

The Twi'lek takes you across the alley, and through a door into a private building, which has heavy, blast-proof doors and several guards. You follow him down some stairs into a large, plain chamber. At one end, there's a table and a chair. T'blisk is sitting in the chair, with his feet up on the table. He's cleaning his nails with a knife. There are no other seats, so you amble forward to stand opposite him.

After a few moments, he looks up, as if he had just realised you are here. He doesn't seem pleased to see you, and turns his attention to Tann. He snorts loudly. Holrga translates. "Do you believe in coincidence?" Tann stumbles over his reply. "T'blisk doesn't either," continues Holrga. "So what are we going to call this payment you have made?"

"40,000 credits," you butt in. "Probably all of what Tann owed you people before you started charging him 30% interest every month. More than enough to prove that he means to pay off the rest of the balance, if you release his ship and let us get out into space and hauling cargo, instead of festering down here." As he listens to Holrga translate this into Gamorrean pig-talk, T'blisk turns his large, brutish head in your direction. He starts cleaning one of his tusks with the curved blade of his knife. The scraping noise makes your own teeth itch. He feeds Holrga his next line. "40,000 credits. That's just what we mean. Recently, someone stole almost exactly the same amount from Ziggy's place. You see what I mean about coincidence? A few days ago, you don't have the price of a bowl of soup. Now you come in, and say you have 40,000 credits. And T'blisk says, what luck, because Ziggy just lost 40,000 credits! What you think of that?"

"Do we get the ship back, or what?" you ask, painfully aware where this conversation is heading. T'blisk is getting pretty steamed with you, and with being excluded from the majority of the conversation. He grunts and growls in what has to be a threatening tone. Holrga nods. "T'blisk would put it another way. Ziggy works for his magnificence, Jabba the Hutt; he runs the loans franchise on Toprawa. T'blisk also works for his excellency, Jabba the Hutt; he controls debt collection and trade out of the spaceport. He wonders – and I am curious about this myself – do you think he is stupid enough to take money from you that you stole from Ziggy? Do you think T'blisk is stupid enough to let you pay off a debt to the all-wise Jabba the Hutt with money you stole from him in the first place?"

Well, yes, actually.

If you have checked 574, go to 188

Otherwise, read 575

178

You defeat T'blisk and his cronies, but there is a terrible price to be paid. Tann has been killed; Surna is weeping over her brother's body. She looks up at you, and you can feel the hot blaze of her anger through the tears. "Why did you open fire, Havet?" She cradles his head in her hands. "T'blisk wasn't going to do anything – I'm sure of it. What made you start a fight?"

You walk away, unable to face her. T'blisk is down behind the table at which he had been sitting. You find an electronic key in his pocket, the kind you use to unlock the control surfaces on a landspeeder or a ship. This must be for the *Rust Bucket*. You've finally got your hands on the ship, but lost your pilot. You turn round to explain to Surna that it wasn't your fault, but find she is standing at the door. She has hefted Tann into her arms, and is carrying him out, strain etched deep in her face. She pauses to say: "You're on your own now, Havet." Then she leaves.

You wait a few moments, then head for the door yourself. Your best option for getting off the planet having been lost, you head back towards the cantina to see if Al can suggest some other way of getting away from Toprawa.

Go to 172

179

Holrga gathers up the money, and heads for the back door. Outside, in the secluded back alleyway, he hands it over to a very large apezoid character, who drops it into a landspeeder and disappears. Should you just allow this to happen? Maybe not, but if T'blisk is going to rip you off, there are plenty of other ways to do it. Besides, what are you going to do – ask for a receipt?

The Twi'lek takes you into a private building, which has heavy, blast-proof doors and several guards. You follow him down some stairs into a large, plain chamber. At one end, there's a table and a chair. T'blisk is sitting in the chair, with his feet up on the table. He's cleaning his nails with a knife. There are no other seats, so you amble forward to stand opposite him. After a few moments, he looks up, as if he had just realised you are here. He seems quite pleased to see you, and grunts heartily. Gamorreans can't speak Basic, and so Holrga translates. "T'blisk is very pleased," he says. "He gave up on you a long time ago, but the magnificent Jabba said we should be patient. How wise he was! Now you have made this large payment!"

If you have checked 563, go to 202

Otherwise, go to 190

180

The old guy tutts audibly. "I wouldn't like to be in your boots if Boba Fett heard you talk that way." Man, there's nothing wrong with the oldster's hearing. "Will you butt out? This is a private conversation!" The gnarled old hand clenches into a fist, but he says nothing. Good. "I have to get off this planet," you continue, dropping your voice to where even Al has trouble hearing you. "Can you help?" Al scratches his nose and thinks it over. "I can get you into the Port, Havet; but what about a ship?" Good question. "I'll need one of those too," you reply. "It'll make life a lot easier," says Al, with the trace of a grin.

Check 574

Go to 137

181

The old man seems a lot stronger than you expected, but you wrestle the rocket dart launcher from his hand.

Read 584, and use the combat rules from the beginning of this book. Record this paragraph number so you can find your way back here.

If you win the combat, go to 204

If you lose, go to 214

182

You wait, expecting T'blisk to start something. He grins, showing the full length of his yellow tusks. He's enjoying himself, but it doesn't appear that he or his goons are going to start a shooting match just yet. The silence lasts for quite a while, and it is T'blisk's patience which snaps first, although he still seems in a pretty good mood. He grunts some instructions to Holrga.

"You may go," the Twi'lek orders. T'blisk waves his hand dismissively for emphasis, and goes back to his hygiene routine. "Is that it?" you ask, incredulously. "What do you expect?" Holrga scoffs. "You think T'blisk is going to pull my blaster and start a fight in here? You've been watching too many old gangster vids! We are businessmen, not thugs." As Holrga says this, T'blisk gets on with a particularly aggressive bit of weeding with his knife. "And besides..." Aha! Now we're getting to it. "...Boba Fett is here on Toprawa. He will look after the incalculable Jabba's interests in this area."

In other words, T'blisk would like to shoot you down like a dog, but he isn't going to tread on Fett's toes.

"That's it, then?" you ask. "Doesn't it worry you that we could just take you guys on anyway. I bet you have the key to Tann's ship on you somewhere. What's to stop us just taking it?" Holrga isn't at all phased. "You want the key?" He speaks to T'blisk in Gamorrean. T'blisk reaches into a pocket and fetches out the key for an electronic immobiliser, the kind of thing you get on a landspeeder. He tosses it to Tann, who looks at it in a way that suggests he recognises it well. "Here – take it," says Holrga. "Why should we fight? We have nothing to gain. And for you, there will still be Boba Fett. Sooner or later, you are going to have to face him."

Check 557

If you have checked 574, go to 198

If not, go to 209

183

T'blisk starts moving towards the exit, looking as nervous as 150 kilos of porcine muscle ever can. "One thing," says Fett, and the Gamorrean and his companions halt immediately. "The ship – the *Rust Bucket* – you have the key?" T'blisk produces it after Holrga's translation. "Give it to the pilot." T'blisk hesitates. "You want us to give him his ship back?" asks Holrga. Fett's voice becomes just a little impatient with whatever game he is playing. "Of course. It won't be much of a lesson if no-one ever gets to hear about it, will it? Of course, we could disturb your master, the illustrious Jabba, with whom I have already spoken, to see if he concurs. Have you ever questioned his orders before?" T'blisk hasn't, but he obviously knows a man who did. He tosses an electronic panel key to Tann, then leaves as quickly as he can.

"You two can leave also," Fett says to Tann and Surna, quietly controlled now. Surna shoots you a worried look. "Go!" you order. They head for the exit.

"Havet, I have just passed up a perfectly good bounty," says Fett, now you are alone. "Do you know why?" You can guess. "I want to kill you for myself. Just because I'm a 'psychotic madman', I suppose." Sheesh! What a touchy guy he is! "You shouldn't hold a grudge," you say. "Carrying that kind of thing around can do you all kind of harm." Fett chuckles. "I'm not carrying this grudge around much longer, Havet Storm. Let's go."

Check 557

Read 580, and use the combat rules from the beginning of this book. Record this paragraph number so you can find your way back here.

If you win the combat, go to 205

If you lose, go to 216

184

Just when you think it's all over, there's a small, popping noise just behind you, followed by a thick WHOOSH! Boba Fett is struck square by a jet of high-pressure foam, which coats his visor in a dark, sticky cloud of bubbles. Instinctively, he pulls the trigger on his slug-thrower, but you have thrown yourself aside, and the slug passes through a fold in your coat, and cracks into the bar. Picking up a chair (and dropping the small, thin humanoid who was sitting in it), you heave it at Boba Fett. It hits him hard enough to throw him off his feet, and the slug-thrower spins out of his hand. Of course, Boba Fett still has an arsenal of weapons attached to his armour, but it's nice to see him partially disarmed.

With this small advantage, you think about finishing Boba Fett off, but he isn't that ready to be a victim. A huge plume of smoke erupts from his pack, reducing visibility in the cantina to zero in about a second and a half. Now you're as blind as he is. Drawing your weapon, you crouch low, listening, but the uproar in the cantina as everyone heads for the exit is too loud. The smoke detectors have been triggered, and extractors gradually reduce the thick, inky cloud. By the time you can see the whole room, Boba Fett is gone, along with everyone else. Behind the bar, Al rises up from the floor, still clutching the bottle of fizzy wine he used to spray Fett.

"People drink that stuff?" you ask. "Hardly ever. After a few decades in the bottle, it goes kind of oily, you know?" You saw that for yourself. "It's the last bottle of Daruvvian Champagne I had. I really think it's time we left now." You nod. "Make the arrangements." While he goes off to make a call, you check cautiously outside to make sure Boba Fett has gone.

Go to 144

185

The cantina has its usual mix of customers; humans and aliens, mixed wildly together. Everyone seems to be having a good time, as if trying to forget the miserable existence they are forced to endure on Toprawa. The Empire may have cut off Toprawa from the rest of the galaxy, but they haven't managed to keep Al the Alchemist from contacting his suppliers, and there is plenty of cheap food and drink to be enjoyed. Why does Al want to leave all this behind?

There's a small movement to your left, where the old man is sitting. You notice that he has a severely humped back. Man, he must be really hot under that cloak; you're gasping for air in here yourself. He has put down his drink, and is rummaging around under his cloak for something.

A flash of intuition jangles in your mind. Your hand starts moving even before you see the weapon appear. Much faster than you have seen him move until now, the old man produces a rocket dart pistol. You instinctively move to defend yourself against him.

Read 579, and use the combat rules from the beginning of this book. Record this paragraph number so you can find your way back here.

If you win the combat, go to 203

If you lose, go to 214

186

You walk purposefully over towards the ore freighter, trying to look like you belong. Despite all the Imperial technicians and flight crew around the ship, no-one pays you much attention. At the rear of the ship, you find an access hatch, and crawl in. The hatch leads into the crawl space beneath one of the large holds. Dragging yourself along, you come to another door, one which you hope leads out of the freight area. You push against the lock – it doesn't move! You heave again – still nothing. Throughout the ship, you can hear the whine of repulsorlifts, as the freighter powers up to leave the port.

You can't stay here! Once the ship leaves Toprawa's atmosphere, this area will be in a vacuum – and you don't have a space suit!

If you want to try to force the door open, look at your Strength score (on your Character Sheet). You may spend Jedi Power Points to increase your Strength temporarily (but not to more than 6). Now take this total, and add it to 240. This is the number of the paragraph you should read next. So, if your Strength is 4 and you spend 1 Jedi Power Point, you would now go to 245

Alternatively, if you crawl back the way you came, look at your Speed score (on your Character Sheet). You may spend Jedi Power Points to increase your Speed temporarily (but not to more than 6). Now take this total, and add it to 230. This is the number of the paragraph you should read next. So, if your Speed is 1 and you spend 1 Jedi Power Point, you would now go to 232

187

Keeping in the shelter of the shadows cast by the port's buildings, you scamper across to the gun tower. From close up, you can see why Tann was so nervous. Twin Kormalite 225 heavy blasters are mounted on a swivel platform with a wide field of fire. Not only would the weapon provide good defence against an airborne attack, but its firepower could be quickly brought to bear on any ship on this sector of the port apron, blasting it to atoms before it could rise to manoeuvring height on its repulsorlifts.

There is a narrow stairway winding up the slender tower. You race up the steps. A stormtrooper at the top of the ladder hears you approach, but he is too slow reacting. You stiff arm him, and he topples over the stair rail. Crashing open the door, you face the gun crew.

Read 581, and use the Combat Rules from the beginning of this book. Record this paragraph number so you can find your way back

If you defeat the tower's defenders, go to 207

If you are beaten, go to 218

188

T'blisk blazes with anger. You're just on the point of deciding whether to fight your way out when there is a very brief commotion at the door, and a voice interrupts the proceedings. "This isn't about how stupid T'blisk is, Holrga. It's about how stupid these Rebels are, and about how they're going to pay for their mistakes." You look round to see who has entered... it's the old man from the cantina! He has his hooded cloak pulled up, so that the face is still invisible (it's pretty gloomy in this room anyway); he clutches a blaster rifle in one hand and an unconscious member of T'blisk's entourage in the other. He's certainly full of surprises for an old guy!

"Who *are* you?" asks Holrga. The same question has been on your mind too. "How would Jabba the Hutt deal with these thieves?" continues the old man, ignoring the question. "What would he do, if he learned that his money had been stolen?" T'blisk growls once. "He would place a bounty on their heads, and have them hunted down as a lesson to the rest of the galaxy," says Holrga, translating pretty loosely.

"How much?" The old man's voice has lost its quaver. It has a definitely familiar ice about it. "5,000 credits," replies Holrga, who looks very uncomfortable. "I'll do it for free," says the other. The room temperature drops about 10 degrees. "Are you a bounty hunter, then, ancient one?" mocks Holrga. It isn't something you'd have done yourself.

The old man throws the part conscious guard aside with cruel strength; the man skids across the floor and crunches into the wall. Next, he unfastens his cloak, not once allowing the barrel of his blaster rifle to waver. Moments later, he throws the cloak aside, and you find yourself gazing once more into the cold metallic mask of Boba Fett's battered old helmet. What does it take to get away from this guy?

T'blisk utters some indelicate, strange, nervous noises. "I – I – I'm so glad you're here, Boba Fett," Holrga gibbers. "Your generous offer will be gratefully received by our most honoured master." Fett steps a little closer. "I'm sure it will be," he says. "However, for such a price I can only take one life. Will that be enough of a lesson to the rest of the galaxy, do you think?" Where is this leading, you wonder? T'blisk must be wondering the same thing, but he agrees anyway. "Whatever you think is best, Boba Fett," says Holrga.

Go to 183

189

"Surna will be alright," you tell Tann after a few moments. The relief shows on his face. "We have to get her to a doctor, right?" he says. "I don't think she's in any danger, Tann. If we take her to a hospital, they'll want to know how she got wounded. It would be better if we got off Toprawa altogether. Do you agree?" He isn't happy about the idea, but Surna nods her head.

You search T'blisk and the other crooks. You find an electronic key, which Tann recognises as being from the *Rust Bucket*. Good. Between you, you manage to carry Surna from the room, and back across the alley to a private room at the back of Al's cantina, where you leave Surna in her brother's care. "Where are you going?" asks Tann.

"Back into the cantina to ask Al for help. I'm just going to walk through the front door as if nothing has happened. If there's trouble, no-one will look for you out the back."

Check 557

Go to 43

190

Holrga and T'blisk swap grunts. T'blisk grins, showing his brutal tusks. Holrga snorts and grunts a few more 'words', and the grin fades. That must have been where Holrga explained that you weren't prepared to pay any more. Just to make sure he gets the idea, you say: "That's all the money you're going to get, T'blisk. We have to have that ship back now. There isn't going to be another forty-six thousand three hundred and whatever –" Holrga looks as though he might chime in with the rest of the figure, but you silence him with your best threatening look. "Give us back the ship, T'blisk."

The Gamorrean twists his face in an ugly grimace, and leans back on the fragile-looking chair as Holrga gives him the gist of what you have said. T'blisk isn't impressed, and so you up the stakes a little. "Look, let's be rational. If we can't get off this planet, we're pretty much dead anyway. So, we're willing to take our chances right now. If you don't give us the ship, we'll take it. And we'll start by frying your hide right here and now." When this is translated for him, T'blisk smiles widely. You can see that's he's much happier dealing with threats; threats are something which he can cope with. "There are five of us, and only three of you," comments Holrga. "You'll never make it." You shake your head, trying to persuade him that he has missed the point. "Tell T'blisk he'll never know. All three of us will aim for him first. Even if we get killed, he'll be dead too. You too, if I have my way."

In several old vids you watched in your youth, that kind of reasoning always worked on the bad guys. T'blisk, though, just gets angry, and grunts loudly for several seconds. Holrga finally manages to offer an edited version in Basic. "Don't threaten us. Even if you had the ship, you would never get to fly it. The exalted Jabba will place a bounty on your heads, and there is a Bounty Hunter already on Toprawa. Boba Fett will kill you before you ever leave the ground."

"Do not make the mistake of thinking we are stupid, Havet Storm," he finishes, puffing himself up to his full height, almost daring you to challenge him.

If you have checked 574, go to 188

If you haven't checked 574, read 575

191-192

Holrga leans forward to count the pile again, while you try to influence his mind to believe that a greater sum of money lies in front of him than is really there. Because of his greed, your plan succeeds.

Go to 165

193-196

Holrga leans forward to count the pile again, while you overpower his weak and greedy mind with the power of the Force. He counts each coin several times over.

Go to 167

197

Al has arranged for you to make his regular delivery to the spaceport. He has a freight speeder parked out the back, loaded with food and drink for the Officer's mess. "Unpack the cases on the landing bay behind the Fleet Quarters," he explains. "There's a door. When no-one's watching, slip through it. It leads past some ready rooms where you can steal a uniform; beyond them, there are passages leading to all the landing bays. Good luck."

It's a risky plan, but it goes quite well. The guards at the gate ask for your papers, but they're more interested in your cargo than you. As Al suggested, you slip them some beer, and they wave you through. The Fleet Quarters are well sign-posted. An orderly meets you at the landing bay, and checks your delivery list. When you ask if he will help you unload, he makes an excuse and wanders off. You leave it a few moments, then slip through the door Al told you about.

Moments later, dressed in a Fleet uniform, and carrying an empty chart case, both stolen from a ready room, you make your way towards the landing bays. Somewhere along here there's Tann's ship, the *Rust Bucket*, but that's no good for you. You can't pilot or navigate a spaceship. That leaves just one choice – you'll have to stow-away.

There are two ships on this side of the spaceport. One is an ore freighter, which has just loaded up, and is in preflight. A great many personnel are wandering about it. The other, on an isolated landing part of the apron, is a small three-crew ship. It has no-one close by at all. In fact, most people give the *Slave I* a wide berth. Should you?

If you check out the ore freighter, go to 186

If you try boarding *Slave I*, go to 212

198

It almost seems too good to be true. With the key in your hands, the three of you start backing towards the door. T'blisk watches, seemingly unconcerned. You're just on the point of turning to leave the room when there is a very brief commotion on the other side of the door. It bursts open, and the old man from the cantina walks in. What's he doing here? He has his hooded cloak pulled up, so that the face is still invisible (it's pretty gloomy in this room anyway); he clutches a blaster rifle in one hand and an unconscious member of T'blisk's entourage gripped by the neck in the other. He throws the poor, part-conscious guard to one side. Pretty tough, for an oldster.

"Who *are* you?" demands Holrga. The same question has been on your mind too. "I thought you were looking for me," says the old man. "I heard you were looking for a bounty hunter." The old man's voice has lost its quaver. It has a definitely familiar ice about it. "Are you a bounty hunter, then, ancient one?" Holrga mocks. "We had hoped to see Boba Fett."

The old man unfastens his cloak, not once allowing his blaster rifle to waver. Moments later, he throws the cloak aside, and you find yourself gazing once more into the cold metallic mask of Boba Fett's battered old helmet. What does it take to get away from this guy? "I – I'm so glad you're here, Boba Fett," Holrga gibbers, while T'blisk offers some quiet, prayer-like whimpers. "I was just saying to these rebel thieves –"

"I heard what you said," says Fett, "every word. You want me to teach these defaulters a lesson. I accept the commission." Hmmm. It looks like he's going to enjoy it too.

Go to 183

199

Moving so fast that the old man scarcely has time to react, you reach out and grab the rocket dart launcher. He has a surprisingly strong grasp, but you snatch the weapon from his hand and fire it at his cloaked body, all in one movement. He grunts as the darts thump into his body, and the powerful sedative is poured into him.

Even before he can fall, you are pulled back from him by rough hands. The other customers are very angry – they can't believe that you would beat up on an old man. It takes a lot of effort to shake them off. Once you are standing in some clear space again, you look around for your cloaked opponent – but he's gone! How could he have escaped with all that sedative inside him? Unless he was wearing armour under the cloak…

"What was all that about?" asks Al, reappearing from the back room. "A small mystery," you answer. "Forget it for now. Have you fixed it up for me to get inside the Port?" He has, but he isn't happy about it. "Are you positive this is what you want, Havet?" You nod. "With the number of enemies I have developed lately," you explain, "I think it's just about my only choice. don't you?"

Go to 197

200

It's a miracle, but you win the combat without any of you coming to any harm. Tann and Surna are breathing hard, but they haven't been injured. They look confused. "Why did you open fire?" asks Surna. "I didn't see anything threatening." You decide that you had better avoid explanation, and go across to search T'blisk instead. The Gamorrean is still alive, but his condition is poor.

You find an electronic key in his pocket. "If this is what I think it is, we'll be long gone before any of your people can find us. So save your breath. I wouldn't understand anything you said anyway." T'blisk sneers, which is a more worrying answer than words he could have spoken You step away, and hurry Surna and Tann out of the room. Locking the door, you lead them from the building.

"What's next in your master plan, Havet?" asks Surna, sarcastically. You can tell she didn't like the way you handled things in there. "Tann, is this for your ship?" you ask. The pilot looks it over. "It was, but the circuits have been damaged. I'm not sure it will work." Perhaps it can be fixed. Either way, you're committed now, you have to go for Tann's ship right away. Surna asks the obvious question: "How are we going to get into the spaceport? Shoot our way in?"

"If we have to. Let's get back and see Al. Maybe he has some quieter ideas."

Go to 43

201

You do what you can for Surna, but it isn't a lot. She's badly injured. Tann's emotions swing wildly from relief that she is alive, to fear for her injuries, to hot anger at the part you have played in all this. "I'm going to find her a doctor!" he shouts, picking his sister up in his arms. You know what that means. If he takes her into any hospital with wounds like that, the authorities will be told, and they'll be arrested. There's no point telling him, though; he's frightened, and he has to do something to help her.

You watch them go, your friend and her brother, the pilot. At one stroke, it just became even more important that you get off Toprawa, and about a hundred times more difficult. Picking yourself up, you head for the door. The only person who can help you now is Al; if his contacts can't provide you with some way to get off this rock, you'll be trapped here forever. You walk slowly back to the cantina.

Go to 43

202

Holrga explains to T'blisk that you have paid off the debt in full, telling him the news in a lengthy series of grunts and snorts. The Gamorrean is surprised, tinged with maybe just a little disappointment. You can see he just *hates* to let a customer go.

He reaches into a pocket, pulls out an electronic key and gives it to Holrga. The Twi'lek tosses it to Tann. "The *Rust Bucket* is yours. This will turn off the explosive charge in the hyperdrive control panel." Is that it? "Your debt to the illustrious Jabba is paid in full. We have no more business to discuss, unless…" Ah! Here it comes. "Even now, you cannot take your ship freely. The Imperials will not allow it to leave Toprawa. However, for a small fee…"

Tann is about to express some interest, but you cut him off. "Many thanks, but we'll take our chances with the blockade." Holrga shrugs. "You take many chances, Havet Storm. For you, there is also the problem of Boba Fett, who you have gravely insulted." What's his problem? "I don't know the details, but he has asked T'blisk to keep him informed about your movements. He will take a personal interest in stopping you leaving, I think." Is T'blisk offering you some kind of deal to get the bounty hunter off your back? "Some things are beyond price," Holrga grins. "You must deal with Boba Fett yourself."

Moments later, you're back outside, and the three of you take a good, long, hard look at the key. "Well," Tann grins, "that's the first part done. Now how do we get into the port?" They both look at you. "What we need is to pick the brains of someone with even more sneaky contacts than T'blisk. Let's go back to the cantina; if Al can't think of something, I don't know who can."

Check 557

Go to 43

You throw your fist into the hooded face of the old man. It's a full-blooded blow, and it's hard to say who it hurts worse. The old man is thrown back from his stool, and clatters to the ground, with the rocket dart launcher flying off into the distance. On the other hand, your hand feels like an AT-AT has trodden on it. You're not stupid; you can't thump anyone in the face with your fist and have it not hurt — there's too much bone in the average head (with the exception of a few species you could mention). But this! It felt like the old man's head was made of metal, like he was a droid, maybe, or had a helmet on under the hood…

You're ready to grab him, and find out just what you're dealing with, when a huge giant of a humanoid grabs you in a bear hug from behind, swinging you round into the centre of the room. You land awkwardly on a table, which gives way. Picking yourself up from the wreckage, you find you are at the centre of a ring of fierce faces from every race in the galaxy. The hairy giant is foremost amongst them, his fierce face furrowed with dark anger. "Never could stand anyone who picks on old people," he growls. "Then you ought to be ashamed of yourself!" you riposte, "I'm 360! I just look young!" His face seems to shrink even further, so that his brows dip closer to his mouth, and his eyebrows start tangling with his beard. "Anyway," you continue. "That isn't an old man, it's a droid of some kind. Take a look!"

The crowd parts somewhat as they look round for the 'victim' of your attack. You can see the corner of the cantina where you had been standing – and there's no-one there. Everyone shuffles around, wondering where the old guy has gone, wondering what to do next. Al reappears. He looks unhappy. "I know you're leaving, Havet," he says, "but don't break up my furniture."

Go to 197

204

You fire the rocket dart launcher at point blank range into the gnarled hand of the old man. To your great surprise, most of the darts don't penetrate his skin, but fall off, carrying their sedative to the floor. While you're trying to work this out in your mind, he swings his fist at your head. You manage to duck partially, but he cuffs you across the top of the head, and you end up sprawled on your backside.

The old man is trying to drag yet another weapon from the inside of his cloak, but he sways on his feet, and staggers back. Some of the darts must have got through. He clutches at the bar for support, then pushes away, and heads for the door. It would be easy to intercept him, and you have a burning curiosity to find out who he is, but you decide to let him go. You have more important fish to fry.

"What was all that about?" asks Al, who has reappeared from the back room. "You're asking the wrong man," you reply. "And – frankly – I'm not that bothered with the answer. Have you managed to find a way to get me into the spaceport?"

Go to 197

205

Fett clearly thinks he can beat you with the force pike; this is his way of having revenge. However, you spoil it for him. He over-reaches fractionally with one attack, and you slap his pike aside, and thrust forward at his shoulder. He tries to spin back, so that he is already off-balance as you tap him with the business end of the pike. There is a loud crack, and a sharp flash of green-blue light. The charge kicks Boba Fett round even faster, and he loses his footing. Even in defeat, he makes one last attempt to ram his pike into your face as he topples off the narrow roof into the street.

It's a long drop, and it would have been a fearful thing if you had lost the battle. Fett, though, has his armour, and it protects him from some of the impact as he smashes through the roof of a parked land-speeder. Even so, he lies quite still.

You feel a great wash of triumph. You have defeated the bounty hunter! Even if he has survived, you have humiliated him, and proved who is the better fighter. Sensibly, you realise that you ought to finish him off, that he will never let you rest as long as he lives. However, you are not the same as him, and your sense of personal honour doesn't allow you to consider it. It doesn't stop you dropping your force pike on him, though.

You retrieve your weapons, and leave the roof. You go down into the alley, and approach the broken landspeeder cautiously, almost expecting what you finally see. The landspeeder is empty. The two force pikes are there, but Boba Fett is gone.

There will be another time for you and Boba Fett. Turning away, you cross the alley and go back into Al's cantina through the back door. Surna and Tann are extremely pleased to see you, and the word of what you have achieved sweeps round the cantina like wildfire. You're famous now! Al wants to know all the details, but you're much more interested in how you move onto the next phase of your plan – getting into Toprawa spaceport.

If you have checked 569, remove it

Check 511

Go to 122

You run over towards the Control Centre. No-one questions you; it would be quite common for pilots to come in and file flight plans, and check details of the position of the blockading ships, etc. When you rush past the duty desk, however, you excite a little more interest. A security guard tries to halt you, and you push him aside as you leap up the stairs towards the control tower.

"What are you doing in here?!" yells an Officer as you crash through the door, knocking an orderly aside. "Are you the pilot of that freighter out there?" You nod, taking the time to check out the opposition. There are a few Officers with side-arms, but most of the crew are just technical staff, with no weapons. "Look, there's been a foul-up, that's all. We don't have a flight plan filed for your ship. Where are you heading for?"

"That information is classified," you insist, hoping that you can bluff your way out of this. The Officer looks sour, unimpressed. "Don't be ridiculous. If you don't file an approved flight plan, the fleet won't allow you to pass. You'll be destroyed!" That isn't part of the plan. "We're due to fly to Coruscant." The Officer pulls a data pad from a nearby console and enters this information. "What about cargo? he asks. "Documents... recently captured from the Rebels." He looks up briefly, with a disbelieving look. "On whose orders?"

"General BlasTech," you reply. He looks down to enter this information, but halts as he realises what you've said. "That's not a general's name," he says, "it's a... weapon..." He utters this last word after looking up and realising that you have drawn a weapon and aimed it at him. "Contact the fleet," you order. "Tell them to let the *Rust Bucket* through."

"I can't do that!" he insists, but he doesn't sound very certain as you jab your weapon closer to his eyes. He bends over the console, and keys the microphone. As he passes the information up to the flagship of the Imperial blockade, you look around the rest of the personnel in the room. None of them are keen to interfere. The Officer completes the message. "That's it. They'll pass you through." Good. But what are *you* going to do? If you leave the Control Centre, they'll just change the orders to the Fleet, and the *Rust Bucket* will be destroyed.

If you lock up the staff of the Control Centre, and run back to Tann's ship, go to 219

If you tell Tann to take off, go to 240

207

You take out the crew of the gun tower, and then break the trigger mechanism on the weapon itself. There's no way they can use this weapon against Tann's ship now!

You go back to the door. There's no alarm sounded outside. Perhaps this scheme is going to work out after all!

Check 583

If you run back to Tann's ship and take off, go to 217

If you investigate the Control Centre, go to 206

208

Tann fires up the repulsorlifts on the *Rust Bucket*, and the ship begins to rise slowly from the ground. Alarms sound immediately, and a voice comes through the speakers of the ship's communications. *"Rust Bucket!* This is Toprawa Tower. You are not cleared for take-off. Cut your engines immediately, or we will open fire." Tann tries to speed up the take-off, manoeuvring the ship to present a smaller target to the gun tower, but it is a hopeless task. No more than thirty metres off the ground, the ship takes several hits from the heavy blasters, and lurches heavily to one side. Power to the engines dies, and the *Rust Bucket* sags, then dives to the ground.

The landing is heavy, and you are fortunate that Tann's ship doesn't explode when it smacks onto the apron. As it is, there is a great deal of smoke and dust. You know that you have only a moment or two to react before Port Security troopers arrive. "Get off the ship, fast!" you instruct the others, blowing open the emergency hatch from the crew compartment. "Use the smoke for cover! There's a ship no more than fifty metres away. Run to it, and we'll try and get ourselves out of this mess!"

Surna leads the way; Tann and Al follow, and you bring up the rear, sprinting through the oily smoke. The dark shape of another ship looms up in front of you. The other three are sheltering underneath. "This is Boba Fett's ship – the *Slave I*!" yells Al. So it is. What a strange place to find shelter.

If you have checked 538, check 590 and go to 229

If not, go to 223

209

"I'll deal with Boba Fett, if and when the time comes," you tell Holrga. T'blisk grins spitefully. You still find it hard to believe that he is going to let you just walk out of here! Backing away, you go through the door and out into the street. Surna and Tann laugh out loud with relief. "He just *gave* us the key!" grins Tann. Maybe, but in your experience nothing ever comes that easily. "Let's go back to the cantina," you tell the others. "We still have a lot to do if we're going to get away from this planet."

Go to 43

210

You fail in your clumsy attempt to take the rocket dart launcher away from the old man. He fires, and the slender darts sting your flesh. Within seconds, the powerful sedatives are acting on your system, and you feel the ground swing wildly up from under your feet. Then comes blackness.

You wake after who knows how long, to find yourself in some kind of cell. It takes a while for you to realise that the cell is inside the hold of a ship. It takes even longer to understand the rest of it, when a bulkhead door opens and Boba Fett walks through from the crew compartment. "You're awake! Good! How do you feel? Have you realised where you are yet? This is my ship, the *Slave I*. I left Toprawa a few days ago, bound for Yavin. You? I'm not sure how far you'll be travelling." Even in your befuddled state, you know this isn't good news.

Go to 43

211

"We have ground clearance," you announce, which comes as a surprise to just about everyone. "OK..." says the Imperial technician (in a way which suggests he's thinking 'it's your funeral'). "Then the only other thing you have to worry about is the fleet. If your flight plan hasn't been logged with them, they'll treat your flight as an unauthorised lift-off, and blow you out of the sky."

"Who tells them that a flight has been authorised?" you ask. You can't think of any clever way to avoid the blockade. "The control tower," says the technician. "Right."

There's a medical kit on the ship, and you use some sedatives to knock out the technician. Surna ties him up, and hides him in a large storage bin on the edge of the landing bay, while you scout out the rest of the landing field on this side of the port. The control tower is about 250 metres away, a squat building topped off with a slender mast, and a transparent bubble housing the port management staff. Some distance further away, and at a right angle to the control tower, there's one of the port's defence stations, a tall gun tower. If what the technician has told you is correct, the gun shouldn't open fire – its operators should believe you have clearance to take off (assuming your earlier trick hasn't been discovered). The fleet, on the other hand, is still a problem. All the same, there doesn't seem to be an obvious way of beating that problem, short of a mad raid on the control tower.

Tann calls down from the flight deck. "I think I've got it ready! Are we going, or what?"

If you go to the gun tower, go to 187

If you attack the control tower, go to 206

If you take off, go to 217

212

Something Al said before comes back to you. Every ship which takes off from Toprawa is checked for any excess mass – every ship except Boba Fett's. Which means, even if you could get onto the ore freighter, you'd be discovered.

Which leaves *Slave I* as your only way out. Within a few moments, you're standing outside its closed entrance hatch, wondering just how you can get onto a ship most people would sell their grandmother to stay a long way away from...

If you have checked 538, go to 229

If not, go to 220

213

You look up into the sky a few times as you run across the port apron, even though the *Rust Bucket* is well out of sight. There are no pinpoint flashes of flight, no trails left by burnt-up ships. With luck, that means Tann has successfully bypassed the fleet, and gone into hyperspace.

Check 585

Go to 212

214

The old man proves to be a very deadly opponent. Somehow, you are defeated.

There's a mystery to be solved here. Can you do better in your next attempt?

215

The port's guns are silent. "Which console monitors their progress?" you ask the Imperial Officer. He points at a console. A small icon moves above a diagrammatic view of the port, gaining altitude, until it is beyond the limits of Toprawa's atmosphere. The view changes automatically, and you see the larger icons representing the Imperial fleet. No shots are fired. Seconds later, the *Rust Bucket's* icon changes to red. "What does that mean?" you ask. "He's engaged the warp drive." Another few moments pass by, until the icon disappears, except for a ghost image with its last known heading and projected speed shown. You know Tann will make just a small jump at first, and then change course violently to throw off any trail.

He can be left to look after the others now. The question now is, what are you going to do? "You might as well surrender," says the Officer. "Your friends have escaped, but there's no way you can get out of this port alive." You lock him (and the others) in a small, interior rest room while you think about the truth of that statement. Back in the main control room, looking out through the bubble, you can see a ship, sitting on its landing pad, challenging you to find a way onto it, and to follow Tann into space. It is Boba Fett's ship, the *Slave I*.

Check 585

Go to 212

216

You're not sure what Boba Fett hoped to prove in this battle on the roof. He is much more practised with the force pikes than you, and the struggle is gloriously one-sided. Just watching the way Fett's pike sparks as it clashes against yours makes you very wary of being hit. Above all else, you can't let him strike you with the metal tip. Well, you're successful in that. Parrying a long thrust by Fett, you try a counter-attack, but walk straight into the butt of Fett's pike. It catches you on the chin, and throws you off the roof.

It's a long fall, but your good fortune stretches out a little further. A soft-ish pile of rubbish, stacked close to the wall in the alley, breaks your fall. You bounce off with no more than a few bruises to show for your defeat. Looking up, you see Boba Fett glowering down at you. He's very disappointed that you have survived, and when he disappears, you know he has gone to fetch something that will change that situation at once. Well, you don't want to be a spoilsport, but you have other plans, so you duck back into the cantina, to lose yourself in the crowd. You don't expect Fett to come after you at once – Al can slip you out of one of the other exits anyway. You tell Al what has happened, and he gets very excited. You'd sooner he came up with some ideas about how you could get into Toprawa spaceport.

If you have checked 569, remove it

Read 587

If you have checked 503 (you had your lightsabre on your belt), also read 588

Go to 122

217

"Yes!" you yell. "Let's get out of here!" You make sure everyone is on board, and close the hatch. You join Tann on the flight deck as he finishes the last of his preflight checks. There's no sign of any special activity outside, but you know that this could all change as soon as Tann starts up the engines.

If you have checked either 540 or 583, go to 228

If you haven't checked either of these, go to 208

218

The crew in the gun tower are too good for you. Wounded, you collapse to the floor. Your weapons are removed, and you are searched for any other devices. The surviving gunners are still a little shocked, but they are reacting quickly. They call into the Security Centre, and post a new guard on the door.

You are drifting in and out of consciousness, but you catch a sudden burst of excitement. You realise what has happened. Tann has seen the security detachment on their way to the gun tower, and worked out that you have been killed or captured. He will have figured that you may have taken out enough of the gun crew to disable the tower, and has decided to take his chances.

The gun crew move quickly. They check that the ship has no clearance to take off, and then operate the controls to swing the double-barrelled heavy blaster towards the *Rust Bucket*. Seconds later, they open fire…

Your adventure has come to a sad end. Start again from paragraph 1

219

You lock up the crew of the control tower, finding a small rest room they can all be jammed in. You make your way back downstairs, where the security guards give you a hard time for barging upstairs. You manage to convince them that you are just a man in a hurry. Even so, it wastes precious time. As you step outside, you see two engineers looking up at the transparent bubble, realising that there is no-one visible up there. One of them starts trotting across towards the door, probably to get someone to check what is going on.

The *Rust Bucket* is still over 200 metres away. Even if nothing has happened by the time you reach the ship, it looks as though the port will be alerted before you can get clear. You just aren't going to make it. As the engineer scampers past you, you signal frantically to the ship, instructing Tann to take off immediately.

Turning back, you follow the engineer towards the control tower. Even as you reach the door, you hear the growing whine of the *Rust Bucket's* repulsorlifts.

Read 589, and use the combat rules from the beginning of the book. Record this paragraph number so you can find your way

back here

If you win the combat, go to 230

If you are defeated, go to 247

220

The access hatch into *Slave I* is closed and locked tight. There's no way onto the vessel.

Well, not for you, perhaps, but here comes someone who can certainly get on – Boba Fett himself! He's walking across the port apron as if nothing and no-one else mattered. You keep out of sight, and watch him approach the access hatch. He keys in a number – you can't see what the code was – and the hatch swings down. Without even looking round, Fett goes up onto the ship.

This is your very last chance to get off Toprawa! Fett has already keyed the ramp to start closing. You have just a few seconds to get through the narrowing entrance and onto the ship.

Look up your Speed score from your Character Sheet. You may spend Jedi Power Points to temporarily increase this score (but not to more than 6!). Now add this total to 250. This is the number of the paragraph you should go to now. So, if your Speed score is 2 and you spend 1 JPP, you would next read 253.

221

"Boba Fett isn't going to have landed on a deserted planet. We have to take this chance to escape." The others agree. Being cooped up in the slave pens of Fett's ship has made them extremely nervous! Grabbing your belongings, you slip out into the dark hold, and move across to the rectangle of light that marks the access hatch.

Outside, you realise that you're not on a planet at all, but some kind of moon. The bright disk of a nearby world dominates the sky. The surface of the satellite you have landed on is dusty and dark, and there is no sign of life. The sky boils with dust clouds. "Where are we?" asks Tann. Who knows? Nowhere you'd want to stay, that's for sure.

Boba Fett is striding off into the distance, towards a shadowy mound. Some kind of flickering glow is shining from inside. A tunnel

entrance, maybe. Perhaps the people on this moon lived underground? Man, it's frustrating not knowing where you are. "We need
to know if we're going to be able to get off this mudball," you tell
the others. "Scout around; see if you can find any sign of ships coming and going, or any sign of life on this rock." Surna looks worried.
"Where are you going?"

"To follow Boba Fett. I want to know what's he's up to." She shakes
her head. "That's crazy! He wants to kill you, and you're following
him around?" She has a point. All the same, you need to know when
Fett is leaving, to avoid being stranded here. The others move off,
looking back anxiously to see if you change your mind and go with
them. You turn away, wondering if you will ever see any of your
friends again.

If you follow Fett towards the mound, go to 238

If you stay close by his ship, go to 249

222

"OK, so how do we organise ground clearance?" The technician
looks very unhappy. He knows you aren't going to like what you
hear next. "I don't see how you can. The Departures Officer would
have you logged in as being ready to fly out. A security sweep would
be run on the ship, and then…"

"I don't think we have time for all that," mutters Al. "Isn't there
someone we could bribe?" The technician doesn't offer an opinion.
"OK, let's face facts," you announce. "If we try to take off without
clearance, that gun tower over there is going to fill the *Bucket* full of
holes. We can't get clearance without wasting too much time, so the
only other option is to take out the tower." Al and Surna look at you,
seriously concerned for your sanity. "Attack a heavy blaster tower?"
asks Surna. "Hey, it doesn't make much difference how big the
blaster is," you reply. "You can't get killed by degrees. Besides, I
wasn't thinking of standing outside and challenging them to a gun
fight." You look over towards the tower. There's a guard on a bal-
cony around the outside, but he's the only defender you can see.
"You're considering being sneaky again, aren't you?" asks Al. He
doesn't have any faith in you at all…

You turn back to the technician. "Assuming we had ground clearance
– or the gun tower developed a sudden malfunction – what then?" He
thinks it over "Well…" he says (in a way which suggests he's thinking 'if Marrovian pigs could fly'), "the only other thing you have to

worry about is the fleet. If your flight plan hasn't been logged with them, they'll treat your flight as an unauthorised lift-off, and blow you out of the sky."

"Who tells them that a flight has been authorised?" you ask. "The control tower," he replies.

That's all you need to know. There's a medical kit on the ship, and you use a sedative to knock out the technician. Surna ties him up, and hides him in a large storage bin on the edge of the landing pit, while you scout out the rest of the landing field on this side of the port. The control tower is about 250 metres away, a squat building topped off with a slender mast, and a transparent bubble housing the port management staff. Some distance further away, and at a right angle to the control tower, there's the tall gun tower.

Tann calls down from the flight deck. "Everything's ready in here! Are we going, or what?" You look from the gun tower to the control tower, and back again. "Just a minute, Tann. There are a few details to be worked out at this end."

If you go to the gun tower, go to 187

If you attack the control tower, go to 206

If you take off, go to 217

223

You inspect the exterior lock on *Slave I*. As you expected, it's a sophisticated code-programmable device, with a fail-safe against repeat random entries. There's no way you can just hook Arf up to the lock and keep trying different combinations until the door opens. "What are you doing?" asks Surna, urgently. "I'm trying to find a way to get on this ship!" you reply, equally forcefully. "Are you crazy?!" she hisses. "There's no way I'm going to get on that ship! You know I can't!" Surna's phobia about being locked up is going to make life rather difficult...

"It doesn't matter anyway, I can't unlock the door. Short of getting an invite from Boba Fett himself, I don't see how we can get on this ship." You hear an audible groan from Al, who has been keeping watch. "You had to say it, didn't you?! Here he comes! It's Boba Fett himself!"

Sure enough, the bounty hunter is walking across the apron towards his ship, his blaster rifle sloped against his shoulder. Surna readies her weapon. You place your hand over hers, and shake your head. "I thought you'd be only too pleased! He's your worst enemy!" True, but... "If we fire, we'll attract the Port Security Detachment. Keep cool. We might be able to sneak onto the ship behind him." You press her down, and duck your own head. You hear the bounty hunter reach the hatch and enter the code. The hatch hisses, and lowers to the ground. Silence, and then a voice. "Are you coming on board, Havet Storm? Or would you prefer to surrender to the Imperial forces?" Oh, rats.

Check 592

Go to 250

224

As you run across the port apron, you keep looking up into the sky, as if looking for reassurance that the others have escaped. Of course, what you want to see is *nothing*; if Tann has got past the blockade and entered hyperspace, nothing will be visible from the ground. If the fleet intercept him, you might just see the flash of their weapons. If –

Your thoughts and progress across the apron are interrupted by a sudden bright flash in the sky directly above you. It's not a weapon discharge, it has to be...

You feel sick as the idea lodges in your mind. You can hope, of course, that the flash was something different, but you know in your heart of hearts that it must have been the destruction of the *Rust Bucket*. But why? It didn't look as if the ship was intercepted by the fleet – you did enough to prevent that, surely. What then?

The answer comes to you straight away. Of course – T'blisk must have had some kind of security device on the *Rust Bucket*. A booby trap, or something like that, attached to the hyperdrive motors. When Tann tried to enter hyperspace, the ship exploded. You feel deep anger in your guts at having been fooled so completely. As you reach Boba Fett's ship, and find a place to hide, you realise that it has just become even more important that you get off Toprawa, and make some sense of all that has been lost. Shedding a tear, you promise Surna and the others that they will be avenged.

Go to 212

The journey from Toprawa lasts several days; exactly how long, you don't know, because watching your chrono crawling slowly through the minutes and the hours would drive you mad, so you have taken it off. You try to sleep and rest as much as you can, eating and drinking sparingly from the meagre supplies you have brought. At last, you hear a change in the steady beat of the ship's engines. The *Slave I* is coming out of hyperspace.

You recover all the Jedi Power Points you have spent so far; your JPP score returns to its starting value

Go to 227

226

The port's guns are silent. No alarm sounds in challenge to the *Rust Bucket*'s departure. "Which console monitors their progress?" you ask the Imperial Officer. He points at a console. A small icon moves above a diagrammatic view of the port, gaining altitude, until it is beyond the limits of Toprawa's atmosphere. The view changes automatically, and you see larger icons representing the Imperial fleet. No shots are fired. Seconds later, the *Rust Bucket*'s icon changes to red. "He's engaged the warp drive," the Officer explains. Suddenly, the icon disintegrates, scattering pixels across the screen. A small alarm chimes. "What is it? What does that mean?" The Officer leans forward and cancels the alarm. "The ship exploded as the warp engines came up to full power," he explains, barely able to keep the smug grin off his face. "A fault in the ion convertor, or sabotage…" Of course. T'blisk had some kind of insurance policy. "Your friends are dead. You may as well surrender." Just for a second, you consider doing just that. Then you lock him (and the others) in a small, interior rest room. It isn't going to end like this.

Back in the main control room, fighting back the tears, you look out through the bubble. Down below, you can see a ship, sitting on its landing pad, challenging you to find a way onto it. It is Boba Fett's ship, the *Slave I*. Your last chance to get off Toprawa.

Go to 212

The *Slave I* switches to its sub-light drives, and you feel the rhythm of its movement change. There are subtle changes in the on-board gravity; you remember the same sensations from other landings on other worlds. Boba Fett has reached another planet, and is bringing the ship into land. You wait, listening for every clue. You hear the rasping of the planet's atmosphere against the hull, and the main engines hand over to the repulsorlifts for the last glide into the landing. There is a gentle bump as the skids hit the ground. Who knows where, but you have landed somewhere. The interior hatch opens, and Boba Fett comes through from the crew compartment, activating the exterior door. With a hiss of hydraulics, the door swings down, spilling a small pool of white-yellow light into the hold. You shield your eyes against the brightness.

If you have checked 592, go to 257

If you have checked 590, go to 237

If you have checked 593, go to 269

If you haven't checked any of these, go to 277

228

You get off the ground, and Tann steers the *Rust Bucket* up through the atmosphere, and out into space. The atmosphere on the ship feels oxygen-starved and cold. No-one speaks. Sooner or later, you will be faced with the Imperial blockade.

Sooner rather than later. A voice comes over the speaker. "Unidentified freighter, this is the Imperial Corvette *Nunchuka*. You have made an unauthorised departure from a restricted planet. Do not attempt to engage your hyperdrive motors. Any attempt to leave Toprawan space will be met with extreme force. Close down all engines and prepare to be boarded."

You can just about make out the shape of the distant corvette through the main viewport. Tann checks the sensors. "She's powering up her turbolasers." A diagrammatic view of the corvette appears on a monitor; the *Nunchuka* has six double turbolaser batteries. "How long until we can jump through lightspeed?" you ask. "Too long. They'll be watching us carefully. We don't have any weapons – I had to sell them to help pay off the debt to T'blisk. As soon as I wind up the hyperdrive, they'll fire. The shields will take one hit, maybe two. I still need a few moments to programme the navigation computer."

"Don't you have any good news?" you ask. "We're not dead yet," he replies. That's something. "What are our options?" Tann considers this for a moment. "There are only two. Give up, or take our chances. And our chances lie somewhere between Not Many and None At All."

If you tell Tann to engage the hyperdrive, go to 248

If you allow the corvette's troops to board you, go to 267

229

You pull Arf from the deep pocket of your coat, and activate the little droid. "Arf, access the ship's door mechanism." Arf huffs happily as he extends a probe into the lock. "Open the hatch." The droid whimpers, picking up the nervous tension in your voice. "I know. Let's just hope he isn't at home." Arf transfers the codes through the probe, and you hear the locks disengage. The hatch drops down, and a little daylight spills into the gloomy interior. You catch sight of the prisoner pens, and a shiver passes through you. Arf whimpers even more sadly. "Don't knock it. This is going to be home for the next few days."

Go to 268

230

You manage to overcome the guards in the control tower, but it takes too long. From distant parts of the spaceport, alarms have summoned still more Imperial soldiers. As you run from the control tower, you fall headlong into a hail of blaster fire.

You have been defeated. Violence is rarely the right answer. As you start a new adventure, try thinking of other ways you could have handled this problem

231-232

You crawl back through the freighter as fast as you are able, but not fast enough. By the time you get back to the hatch, it has been electronically sealed tight. You can feel the ship rising, climbing through the atmosphere on its repulsorlifts. After a while, the air starts becoming thin…

You have escaped from Toprawa, but you won't live to see it! Start a new adventure

233

You crawl back through the freighter as fast as you can. As you reach the hatch and smash it open, you realise that you are already several metres off the ground. The jump is dangerous, but to be caught up in space with no air…

You drop through the hatch, hearing it close automatically behind you. You only just made it in time! You don't have a lot of time to think about this, though, as the ground rushes up to meet you. You land hard, smacking onto the apron floor, surrounded by dust kicked up as the freighter lifts away. There's a savage pain in your leg. You have to ignore it at first, as you hobble away from the freighter's landing bay, and into the shadow of another ship.

You look up, and find that you have taken shelter beneath the *Slave I* – Boba Fett's own ship!

Check 591

Go to 212

234-236

You crawl rapidly back through the freighter. Before the first jolt as the ship leaves the ground, you reach the hatch and kick it open. You drop through and land softly on the ground, enveloped by smoke and dust kicked up as the big ship leaves the ground. The hatch swings shut. No-one will ever know you tried to get on board.

Scrambling across the landing apron, you hide in the shadow of another ship, parked in a neighbouring pit. You watch the freighter rise up; no-one comes to investigate, so you figure no-one saw you jump. Well, that didn't work. That leaves just the one avenue to explore; can you get aboard *Slave I* – Boba Fett's own ship?

Go to 212

237

You watch Fett leave the ship, disappearing into the glare of the world outside. "What do we do, Havet?" hisses Surna.

If you leave the ship, go to 221

If you explore the ship, go to 258

If you sit tight, go to 278

238

As cautiously as you can, you set out to follow Boba Fett towards the strange mound. Along the way, you find some battered proof that this is indeed Yavin Four, a moon circling a minor planet not too far from Toprawa. For a while, Yavin Four was the most important military base in the Rebel Alliance – but they were forced to abandon it, even after defeating the Death Star, and to go off looking for another home.

The Imperials have vented their anger on what little was left behind. With the Death Star destroyed in the skies above, they no longer had the capacity to destroy the moon with a single blast, and Darth Vader is not the kind of man to waste precious ships in a gesture of vengeance. So, the moon was subjected to a vigorous 'search' by the Imperial army, a search which rampaged through the underground bunkers and other facilities, reducing the abandoned base to rubble and ash.

The mound ahead of you appears to be the entrance to one of the underground bunkers. It is not the only entrance now. The bunker's roof is missing, and the interior is open to the sky. The flickering light proves to be a fire, lit on the floor of the interior. As you pass by the mound, and skirt the wide crater where the roof fell in, you can see that someone is sheltering there. Fett entered through the old entrance some moments before. You hear his voice as you come closer, arguing loudly, threatening. You crawl towards the edge of the crater, so that you can listen more effectively. Just as you arrive, you hear the sharp crack of a blaster rifle.

"Tell me what I want to know," hisses Fett, "or I'll kill you all, one by one." You can see now that he is standing in the doorway of a large room. Several men and women are seated round a fire, sitting perfectly still with their hands raised. One is sprawled in the dust. Fett has them covered with his blaster rifle.

"Where have the Rebel leadership flown to? Where is the new Rebel base?" A woman, her face lit by the fire, glares angrily back at him. "We don't know anything! We came here long after the Rebels departed! We're just scavengers. We came here hoping to find some scrap, or some forgotten equipment we could sell. We can't tell you anything about the Alliance!" Fett swings the blaster rifle in her direction. "Scavengers, eh? Not much of a life, I hear. How would you like to lose yours?"

If you open fire on Fett (you must have a weapon checked in your Equipment Box!), go to 289

If you do nothing, go to 307

239

You abandon the *Rust Bucket*. From the outside, you see that the ship has been very badly damaged by its crash-landing. The engines are shattered, and the hull has more holes than a sponge in a blender. Tann is furious. "What was that idiot playing at?" You decide to go and ask the idiot for yourself. The port is a long walk away, so you grab some gear, and set off at once.

The moon is a dusty rock, with a thin atmosphere marked by hot, broiling clouds. In no time at all, you are filmed with sweat and breathing hard. The few buildings you see are in ruins. Underground bunkers which once housed the Rebel base have been destroyed by explosives. In fact, Yavin Four is a ruin. You walk on, finally reaching the spaceport area. The perimeter fence is down, so you just stroll onto the ravaged apron. The port has been severely battered, and there are no intact ships parked on your side of the apron. Walking cautiously past the shell of a command centre, you see just one ship on the other side of the landing field – a ship you can't believe is here! "I don't believe it!" you whisper back to the others. "It's *Slave I*!" The others jostle to look past you. "How can Boba Fett possibly have followed us here? It can't be coincidence." Tann grimaces. "There must have been a tracer on the *Rust Bucket*. I didn't have time to search properly."

"I don't care how he got here, I'm wondering why." you tell the others. "I'm going to take a look." Surna squeaks with alarm as you jog across the apron. She doesn't follow you.

Boba Fett's ship is sitting in the open, it's hatch closed. Ducking into the shadows, you search around. There he is! Fett is walking across the apron, heading for a dark mound on the edge of the port. You could follow him or wait for him to come back. Either way, you know that the only way to find out what he is doing is to get close to him.

If you follow Fett towards the mound, go to 238

If you wait by *Slave I*, go to 249

240

It's obvious what you have to do. Keying your comlink, you open a channel to the *Rust Bucket*. "Is that you, Havet?" Tann's voice sounds astonished through the speaker. "Yes. I've neutralised the control tower, but I can't get back to the ship. Take off without me." After a brief commotion, Surna's voice breaks in. "Hold tight," she snaps, "we're coming to get you."

"You can't!" you shout into the mike. "Take off now! I can only keep a lid on things up here for a while." The Imperials are smirking, pleased with your discomfort. You stare hard into their eyes so that they remember just who has a weapon pointed at who. "What will you do?" asks Surna. "You want me to broadcast my plans, dimwit?" you scold her. "I'll be fine. So, take off now and get past that block-ade." There's a long silence. Tann comes back on line. "We copy, Havet. We're taking off right away." Looking through the bubble, you see the *Rust Bucket* rising up on its repulsorlifts, lifting clear of the apron, and turning to point its nose at the sky. Just before you close off the communications channel, Surna comes on. "You'd bet-ter have a plan," she says. "I love you, Havet. And I'm not a dimwit!" The channel cuts out before you can answer, and you pull the mike from its socket.

You turn back to face the Imperial controllers in the room. "Women! You have no idea how much trouble I've had getting rid of her."

If you have checked 557, go to 215

If you haven't checked 557, go to 226

241-243

You heave against the locks of the door, but to no avail. Built to resist the vacuum of space, the door locks are too powerful for you. You can feel the ship rising, climbing through the atmosphere on its repulsorlifts. After a while, the air starts becoming thin, and your hammering against the bulkhead door grows slowly weaker...

You have escaped from Toprawa, but you won't live to see it! Start a new adventure

244-246

There's no way you can hammer your way through the heavy bulkhead door, built to withstand the vacuum of space. However, you do manage to cause sufficient damage to the lock to trigger some kind of alarm. The gradual rise of the freighter halts, and you feel it settle back down towards the ground.

You head back to the maintenance hatch you entered by, and manage to kick it open as the ship lands. Hidden by the clouds of dust kicked up by the freighter, you scramble away across the landing apron, to hide in the shadow of the ship parked in the neighbouring bay. Ground crew start swarming all over the freighter as the landing is completed. They find the open hatch, and some security guards are called. Did anyone see you jump clear and run this way? Will they come and check? You'd be a lot safer if you could just get on board this ship. You look up, and realise which vessel it is. It's Boba Fett's ship, the *Slave I*. Did you say you'd be safer?

Go to 212

247

The battle in the control tower goes against you. Even as you hear Tann lift the *Rust Bucket* clear of the port, you are surrounded and brought down.

You were unlucky to have got so far, and then lose. Why not start the adventure again?

248

"I've had just about enough of this," you remark, sourly. "Let's take our chances. Fire up the hyperdrive, Tann." The others give you anxious looks, but you can see Surna is of the same mind as you; she can't face the thought of an Imperial prison.

Tann completes the programming of the navigational computer, while the *Nunchuka* closes in, repeating its warning. You stall as best you can; pretending your communications are breaking up, then trying to bluff that you have a secret mission, finally falling back to try the "will you check with the surface; they told us we had clearance!" approach. "Are we ready yet?" you ask Tann. "My mother said I wasn't supposed to tell lies." Tann hits the hyperdrive start-up. "Give it another fifty seconds, Havet; we have to bring the drive up to full power."

"Unidentified space freighter, this is *Nunchuka*. Our sensors have detected your warp engines being engaged. Shut down immediately, or we open fire." Forty seconds. You open a channel. *"Nunchuka*, this is Imperial Freighter *Mass Destruction*. Stand by for a message from Commander Diamond, Head of Security, Toprawa Station." Thirty seconds. Silence at the other end; just the name of the former commander of the Imperial Research Station's security branch is enough to freeze the Imperials, even if only for a few moments. You hand the microphone to Surna. "Be nasty," you tell her. She looks at you with a 'I can't pretend to be Diamond!' expression, but her brother swats her with his palm, so she gives it a shot. *"Nunchuka*, this is Commander Diamond. I'm – errr – engaged on an urgent mission to report to the Emperor." She shuts off the mike. "They'll run a voice-print on this, you know. It won't take long for them to know it isn't her."

"We don't need long. Demand to talk to the Captain. Get heavy." Fifteen seconds. Tann shouts in alarm. "The *Nunchuka*'s turbolasers are being activated! I'm throwing power to the forward shields!" Surna starts blasting into the microphone. *"Nunchuka!* This is Diamond, I want your Captain on the line now!" Another second or two pass, then Tann shouts. "Incoming!"

The turbolasers strike a glancing blow to the front shields, throwing the nose of the *Rust Bucket* up, and spilling those of you unlucky enough to be standing into a heap at the back of the crew compartment. Warning lights appear all over the board in front of Tann. "Shields faltering, trim stabilisers damaged, we have atmosphere leaks from the hold." You can't take another hit. "Hyperdrive at 85% – here comes another salvo!!!"

"Hit the hyperdrive!! NOW!!!"

Check 618

Go to 259

249

You decide to stay close to *Slave I*, so you can see when Boba Fett returns.

If you have checked either 592 or 590, go to 290

If not, go to 308

250

You are taken onto *Slave I* by Boba Fett, disarmed and thoroughly searched. It's a very frustrating moment. It seems as if it would be so easy to overpower Fett, but there's no point. You can imagine the large squad of soldiers gathered outside the ship, keeping a close eye on the hatch. There's nowhere you can run, nowhere you can hide. You actually need Fett to keep you out of the Empire's clutches.

Fett is quite surprised when he finds Arf in your coat pocket. "A toy dog, Havet? I didn't realise what a child you were." He takes it from you. All your gear is placed in a locker on the far side of the hold, and secured by an electronic lock. He points towards the cells, and you step in. The cage is closed, and powerful bolts are thrown, sealing the door tight. You can also hear the hum of a force field. Fett steps away from the controls.

"What happens now?" you ask. The bounty hunter halts near the door through to the crew compartment. He looks back at you, barely visible in the deep gloom of the hold. "Do you know, I'm not entirely sure. My plans for you didn't allow for this. I thought you would escape on the *Rust Bucket*. I had it covered in tracers." Huh? "You were going to follow us? Why?"

"Where would you have gone if you had escaped? Let me tell you; you would have tried to find other members of the Rebel Alliance. Given the amount of outrageous luck you have, I figured you might have made it. It so happens I need to find a particular member of the Alliance, and I hoped you would lead me to him." You have to admire Fett's sneakiness. "So, what will you do instead?" He hits the door release on the inner hatch. "We'll see," he says, and disappears from view. The outer hatch closes shortly after, plunging the hold into pitch blackness. You find a small bunk in your cell, and sit. After about an hour, you hear the repulsorlifts start winding up, and *Slave I* lifts off from Toprawa. Well, that's what you wanted... It would be nice, though, to have some idea where you were going, or what might happen to you when you get there.

Make a note; you have none of your weapons, and you have been separated from Arf. Don't remove them from your Equipment Box altogether – you might get them back (you'd better!)

If you try to recover your weapons and other possessions, you must extend your Jedi Power to see if you can open the lid on the locker. Decide how many JPPs you will spend (no more than 6), and add that number to 260. The total is the number of the next paragraph you should read. So, if you spend 1 JPP, you would read 261

If you get as much sleep as you can, go to 225

If you try to keep alert until you reach your destination, go to 227

251-254

You allow Boba Fett to disappear from view, then race for the hatch. Too late! It closes before you can get aboard the ship!

As you stumble in the dirt of the landing bay, you are seen by a security guard searching close by. Moments later, he has summoned his colleagues, and your adventure is at an end.

Return to the beginning of the book

255

You allow Boba Fett to disappear from view, then race for the hatch. It's almost closed as you dive aboard, and you fall into the hold with a great clatter, cracking your head on the floor. When you come to, you are sitting back outside the ship, covered by the business end of a blaster rifle. Boba Fett is explaining to some Imperial lackey that you are his prisoner, and that he intends to take you with him when he leaves Toprawa. The Imperial Officer argues for a while, then shrugs and leaves. Fett looks at you, sunlight glinting from his visor. "You seemed so keen to come aboard," he says. "I couldn't leave you behind, could I?"

Check 593

Go to 250

You allow Boba Fett to disappear from view, then race for the hatch. It's a close call, but you just manage to slip through the hatch before the door hisses shut. The interior of the ship is gloomy. Fett, his back to you, is going through a second, interior door, into what you would imagine is the crew compartment. The door closes, leaving you alone in the hold.

Go to 268

Boba Fett slips through the hatch, leaving it open. "Where are we?" asks Al. "We didn't travel far," says Tann, trying to calculate the variables. "Pinoora, maybe. Or Glade." Or any of about thirty or forty others. It hardly matters as long as the planet is out there and you're in here.

You catch the slight ring of a boot on the ramp. Fett? Back already? But no – the sound of these footsteps is very different. "Who's there?" you call. A head appears in the hatchway. It's human, rough and pale, stippled with a scraggly beard. All four of you leap to your feet. "We're prisoners! Did you see the guy who got off this ship?" The guy nods. "That was Boba Fett; you heard of him?" He nods again. "We're dead if we stay in here. Won't you get us out?"

Scraggly beard springs into the hold. He has an antique slug-thrower in his fist, a real pre-Old Republic gun. "What do you want?" he grunts. You point him at the cell door master control on the wall. "Think you can open the doors?" Actually, there are several ways to open an electronically-controlled security gate. You can bypass the controls, or patch in a droid like Arf to squirt millions of combinations through the lock until it hits the right one, or you can use a polarity disrupter, which convinces simple systems that they're closed when they're open and vice versa. What you can't do is blow the mechanism to pieces and expect the doors to just fly open. So, when scraggly beard pumps two rounds through the box, you feel your heart stop. You're just about to call him all the names you've ever heard of when the cell doors swing back.

"Neat," you smile, as you leap out of the cage. Surna looks pretty happy to be out, and she is halfway down the ramp before you can think. You think about the gear in the locker, you think about trying to steal the ship. You smell the fresh air of the planet outside.

Check 594

If you look outside the ship, go to 221

If you explore *Slave I*, go to 258

If you examine the locker, go to 270

258

You decide that this is an ideal opportunity to explore Fett's ship. You gave the hold a thorough examination during the flight to Yavin. Now, though, you're determined to get through the door and into the crew compartment.

If you use your lightsabre (you do still have your lightsabre, don't you?) to cut through the door, go to 287

If you use Arf (assuming he hasn't been taken away from you) to tap into the door mechanism, go to 298

If you try to trip the door mechanism yourself, look up your Tech Skills score (from your Character Sheet). If you wish, you may increase it (but not to more than 6!) by spending Jedi Power Points. Now add the total to 270 – the result is the number of the next paragraph you should read. So, if your Tech Skill score is 2, and you spend 1 JPP, you would read 273.

259

"Look on the bright side!" smiles Al, breaking out some lunch. "We're alive."

"Yeah," murmurs Surna, "just barely." She tries to restore power to the sensors once more, but all she gets is a shower of sparks, and about half a nanosecond of snow on the monitor before the system folds again. She screams in frustration. "There's no way these things are ever going to work again!" She slams down her tools, and takes a seat. Al pushes a sandwich at her, and she eats with undisguised anger.

Tann isn't happy either. The damage assessment has shown up the destabilisation of the navigational computer, damage to the shield generators, and the partial shearing of the trim stabilisers. He locks off a few systems, and comes back to the pilot's station. "It's not good. We're leaking atmosphere, and recycling is shot. We have maybe twenty days of air with four of us on board." That's not so bad! You can get a long way in twenty days. "Problem two: we've lost sensors, and the calibration of the navigational computer is out. We can trust the ship to make this first jump OK, but after that we'd be bouncing around in the dark." That's not so good, but you can stop wherever the first jump takes you, make some repairs... "When we left Toprawa, I set course for Yavin Four. I have no idea what state the place is in since the battle, but I hope they have some dock-yard facilities we can use. Anyway, we're committed now; we'll have to land there." There you go, that's not so bad. "But with the stabilisers shot, we'll probably have a messy landing. In fact, I'm not sure we can land in one piece at all."

You give up listening while Tann lists a few other problems he can't deal with in deep space. You take some of the food Al serves up, and then settle into a deep seat for a rest. There's not much you can do to help, so you might as well catch up on some sleep. In fact, you miss quite a bit of the next few days as the *Rust Bucket* drifts through hyperspace. Every time you wake up, Tann is whittering on about some new problem he has discovered, so you go back to sleep. By the time you reach the Yavin system, you're feeling more rested than at any time in the last two years. Tann, on the other hand, looks very tense. "I'm not picking up any beacon signals from the surface. If there's a functioning spaceport, I can't find it." The planet and its moon are clearly visible through the viewport. He hasn't picked up any communications from either. "You sure this is Yavin?" you ask. Tann shoots you a dirty look.

Tann takes the ship in on manual, dipping it gently towards the atmosphere of the moon. You buckle up; it's going to be a rough ride. Within a few seconds of the approach, the stabilisers shear off, and the *Rust Bucket* starts kicking and swaying alarmingly. The ground appears beneath thick, black clouds. Tann is navigating by memory. "The main spaceport is somewhere just ahead!" he yells. He drops the ship a little lower, running on the repulsorlifts.

Suddenly, another ship roars past overhead. It happens too fast for you to recognise it, but the wash from its passing throws the *Rust Bucket* downwards, perilously close to the ground. Tann shouts that he can see the port ahead, but it is obvious that you aren't going to make it. The *Rust Bucket* smacks into the ground. As crash landings go, it's only a little horrendous. The ship crunches into the dirt in a riot of shattered metal and dust. It bounces twice, then goes nose-first into the ground, finally coming to a stop. The ear-splitting noise dies down. "We're down," sighs Tann. No, really...

"What was that other ship?" asks Al. "Who knows," you reply. "We could go and find out."

Restore your Jedi Power Points to their starting score. All that rest has replenished your strength

If you search the area where you have landed, go to 280

If you go looking for the other ship, go to 239

260

Laying down a spray of fire, you leave the control tower at a run. Tann has already lifted the *Rust Bucket* out of sight into the clouds. Hopefully, the three of them will have time to get past the blockade before anyone can warn the fleet. You've done as much as you could hope.

What next, though, Havet? There are alarms going off all over the port. You might be able to take advantage of the confusion to slip back out into the city, but what would be the point? You can't hope to avoid capture on Toprawa forever; sooner or later you'll be captured or killed. You *have* to get off this planet! At the same time, it's unlikely that the Imperials will allow anything to take off without a thorough search. They are going to want to catch you after all the trouble they have been caused! Where could you possibly hide out?

You see the answer, sitting in its landing bay. Boba Fett's ship, the *Slave I*. If any vessel is going to be allowed to leave Toprawa in the next few hours, that will be the one. And didn't Al say Fett was looking to move on; that he had some kind of commission from Jabba the Hutt?

Have you checked 557? If you have, go to 213

If not, go to 224

261-266

There's nothing you can do to recover your weapons from the locker. It has an electronic lock, and your Jedi power can't be used to alter technology. After several attempts, all you succeed in doing is wearing yourself down.

Go to 227

267

"I don't think we should commit suicide," you tell Tann. "Signal the *Nunchuka*; tell them we'll allow them to send over a boarding party. We'll try to bluff our way out of it – you know, act injured, pretend there has been some foul up by those idiots at the port, you know the kind of thing." The others don't look impressed. "OK; if that doesn't work, we'll jump the boarding party, then everyone on the corvette, and we'll take over their ship and escape that way." By comparison, your first plan sounds better by the minute.

The *Nunchuka* comes alongside, and a boarding tube is extended from its waist to connect with the external hatch on the *Rust Bucket*. You sit very still as the door is opened. Imperial navy personnel pour onto the ship, covering you with blasters. A young, arrogant officer follows. He demands to see your papers. You start your dialogue, pretending that you are the victim of a mistake. The young executive officer isn't having any of it. "Save the space debris," he sneers. "We've had a full report from the ground. We know you are Rebels trying to flee the planet."

He snaps his fingers, and you are led off the ship, and onto the much larger corvette. There is a heavy guard. They take you into the main control room to face the captain. He looks as though he has just been wakened from a lengthy sleep, but he's happy enough about it. This is the most action they've seen in two years.

"Welcome aboard the *Nunchuka*, Rebel scum," he gloats. "I'm delighted to see you. We thought you Rebels were going to just give up tamely, but it's nice to see you have just enough guts left to make a bit of sport out of it." Some sport; the man must be easily pleased. "I shall look forward to arranging your trial and execution." Oh, he does look pleased with himself.

Another young executive officer – he looks like a clone of the first one – steps forward with a data pad, and shows it to the captain. The happy smile disappears. "Are you sure about this?" he squawks. The Exec shrugs. The captain bangs his hand down on his console, fuming. No-one explains what is going on to you, but then you can't expect any favours, can you?

There is a lengthy delay before things are resolved. Judging by the activity, another ship arrives, and docks with the *Nunchuka*. The new arrival is brought onto the bridge and presented to the captain. It comes as no surprise to you when it proves to be Boba Fett. It feels as if he is connected to you by some kind of force chain! He ignores you, and goes across to whisper to the captain. There is lengthy discussion, and the captain's voice gets loud enough to hear on occasion; it's quite clear that he isn't a happy man. Eventually, though, he says: "Very well, bounty hunter, take your prisoner."

Fett walks across towards you, and points his blaster at your head. You take the hint, and let him push you towards the docking bays. You catch Surna's frightened glance as you leave the bridge; there isn't anything any of you can do.

Check 593

Go to 250

268

So, for good or ill, here you are aboard *Slave I*.

The rear hold, which is lined with the cells Fett uses for transporting prisoners, is a dark, chill place, with a stale atmosphere. The cells are narrow, barred rooms, each with a small cot, dispensers to dole out the basics of life, and waste disposal facilities. The bars are physical, but they are meshed with force fields, which can shut each cell off completely from its neighbours. The force fields and cell doors can be controlled from the flight deck or through a control panel in the hold.

Apart from some general storage space, that is the full sum of it. You can imagine the feelings of the poor souls who have been transported in these cells, carried in darkness through the emptiness of space, fearful and alone. Now you must make the same journey.

The best hiding space is a space behind one of the rear cells, where there are some small drums of maintenance equipment. There is no reason why Boba Fett should ever come back here, unless a major fault develops on the ship. You can hide out here until the ship makes a landfall, and then slip out. With luck, Boba Fett will never be any the wiser.

The alternative, of course is to attack and overpower the bounty hunter, and take control of *Slave I*. You give it some serious thought, and investigate how practical an idea it might be. The door through to the crew compartment is solid and acts as an internal bulkhead. If he was really in trouble, Boba Fett could just pump all the atmosphere out of the hold. The lock is a simple one, but it appears to have an override to prevent it being opened from this side while the ship is in flight. A lightsabre would cut through the hatch like butter, but you'd still be faced with Boba Fett on the far side, and such an action would be bound to trigger an alarm.

Anyway, so far he is doing a grand job of being a chauffeur, so you decide to leave him be, and to see where your journey will lead you.

If you get as much sleep as you can, go to 225

If you try to keep alert until you reach your destination, go to 227

269

Boba Fett disappears through the hatch, leaving it open. Blinking frantically, you wait for your eyes to become accustomed to the light, but even when your eyes have adjusted, you can't see much through the hatch, just the dust of a landing bay and some broken packing cases.

You catch the slight ring of a boot on the ramp. Fett? Back already? But no – the sound of these footsteps is very different. "Who's there?" you call. A head appears around the frame of the hatchway. It's human, rough and pale, stippled with a scraggly beard. The guy looks pretty frightened. "It's OK! I'm not an enemy – look, I'm a prisoner, see?" He nods, but doesn't look any calmer. "Did you see the guy who got off this ship?" you continue. He nods. "That was Boba Fett; you heard of him?" The guy nods again. "So, you know I'm in big trouble. You want to give me a hand?"

Scraggly beard creeps cautiously into the hold. He has an antique slug-thrower in his fist, a real pre-Old Republic gun. "Who are you?" he grunts, like some kind of throwback. You tell him your name. His eyes narrow. "You a Rebel?" he asks. You decide to take a chance. "Yes, I am. I fought with the Rebels on Toprawa." He pokes around in the hold a little. "Look, friend," you point out the cell door master control on the wall. "That opens the doors. Think you can work it?" He scratches at his beard. "Why should I?" You give that a little thought, while scraggly beard looks round some more. "Look, maybe I can do you a favour," you offer.

"Could you get us off Yavin?" he asks, having a long look at the door into the crew compartment. "Could you help us join up with the Rebel Alliance?" It looks like his goal is the same as yours. "Do you know where they are?" you ask. "No," he replies, "do you?" Of course not. "Sure." He thinks about this for a moment. "OK. I'll let you out."

Now there are many different ways to open an electronically-controlled security gate. You can bypass the controls, or patch in a droid like Arf which can squirt millions of combinations through the lock until it hits the right one, or you can use a polarity disrupter, which can convince simple systems that they're closed when they're open and vice versa. All those are valid methods. What you can't do is blow the mechanism to pieces with a blaster and expect the doors to just fly open. So, when scraggly beard pumps two rounds through the box, his handgun roaring in the confined space of the hold, you feel your heart seize up, and you're just about to call the moron all the names you've ever heard when the cell doors swing back.

"Neat," you smile, as you leap out of the cage. Scraggly beard glares at you impatiently. "Now, suppose you tell us how we're going to find the Alliance?"

Check 594

If you look outside the ship, go to 303

If you explore *Slave I*, go to 258

If you examine the locker, go to 270

270

Before you do anything else, you know you have to retrieve your weapons. You examine the lock on the box. If you had Arf, this would be easy, but he's inside with the rest of your gear. You'll have to rely on your own skill.

Lock-cracking isn't a skill many people would associate with a Jedi, but you found it a very useful skill while you were on the run as a kid. The trick is to get the lock to believe that the combination you give it is the right one, which means feeding the 'right' information through its circuits no matter what keys you actually press. You raid Fett's repair kit for the gear you need, and hook up a magnetic reader and a binary pulse generator to the lock, along with a small computer console. You program the computer to start feeding random numbers into the lock mechanism. Watching the display on the reader, you watch for any fluctuations which show that the lock has recognised a number or a combination of numbers. Then you program the pulse generator to mimic the fluctuation patterns.

Hey – you can either do this stuff, or you can't. Normally, a lock like this would be all yours in just a few seconds. Knowing that you could be interrupted by Boba Fett's return at any moment makes you a little more nervous.

Find your Tech Skills score (from your Character Sheet); you may increase it (but not to more than 6!) by spending Jedi Power Points if you wish. Now add the total to 280 – the result is the number of the next paragraph you should read. So, if your Tech Skill score is 1, and you spend 3 JPPs, you would read 284.

271-274

The bulkhead door through to the crew compartment is well-protected. There's an alarm coupled to a system which would release stun gas into the hold. The lock itself is extremely well-designed, and you can't find a way to bypass it.

If you leave the ship to go exploring, go to 304

If you sit tight, go to 278

275-276

The bulkhead door through to the crew compartment is well-protected, but you manage to bypass the alarms and booby traps, and to spring the lock. The door hisses open.

The crew compartment of Boba Fett's ship is not a large area. The bridge is a simple work-station, as you would expect of a one-man vessel. The quarters are spartan, with no decoration. On ship, Boba Fett leads a very simple life. You don't find anything which gives anything away about him.

If you have your lightsabre, either on you or stashed in Arf, go to 288

If not, go to 299

277

You watch Fett leave the ship, disappearing into the glare of the world outside. He leaves the hatch open, as if inviting you to follow him outside.

If you leave the ship, go to 303

If you explore the ship, go to 258

If you sit tight, go to 278

278

You decide to stay on *Slave I*.

If you have checked either 590 or 592, go to 291

If you have checked neither of these, go to 309

279

"My name is Kelleg," says scraggly beard as you follow him. "I was with the Rebels here, but I got left behind when they left Yavin. I'd been wounded in a battle with a TIE fighter pilot who had crash-landed after the battle. Just bad luck, I guess." You sympathise. "So, where did the Rebels go when they left here?" you ask. He looks disappointed. "You don't know?" he asks in return. Everyone looks at each other, shaking their heads. "I was hoping you'd know," says Kelleg, sorrowfully. "I know where there is a ship, but we can't just wander out into space in the hope of finding the rest of the Alliance. What do you suggest we do?"

Check 596

If you have checked either 590 or 592, go to 292

If you have checked neither, go to 317

280

"Forget the other ship," you tell the others. "We need to find out where we are, and if there is any way we can get off again." They agree, although Tann would dearly like to meet up with the maniac who wrecked the *Rust Bucket*. "Did you see that other ship?" he moans. "It looked awfully familiar."

You explore the area around where the *Rust Bucket* came down. As Tann expected, this is Yavin Four, the moon where the Rebels won their first major victory, destroying the Emperor's Death Star. News of the destruction of the Empire's ultimate weapon by a few brave X-Wing pilots was one of the last pieces of information to reach Toprawa, well over a year ago. It was a victory purchased with blood sacrificed by the Rebels on Toprawa, which bought the Alliance time to organise the evacuation of their headquarters. Imperial propaganda has been boasting about how they chased the Rebels off Yavin, and about how they have chased them across the galaxy ever since.

Yavin appears to be deserted. The underground bunkers and reinforced buildings in which the Rebels had been based have been destroyed. It's eerily quiet. Then a young man with a scraggly beard appears from behind a shattered communications mast, running over to meet you.

"Are you the crew of that freighter which just crashed?" he asks, gasping for breath. Is there any point in denying it? "Who wants to know?" you ask. "I'm one of the surviving Rebels. Listen, if you follow me, I might be able to help you."

If you follow the man, go to 279

If you ignore him, go to 293

281-282

You can't get the locker open.

If you want to try again, you must spend 3 Jedi Power Points. Go to 297

If you give up, and explore the ship instead, go to 258

If you take a look outside the ship, go to 304

283-286

After a great deal of effort, you manage to break into the locker. What a relief! You have recovered Arf, your weapons and the rest of your gear.

Check 597

If you now explore Fett's ship, go to 258

If you go outside, go to 304

287

Your lightsabre does the trick all right, slicing through the door like butter. However, an alarm goes off at once. Boba Fett would be able to hear the noise if he was on the other side of the planet! You don't dare look round the crew compartment now – you had better look for somewhere to hide!

Check 598

If you leave the ship, go to 304

If you look for a hiding place on board, go to 278

288

You complete your look round the crew compartment of *Slave I*, careful not to touch anything. Looking through the viewport, you see that Fett is walking back towards the ship. Time to get out of here, Havet my boy!

If you have checked 592 or 590, go to 300

If you haven't checked either of those, but you have checked 594, go to 310

If you haven't checked any of those paragraphs, go to 320

289

You can't allow Boba Fett to massacre these people one by one. Pulling your weapon, you open fire.

Read 601, and use the combat rules from the beginning of the book. Record this paragraph number so you can find your way back.

If you win the combat, go to 294

If you are defeated, go to 318

290

Surna and the others go off to scout around, while you keep an eye out for Boba Fett's return. After all, *Slave I* might prove to be your only way off this planet. You have arranged a visual signal system to alert Surna when you see Boba Fett returning.

Before you can even start feeling uncomfortable in your cramped hiding place, you see Surna waving to you from the shell of a distant building. From the signals she's giving, they've found something. Could it be a ship? You give her the thumbs up to show you have seen her, and get ready to go over and join them. Suddenly, you see Fett – just a few metres away, heading purposefully towards his ship!

How has the bounty hunter got so close so fast?! He must have come back from a different direction. Fett boards his ship, but doesn't close the ramp immediately.

If you go back on board *Slave I*, go to 319

If you wait here, go to 329

291

Surna and the others can't believe their ears. "You want to stay on this ship? Why?" You try to explain, but they don't want to listen. "This is our best chance to get away from here!" wails Surna. "I can't spend another minute on this death-ship!"

"There's no way of telling if we'll find another craft outside if we get off. I'm not prepared to take that chance." You can see they don't feel the same way. "I'd sooner be trapped on this planet than stay here!" insists Surna. "I'm getting off. We'll find a ship, you'll see. Come with us!"

"I can't," you tell her. "Boba Fett has been trying to kill me since I first arrived on Toprawa. I can't keep running away, or I'll spend the rest of my life waiting for him to track me down. It just makes better sense to stay hidden on *Slave I*, let Fett take me to somewhere with some better opportunities than this, and face him there." Surna looks fit to bust. There are tears in her eyes. "You're mad!" she says. "I won't stay here and die with you because of some stupid feud with Boba Fett!!" With those words, she spins on her heels and leaves. Tann follows. Al hesitates for a few moments, then he says "You can't beat him, you know. Sooner or later, he's bound to kill you." Then Al is gone too. Thanks for your vote of confidence, Al.

Alone on the ship, you seek the best hiding place you can find in the dark hold, and settle down to wait.

292

An idea comes into your mind. It's as if you have suddenly realised what Boba Fett is after. You pull Surna away from Kelleg, and whisper to her. "Listen, if Kelleg knows where you can find a ship, then maybe you should go with him and check it out. I'm going back to *Slave I*." Her face goes white. "Are you crazy? This is our chance to get away from him!" You take her hand in yours, trying to reassure her. "Is it, Surna? I don't think so. As long as Fett is alive, he's going to keep coming after me. I can't go on looking over my shoulder.

"Besides, I think I know what he's doing here on Yavin. He's trying to find where the Rebel Alliance is based! I have to do something to stop him."

"Then let's all go, and take him on!" insists Surna, anxiously. "No," you reply. "I'll feel better if I know you guys are safe. Besides, it makes more sense if you try and find out where the Rebel base is, and warn them about Fett's plans."

"But what about you?" she asks. "I'll be OK. He's tried to kill me before, and never managed it yet! I'll blow his plan out of space, and then meet up with you later. Don't argue. Go with Kelleg; find this ship." You can see that Surna would happily keep this discussion going all day, so you break away, and start back towards Fett's ship. Along the way, you try to figure out just what your true motives are. Sure, you don't want to place Surna and the others in any more danger, but is this the way to do it?

You find *Slave I* much as you left it. The hatch is open, the ramp is down. Looking around, you can't see any sign of Boba Fett. You climb cautiously up the ramp, and slip on board. The hold is empty. Breathing a sigh of relief, you seek the best hiding place you can find, and settle down to wait.

Check 603

If you have checked either 598 or 594, go to 327

If you have checked neither of those, go to 335

293

You ignore the young man with the scraggly beard, and continue your journey. Suddenly, you hear shots from nearby. Is someone firing at you? No, it seems someone else must be the target. "What do you think?" asks Tann. "Let's check it out," you reply. You run quickly in the direction from which the shots came. The air is still; the fight must have ended quickly. Ahead of you, there's a low mound. Shattered blast doors hang in twisted shapes over a wide entrance. Behind the mound, there's a deep crater, lit from within by firelight. That must be where the shots came from; some kind of underground bunker, now destroyed and opened to the sky. Drawing your weapons, you spread out to surround the crater.

You slip down a steep slope. Inside the ravaged bunker, you find a scene of terrible tragedy. Eight or nine poorly-clad people lie scattered about the floor, having been gunned down as they sheltered round a fire. There are no weapons, and it looks as if they were unarmed. You check the bodies, though it seems as if none could have survived, but Al finds a pulse on one of the victims. You all pitch in, trying to keep the wounded man alive. However, he is fading fast, and there is nothing much you can do about it. With his last few breaths, he manages to tell you what happened. He and his friends were scavengers, looking the old Rebel base over for salvage. The killer who mowed them down ambushed them, demanding to know where the Rebel Alliance's new base was located. When they couldn't tell him, he killed them all. "He's... a madman... No-one... knows... the Rebels... long gone..."

"Who was it?" you ask. You know the answer before it comes. "Boba Fett... We told him... nothing... but he has an... agent here... a man called... Kelleg. He... found out our secret... not really space-drifters... Rebel scouts... Came back to make sure... nothing left behind... Kelleg spied on us... told Fett... to go to... Marranis... said Han Solo... had been there..."

The poor man groans with the effort of his tale. "At least we know whose ship that was that forced us down," says Tann. "He must have put a tracer on the *Rust Bucket*, hoping we'd lead him to the Rebels. Instead, we brought him here." The wounded man coughs. "Not your fault..." he says, his voice very low. "Our bad luck. We have... a ship... We are supposed... to rendezvous... ah!... with the Rebel fleet... there is a transmission frequency... you can use..." Tann bends his head to listen to the frequency. He nods once. By the time he leans back, the wounded man has died. You stand up, knowing there is nothing you can do here. "Do what you can for him. For all of them. Then find this ship of theirs, and try to make contact with the Alliance. Tell them Boba Fett is on their trail, and that he may have a lead on them."

Surna jumps up. "What are you going to do?" You pick up your gear. "I'm going after Fett. I'll see if I can't stop him, or delay him." If he's busy with you, he can't be chasing after the new Alliance base, right? "We shouldn't split up!" she argues. "We must," you insist. "It could take a long time for you to find this ship, or to track down the Alliance. In the meantime, Fett could be way ahead of us. I can take him; I've been close before. Trust me." You move off before she can argue any more. You just about catch her say "Be careful!" as you leave the ruins behind.

Finding Fett's ship proves very easy. The Rebel base's spaceport – mostly in ruins, but with some parts of the landing field intact – is close by, and *Slave I* is the only vessel on it. As you close in, you catch sight of the bounty hunter, performing preflight checks. He turns, and climbs up the ramp onto the ship. Seconds later, you arrive at the outer hatch door, and slip aboard. The connecting door to the crew compartment is closed and locked. Back here, the freight hold has been equipped with holding cells, designed to ferry prisoners. They are all empty. While you are checking, the outer hatch closes, and you hear the repulsorlift motors winding up, ready for take off. It looks like you're joining Boba Fett on a little trip…

Check 603

Go to 337

294

No false modesty here – that was some shot (in fact, it's a pity Boba Fett didn't get a chance to see who fired it…). Fett was just about ready to slaughter the poor people trapped in the crater when you brought him down. It looked like you caught him with a glancing blow to the body, which might mean he's survived. You better take a look.

The eight or nine people around the fire are still reacting with shock and amazement as you slide down the wall of the crater and over to ramp from the original entrance where Fett had been standing. Surprise, surprise, there's no body. Fett has survived yet again. Whatever he paid for that body armour he wears, it was worth every credit!

Check 511 (unless you have already done so)

Go to 338

295

You don't quite have the angle to hit Boba Fett from where you are, but you give him a five-star surprise when you hit the wall over his head, and bring a cascade of plaster, dried paint and prefabricated wall panel down on him! He stumbles back, firing a couple of wild shots, too high to hit anything.

The eight or nine people around the fire are still reacting with shock and amazement as you slide down the slope of the crater. You leap across to the ramp where Fett had been standing, but the bounty hunter isn't there. Surprise, surprise, he's vanished, probably back up the ramp to the original entrance to the bunker. You keep watch for a few moments, but Fett doesn't come back. You must have really rattled him!

Go to 338

296

After three days of mind-numbing boredom and a growling belly, you hear the ship's engines change note. *Slave I* is out of hyperspace, and slowing. But you don't hear the repulsorlifts, or the roaring of atmospheric friction. Instead, you feel the subtle changes as the slave-ship comes into the gravitational field of another ship. *Slave I* has made a rendezvous in space.

Moments later, Boba Fett appears through the door from the crew compartment. This is the first time you have seen him in days. He strides into the hold, looking confident and ready for anything. If your chosen mission is to prevent him finding the other members of the Alliance, what are you going to do next?

If you have checked 619, go to 373

Otherwise, if you fire at Boba Fett, go to 301

If you wait, and then follow him, go to 340

At the second attempt, you get the locker open. Great! You've recovered your gear! You slip Arf into your coat, and put your weapons in their place. You hadn't realised how exposed you felt without them. It's taken a long time, however, and as you look out through the open hatch, you can see Boba Fett on his way back towards the ship. There's no time for anything else, you must either get off *Slave I* or go into hiding!

If you leave the ship, go to 221

If you stay on board, go to 278

298

You activate Arf, and order the little droid to access the door mechanism. He slips a probe into the lock, and starts trying to trip the combination. It takes a while, but you get lucky, and the door slides open. Arf barks happily. "OK, you did it," you tell him, "now shut up before somebody hears you."

You step through, into the forward area of the ship. It isn't a large space, and if you didn't know who owned the ship, the spartan living quarters wouldn't tell you anything. There's a holo-vid-projector, with several dozen disks scattered about it. Looks like Boba Fett is into vintage horror movies. That's just about the only clue to his identity you can find. In between killing people or taking them back to clients for them to kill, Boba Fett leads a very boring life.

The bridge is a simple work-station, as you would expect of a one-man vessel. If Tann were here, perhaps he could work out where the navigational computer was set for, but ship controls don't mean much to you. Or maybe he could reprogram it so Fett took a one way ride out of the galaxy. Oh, well.

If you have your lightsabre, either on you or stashed in Arf, go to 288

If not, go to 299

299

Poking around in Boba Fett's crew compartment some more, you find a small, secret panel in one of the walls. Opening it, you are amazed to find your lightsabre, stashed there. You complete your look round the crew compartment of *Slave I*, careful not to touch anything. Looking through the viewport, you see that Fett is walking back towards the ship. Time to get out of here, Havet my boy!

Check 599

If you have checked 592 or 590, go to 300

If you haven't checked either of those, but you have checked 594, go to 310

If you haven't checked any of those paragraphs, go to 320

300

Even as you are turning round to leave the crew compartment, there is a strange hissing sound, and the crackling hum of a force field activating. Your instincts scream at you – trap! – and you leap towards the open doorway, hitting the force field at a gallop. It throws you to the floor, stunned. As you struggle to rise, you feel a strange weakness in your legs and arms. Of course, the hissing sound must be some kind of gas being pumped into the ship. Boba Fett has tricked you.

As your eyes mist over, you see Tann briefly on the other side of the doorway, rubbing his hand where he has tested it against the force field. "Havet!" he calls, and his voice sounds as if he is kilometres away, not just the other side of a room. "It's a trap!" you tell him. "Get as far away as you can!" He looks like he is going to argue, so you summon up the last of your strength to tell him to escape, that there is nothing he can do to help you, then you feel the lights going out in your mind, and you slide into unconsciousness.

Check 600

Go to 302

301

It proves ridiculously easy to finally end the feud you have been running with Boba Fett. A single shot, just as he was opening the outer hatch. Just so you didn't have to shoot him in the back, you even called his name as you squeezed the trigger. Of course, it was a cowardly and dishonourable thing to do, but don't the ends always justify the means? Not in this case. Your victory is short lived, because *Slave I* has docked with Darth Vader's Imperial Flagship. Almost before the echoes of your ambush have died, Imperial stormtroopers overwhelm you...

Your grandfather would be ashamed. Is this what being a Jedi is all about? Perhaps that's why people have always been suspicious of you, Havet! Try again, from the beginning

302

When you wake up, you are in one of the cells on Boba Fett's ship. The force field is active, humming its threat of severe pain should you try to break out. Listening to the sounds beyond the hum, you guess that *Slave I* is in flight. Fett makes no attempt to feed you anything more than a minimum diet, and within a few hours your throat is bone dry. You sleep fitfully.

You see Fett briefly, when he comes into the hold to gloat. "Still with us, I see." Ha, ha! "You'll be glad to know, we'll be making contact with another ship shortly." Big deal. "Just what is all this about, Fett?" you demand. He checks to make sure you are securely locked away, then continues talking while he makes repairs to some damaged parts of the hold (now, how did that happen?). "What do you know of Jabba the Hutt?" he asks. Not much, if truth be told. He's a crime lord, responsible for slavery, black-markets, racketeering and worse besides on scores of worlds throughout the galaxy. Some people say he's a gigantic fat slug of a creature, with a taste for human flesh. Strictly not someone you'd invite back home to meet the family.

"What of him?" you ask in turn. "The illustrious Jabba –" was that a little sarcasm in Fett's voice? – "has hired me to find someone for him. Someone who owes him a lot of money. Someone who has a ship which really belongs to Jabba." For a moment, you wonder if he's talking about Tann. When you mention this, Fett laughs. "No, I'm talking about someone with a much larger problem. This person cost Jabba about 30,000 credits." Yikes! So, who is he? "His name is Han Solo – have you ever heard of *him*?" No, can't say as you have.

Fett watches you closely, as if considering the possibility that you might be lying. Then he continues. "Solo joined the Rebellion some time before the battle of Yavin. It was a natural hiding place for a thief like him, and it made it very difficult for me to track him down." Shame. "When the Alliance abandoned Yavin, the trail went cold. It's well known that the Rebels are looking for a new base, and that the Empire – with all its resources – can't find them. What chance did I have of finding just one man? And then I had an idea. The Rebels are still recruiting, right? What would happen if the heroes of the battle of Toprawa turned up? They'd be welcomed with open arms, right? So, I arranged for a fistful of tracers to be planted on the *Rust Bucket*. I figured that if any of the Rebels escaped Toprawa, they could lead me straight to the Alliance."

A light is beginning to dawn inside you. It's not a pleasant light. You've been set up.

If you have checked either 590 or 592, go to 332

If you have checked 618, go to 359

If you have checked 593, go to 367

If you haven't checked *any* of these, go to 344

303

"I wonder where I am," you ask yourself. It occurs to you that the exact name of the planet hardly matters. Boba Fett isn't likely to have come to a deserted world. Somewhere out there there could be people, maybe even someone who can lead you to other members of the Alliance. "Somewhere out there, there might even be another starship." OK. That settles it. Besides, this new habit you have picked up of talking to yourself has got to stop. Being cooped up in the holding pens of Fett's ship obviously isn't doing you any good! Grabbing your belongings, you slip out into the dark hold, and move across to the rectangle of light that marks the access hatch.

Outside, you find you are on some kind of small moon or planetoid. There are no buildings or other signs of inhabitation, and the dark sky boils with dust clouds. Maybe you were wrong; perhaps Fett has brought you to a deserted world.

Standing at the bottom of the ramp, you take a hurried look around. The ship is parked on a beat-up landing field. There are ruined space-port buildings on two sides. Aha! So, there was life here once. It looks as if someone has deliberately razed every structure they could find. The Empire, perhaps, taking reprisals against a Rebel world? Could this be Yavin Four, the Alliance's old base? It would make sense if it was.

Boba Fett is striding off into the distance, towards a dark mound beyond the perimeter of the spaceport, beyond which you can see the flickering glow of a fire. You watch him for a moment, then take another long look around. No other ships, and every sign that the spaceport has been deliberately made non-operational. Fett's craft is your only means to get back off this dead world. Dare you risk leaving it?

If you follow Fett towards the ruins, go to 238

If you stay close to *Slave I* to avoid being left behind, go to 249

304

You kneel at the exit from the hold, and take a look outside into the harsh daylight. There's no sign of life close by; you hear no voices, and no shadows move to betray a guard. Nothing to stop you venturing outside at all.

If you want to go outside and you have checked 590 or 592, go to 221

If you want to go outside and you have *not* checked 590 or 592, go to 303

If you stay aboard *Slave I*, go to 278

305

Now, you're not suspicious or anything, but you have *everything* crossed as you wait by the door. Maybe you should have a weapon ready, or something?

If you have checked 594 or 598, go to 324

If you haven't checked either of these, go to 341

306

Finding Al is easy. The next bit is decidedly trickier. Al is lying stretched out in the dirt, with the guy with the scraggly beard leaning over him with a blaster at his head. "Don't try anything stupid!" he counsels. As if. You hold your hands wide to show that you aren't going to try anything at all. "What's all this in aid of – um – did you tell me your name before?" Names were never your strong suit. "Kelleg," he replies, tartly. "Right. Now, Kelleg, would you like to tell me why it is you rescued us, then dented a blaster over my friend's head?" Drat! – he doesn't look at the blaster to see if it is dented. You must be out of practice at the old Jedi Mind-influence thing. "You met Al before, maybe? Cheated you on a deal, did he?"

"I'm not after him," he snaps. "I'm after you, Storm." He wipes some sweat from his lip with his free hand. "My master wants to see you." He stands up, and aims the blaster at you. "Fair enough. I'd better warn you, though. I work for the Imperial Tourism Bureau, and you aren't doing anything for this planet's image. Where am I again?"

"Yavin Four," he replies, before he realises that you are mocking him. Gesturing with the gun, he signals that the conversation is over. You turn, and let him take you to his master. The further he is away from Al, the better.

Go to 342

307

You try to look away, knowing what must follow. You hear Fett's blaster crack once, and there is a short-lived scream. Turning back, you can no longer see the woman who had spoken before, but there is a dark shadow on the floor. Fett has swung his blaster rifle towards an elderly man.

"Now you know I'm not bluffing," he growls. "Who's next? Or will you tell me what I want to know?" The old man shakes his head, and holds his hands forward, begging for mercy. "None of us can tell you what you want!" the old man wails, his voice thin and high. "I don't believe you!" shouts Fett, aiming his rifle once more. "And I'll kill you all, one by one until you tell me the truth!"

If you have checked *any* of 505, 506, 507, 508 or 509, read 605

If you attack Fett, go to 289. You must have a blaster in your Equipment box to select this option

If you do nothing, go to 321

308

You take shelter behind some dockyard equipment close by the open area where *Slave I* is parked. The deserted port is hushed. You feel quite drowsy in the thin atmosphere, and your mind wanders. You are almost asleep when you hear a series of rapid shots – a blaster rifle, by the sound of it. The sound seems to be coming from behind a dark mound some distance away, from where there is also a flickering light.

If you rush over to the building, go to 322

If you stay where you are, go to 334

309

Alone in the dark, you trust to the shelter of your hiding place. Time passes slowly. You have a momentary panic when you realise that you don't have very much food left, and that Fett's next journey might be very much longer than the last. You're just about to duck out through the hatch in search of some supplies when you hear soft footsteps coming up the ramp. Fett has returned.

Check 603

If you have checked either 598 or 594, go to 327

If you have checked neither of these, go to 336

310

You turn away from the viewport, and head into the hold. Suddenly, the man with the scraggly beard is there, wild-eyed with panic. "Boba Fett is coming!" he cries. "I know," you reply. "What are we supposed to do about it?" He tugs at your arm. "Come quickly!"

If you follow your new "friend", go to 279

If you decide to hide on board *Slave I*, go to 278

311-313

Lift the hatch? You couldn't lift the lid off a biscuit tin the shape you're in. Would it be worth trying again? Perhaps calling on the Force to help you?

If you try again, look up your Strength score on your Character Sheet and add it to 310. You can spend Jedi Power Points to give your Strength score a temporary lift (but not to more than 6). So, if your Strength is 2, you'd better spend at least 2 JPPs, in which case you would go to 314

If you don't feel strong enough to force the hatch open, go to 325

314-315

Fortunately, the locks that would seal the hatch during deep space flight haven't yet engaged. That means you only have to lift a massive metal door against the press of its hydraulic rams. Simple. The hatch gives slightly, and – with a final heave – a little more. You whisk your coat through the gap, and let the door fall back into place.

It took a great deal out of you, though, and you collapse to the floor, drenched in sweat. You are dimly aware that a small warning light is still blinking on the hatch mechanism above you.

If you have checked 594 or 598, go to 324

If you haven't checked either of these, go to 326

316

Fortunately, the locks that would seal the hatch during deep space flight haven't yet engaged. Throwing your weight and all your power against the door, you feel it lift, just enough to leave a gap that you can pull your coat tails through. A small warning light on the control panel winks once as you let the hatch fall back into place, but no alarm sounds. As a precaution, you take cover in the dark shadows at the rear of the hold, weapons at the ready, eyes fixed on the door leading into the crew compartment. But if Boba Fett saw the partner of that warning light flash on the main panel of his controls, he doesn't react to it.

So, here you are, safely stowed away on *Slave I*, ready for another flight to who knows where. In the old days, when you didn't have the money for a ticket, you just used to beg, steal or borrow until you did. You've escaped from dozens of planets by the skin of your teeth, with cops or vengeful traders on your heels. Right now, compared to trying to steal a lift with Boba Fett, those look like the easiest days of your life.

Go to 337

Kelleg seems very disappointed at your announcement that you know nothing of the whereabouts of the new Rebel base. Even so, he agrees to show you his ship. He takes you by a long, circular route around the perimeter of the spaceport, towards the wreckage of a repair shop which needs more than few repairs of its own. He opens the door, and beckons for you to go in. You can see a large shape in the shadows, hidden under a steelweave sheet. You make to go in, but stumble – did Kelleg just trip you?

Off-balance as you are, you are helpless to prevent a heavy blow which crashes into your from behind. You hit the floor hard. Someone jumps onto your back, removing your weapons with a few deft movements. You decide to prove that you're pretty deft yourself, and you ram your elbow back hard into his middle. With a great gasp, the guy on your back falls away, and you manage to spin round so that you can see what is going on.

Perhaps that wasn't such a good idea. You are facing the wrong end of a blaster rifle. It's a sight you have seen too often in the past. "Fancy bumping into you here," sneers Fett (well, you imagine he's sneering under that helmet; the way he said it, you can't imagine it was spoken with a cheery smile). Kelleg is lying off to the side, holding his stomach and trying to remember how to breathe. "I came with a friend of yours," you reply. "I wondered why I never liked him."

Fett manages an impersonation of a laugh. "Kelleg is an agent of mine here on Yavin. He's helping me track down someone, someone I want to meet very much. I had hoped that you might be able to help, but Kelleg tells me you have no idea where the Rebels are. That makes you rather less than useful." He levels a weapon at you. "Maybe," you butt in quickly, "I know more than I was prepared to tell fuzz-face here." Fett remains perfectly still. "Maybe you do," he agrees. "In which case, I need you to stay alive for just a little longer."

"I'm all in favour of that myself," you grin. Fett cautiously takes one hand from his blaster rifle, reaching towards another weapon on his belt.

If you attack Fett, go to 331

If you put your hands in your pockets, go to 343

If you keep perfectly still, go to 357

318

You don't have much of an angle for a clear shot, and that starts you off on the wrong foot. Boba Fett leaps back, swinging his weapon up towards you. You're heavily outgunned, and he has the advantage of knowing the ground. So, this time, you failed. At least you tried to save those poor people from being massacred.

When you start again, add 1 to your starting Jedi Power Points score. You're starting to act like a true Jedi despite yourself, Havet!

319

The ramp starts to close as you jump for the hatch. Oh, man! It's going to be close!! Too close!! As you crunch into the frame, the hatch closes on the flap of your coat, almost crushing Arf (not to mention your leg!). You're inside – but half your coat, including Arf, is on the outside. Damn!

You tug at your coat, but there's no way you can pull it inside with the hatch closed. Perhaps there's some way you can open it again? The control panel is right beside you, and – oh, oh! – there's a warning light flashing. A counterpart of that light will be flashing on the control panel in front of Fett's pilot's seat. If you get real lucky, he'll open the hatch again, and you'll be able to free your coat. Equally likely, he'll have heard the racket you made as you dived through the hatch, and when he sees the warning light he'll put two and two together and make for the door.

Just how are you supposed to get out of this one?

If you wait to see if Fett opens the door, go to 305

If you try operating the door controls, go to 323

If you try to open the hatch enough to drag Arf in, you must find your Strength score on your Character Sheet, and add it to 310. You can spend Jedi Power Points to give your Strength score a temporary increase (to a maximum of 6). So, if your Strength score is 3 and you add 3 JPPs, you would now go to 316

You race back into the hold. You're heading for the exit when the thought hits you... do you really want to go outside? After all, you have no idea what planet this is. Suppose it's crawling with Imperial troops? Suppose there's no way to get off? You could end up trapped on a very hostile planet, and spend the rest of your life amongst flesh-eaters, zombies or what have you.

Ooops! You let your imagination run away with you for a second there, Havet. Even so, you really don't know what you'd be letting yourself in for if you jumped ship here. So, what is your other alternative? Well, you could go back to the hiding place you found for yourself. Boba Fett hasn't found you so far. Perhaps, at his next stop-off, you might find a better chance to escape. Of course, that means staying another few days trapped inside a prison-ship, eating survival rations and drinking melted ice from the inside of a freezer unit, wondering if you could be discovered by the deadliest bounty hunter in the galaxy at any minute.

Nice choices. It's all the more interesting that you have less than a second to think about it.

If you decide to stay on board ship and continue hiding, go to 278

If you want to leave, go to 304

Fett slays his next victim. Still the others refuse to tell him where the new Rebel base might be. If they know, it is a secret they will carry with them to their graves. Fett becomes berserk, and fires indiscriminately into the group. You choke hard, unable to stop him, unable to prevent the massacre. When you next look, it is all over, and Fett is gone.

You slide down the slope of the crater. All of the people who were sheltering here lie scattered about the floor. It seems as if none could have survived, but you find a pulse on one of the victims. The man is fading fast, but he is determined to spend his last breaths in giving you some vital information. Is he going to tell you where the base is? "Fett is... a madman... but very clever... He had an... agent here... a man called... Kelleg. He... discovered our secret... not salvage-hunters at all... Rebels... making sure... nothing left behind... Kelleg told Fett... what we were told... planet called Marranis... said Han Solo... had been there... Fett thought we knew... more..."

The wounded man coughs. "We have... a ship... We were supposed... to rendezvous... ah!... with the Alliance... there is a transmission frequency... you can use..." You bend your head to listen to the frequency. By the time you lean back, the wounded man has died. You stand up, knowing there is nothing more you can do here. "I don't know what made you think you could depend on me," you whisper into the dry air, "but I won't let you down." Leaving the ruined bunker behind, you go off in search of the bounty hunter.

Check 620

If you have checked *any* of these paragraphs – 505, 506, 507, 508 or 509 – read 605

If you have none of those paragraphs checked, read 606

After you have read one of those paragraphs, look to see if you have checked 590 or 592. If you have, go to 328

If not, go to 346

322

You run quickly in the direction from which the shots came. The port is completely deserted as far as you can see, and no-one else appears, curious about the gunfire. Truth is, this planetoid looks as if it has been thoroughly scourged by the Empire. There's not a building left intact. Ahead of you, the dark mound looms larger. You can see now that it is the entrance to an underground bunker. Huge blast doors, hanging crazily from shattered mounts, frame a ramp which leads down into the space beyond. The bunker has been demolished; its roof is open to the sky. There is a flickering light from the floor – a fire of some kind. You reach the edge of the crater where the bunker once lay, and draw your weapon. Moments later, you slide down the slope, bouncing off rubble and debris, to land in a large, fire-ravaged room. You roll into the dubious cover of a broken table, but no shots are fired. You take a long look around the ravaged building's interior.

It's a brutal, tragic scene. All of the people who were sheltering here lie scattered about the floor, murdered, it seems, in cold blood. There is no sign that they had the means to defend themselves. There doesn't appear much hope that any of them could have survived, but – miraculously – you find a pulse on one of the victims. The man is fading fast, but he is determined to spend his last breaths in giving you some vital information. "Fett is... a madman... but very clever... He had an... agent here... a man called... Kelleg. He... discovered our secret... not salvage-hunters at all... Rebels... making sure... nothing left behind... Kelleg told Fett... what we were told... planet called Marranis... said Han Solo... had been there... Fett thought we knew... more..." The wounded man coughs. "We have... a ship... We were supposed... to rendezvous... ah!... with the Alliance... there is a transmission frequency... you can use..." You bend his head to listen to the frequency. By the time you lean back, the wounded man has died. You stand up, knowing there is nothing more you can do here. "I don't know what made you think you could depend on me," you whisper into the dry air, "but I won't let you down."

You stand up, knowing there is nothing more you can do here. Leaving the ruins behind, you go off in search of the bounty hunter. More than ever now, you are determined to make him pay for what he has done.

Go to 334

323

You make a desperate attempt to open the door, but without the access codes you have no chance. Pressing control buttons aimlessly gets you nowhere – worse than that, it alerts Boba Fett that someone is on board.

There is a strange smell, and you catch the high-pitched hiss of gas being pumped into the hold under pressure. One of Fett's security devices, designed to knock out prisoners who have escaped from the cells somehow. You have no mask, and the gas acts quickly. Your legs buckle, and your eyes fill with water. Slumped awkwardly on the ground, still pinned by your coat, you see the connecting door to the crew compartment open. Fett appears. His helmet must have a respirator built in. "Havet Storm!" he laughs. "What an unexpected pleasure!"

Well, at least someone's happy. You hear Fett's laughter echo in your mind as you slip into darkness.

Go to 302

324

In the awkward position you are standing in – well, sort of standing; actually, it's more like being nailed to the wall – whatever, in that position, drawing your weapon is a tad awkward. In fact, you are still fumbling with the release when you realise Boba Fett has come through from the crew compartment and is pointing a neural stunner at you. "I did wonder who caused all the damage to my ship. I'll just add that to what you owe me, shall I, Havet?" He doesn't wait for an answer. You hear a distant pop, then all the world goes black.

Go to 302

325

You can't stay here like this! At any moment, Fett could come through the other door, and find you here, pinned to the door like a biological specimen, ready for dissection. You'll just have to pay the price for your bad luck!

Taking a broad blade from your belt, you cut the flap of your coat away, leaving Arf on the outside. There's no way the droid will survive the journey through the atmosphere, or the deep cold of space. A tear rises in your eye as you realise that you are saying goodbye to an old friend, and you clench your fists in frustration, knowing that it could have been avoided.

You walk to one of the cells and sit in the gloom. You need to find a more secure hiding place, somewhere Boba Fett won't see you if he comes into the hold during the flight. For now, though, all you can think about is the danger of your situation, and what is has cost you to get this far, trapped on Fett's prison ship, truly alone for the first time.

Read 607

Go to 337

326

To your great relief, after a few moments the warning light goes out. The connecting door into the crew compartment stays closed. If Fett ever saw the light, he dismissed it out of hand. You've made it!

Go to 337

Fett arrives on the ship a few minutes later, striding up the ramp, keying the door controls and waiting as the outer hatch closes. He pauses, like an animal smelling the air for the scent of its prey. He pulls a weapon from his belt. Something has made him suspicious. He hasn't seen where you are yet, so you keep him firmly in your sights, knowing that you'll have the drop on him if it comes to a fight. Then he kills the lights. Drat! It was hard enough to see anything in the gloomy hull anyway, but with the outer hatch closed and the interior lights killed, there isn't an active photon anywhere in the room. You'd bet your life, though, that Fett has some kind of light amplifier on that helmet visor, maybe even a heat sensor. You duck lower down.

Silence. Lying flat on the floor, you pray Fett doesn't find you. As a precaution, you slowly take Arf from your pocket, and tuck him further back into the gloom, behind a few bulky storage containers.

It proves to be a worthwhile move. Time passes by slowly. You're trying not to breathe, trying to pierce the deep silence for some kind of clue as to where Fett is. Nothing. And then you feel the cold ring of metal placed against your temple – the barrel of a weapon. "Get up!" he orders, and you obey. He frisks you lightly, then steps back to switch on the lights. The brightness hits you like a slap in the face. You hear Fett cry out – "Storm!" – but by the time you shake the stars from your eyes, he has recovered from the shock of finding you loose aboard his ship, and has drawn a snub-nosed blaster. "I can explain!" you start, but he pulls the trigger, and the explanations will have to wait a while.

Check 615

Go to 302

Heading back towards the spaceport, you pull Tann to one side to show him the communications frequency given to you by Klopke. "Memorise this. I think it will put you in touch with the Rebels. Also, there may be a ship hidden somewhere. See if you can find it. Make contact with the Alliance, and warn them about Fett's interest in Solo."

Surna pushes past her brother to confront you. "Aren't you coming with us?" You pick up your gear. "I'm going after Fett. I'll see if I can't stop him, or delay him." After all, if he's chasing after you, he can't be chasing after the new Alliance base, right? "We shouldn't split up!" she argues. "We must," you insist. "It could take a long time for you to find this ship, or to track down the Alliance. If it takes too long, Fett might get to the Alliance before us, or he might lead the Empire to the new Rebel base. I have to stop him. I can beat him; I've been close before. Trust me." You move off before she can argue any more. You just about catch her say "Be careful!" as you leave the ruins behind.

You go back to the bounty hunter's ship. As you get close, you catch sight of Boba Fett, performing preflight checks. He turns, and climbs up the ramp onto the ship. Seconds later, you arrive at the outer hatch door, and slip aboard. The connecting door to the crew compartment is closed and locked. The freight hold is empty. You hide in one of the cells until the outer hatch closes, and the repulsorlift motors start powering up, ready for take off.

If you have checked 594, read 642

Check 603

Go to 337

329

You wait for several long, agonising moments. Wild ideas and plans come into your mind, only to be dismissed as you see how impossible they all are. Finally, with a hiss of its servos, the hatch closes. You take your chance, and scamper away from Fett's ship, taking shelter in the blind spot to the rear. Once you're about thirty or forty metres away, you circle round behind some ruins, then make your way slowly to where Surna and the others are.

You find them in a wrecked hangar, a service bay with a shattered door and no roof. In the middle of the floor, there's a large, battered hulk of metal. Surna stands with her hands on what might, in a better light, pass as the leading edge of a wing.

"It's a ship!" she beams proudly. Tann appears from underneath the nose (well, it's probably the nose), rubbing his hand on a cloth the way engineers always do when they have looked over a vehicle that is only fit for the scrap yard. "Only just," he sighs, adding his comment to Surna's optimistic opinion. "It'll take six months, and a pretty extensive list of replacement parts before we can be sure about it, though." Surna pouts. Your guess is that she found it, and signalled the news to you before Tann was able to get a good look.

"It won't fly, then?" you ask. "Please!" wails Tann, in horror. "It's a miracle it can just sit still without falling to pieces." To prove the point, he flicks at some heat-tiles on the underbelly. Three fall off. "We aren't going to get this heap into the air," he states finally. "Let's get back to Fett's ship and get out of here."

"No!" cries Surna. "I can't go back onto *Slave I*. Look, the fact that there's one ship here may mean there are others. We can cannibalise the wrecks, scavenge for parts. Hey – and we've got Al with us! If anyone can help us get this thing together, he can." Where is Al? You have just noticed his absence. "Outside. He's haggling with a guy for some food." Good, you're starving.

"Look it over again, Tann. See what's missing, what you need. Surna's right, we can't risk going back on board *Slave I*." You slap him on the shoulder, and give Surna a conspiratorial don't-rile-him-tell-him-what-a-clever-pilot-and-engineer-he-is-and-how-easy-it-will-be-for-him-to-fix-it glare. She blows you back a kiss. Some women will do anything to avoid travelling with hired killers.

You slip out of the hangar. Fett's ship is still on the landing field. You duck back behind the building, and go round the back to find Al.

If you have checked 594, go to 306

If not, go to 330

330

Finding Al is easy. The next bit looks trickier. The former barkeeper may well still be haggling over the price of some supplies, but he's doing it lying down, and with his business associate holding a blaster at the nape of his neck. You freeze. The guy – a thin youth with a few days worth of growth that even his mum wouldn't call a beard – looks nervous, and there's no way you can close the gap in time to stop him vaporising Al's head.

"You Havet Storm?" he asks, wiping sweat from his lip with his free hand. You nod. "My master wants me to bring you to him." He stands up, and aims the blaster at you. That possibly passes for an improvement in the situation.

Go to 342

331

You leap forward, trusting to luck and your speed.

Do you have enough of either? Look up your Speed score on your Character Sheet. You may spend Jedi Power Points to increase your score temporarily (but not to more than 6!). Add the total to 350 to find the number of the next paragraph you should read. So, if you have a Speed score of 2 and you spend 1 JPP, you would next read paragraph 353

332

Not for the first time, you look at Fett and his helmet visor seems to be wearing a grin. "But the *Rust Bucket* is history…" you begin. Fett completes the sentence. "…so I had to make new plans. Fortunately, you made it easy for me by stowing away on my own ship! When I realised that you and your friends were aboard, all I had to do was arrange to get them off the ship, while keeping you on it. That was no problem. Meanwhile, each of your friends has enough tracers on them that I could find them on the other side of the galaxy if I wanted to. As soon as they leave Yavin, I'll know about it, and I'll follow them wherever they lead. Hopefully, that will be directly to the new Rebel base, and to Han Solo. I get my prisoner, the Empire gets the whereabouts of the Rebel leaders – everyone wins. Except the Rebels. And you. I couldn't let you go, Havet, now could I?"

If you have checked 604, read 617

Go to 349

333

You dump Boba Fett to the ground. He arches his back, fighting to get back up, then falls still. If he's still breathing, it's difficult to see. Maybe, just maybe, the long struggle is over at last…

You hear a foot scuff the floor behind you, and spin quickly. Kelleg! You'd forgotten about Fett's agent. But if you've beaten the master, will it be so difficult to defeat the slave? Apparently, yes. Kelleg has picked up the fallen stun-pistol. He fires, and the glow of victory is replaced with the blackness of the void. Man! Just once, you wouldn't have minded a few minutes to be able to crow about how clever you'd been before something else went wrong.

Read 612

Go to 302

334

Your determination to keep track of Boba Fett pays off. You catch sight of the bounty hunter striding across the battered landing field towards the ship. He takes a look around – was he expecting to see someone? – then performs a few preflight checks on the outside of the ship. You watch him closely. He finally decides he is satisfied, and goes up the ramp and into the ship.

You explode from your hiding place, and cover the ground between yourself and the ship in an instant. Even as you arrive at the hatch, the ramp starts to rise. You take a nanosecond to look inside and check that Fett isn't on the hold, then dive on board. Landing as softly as you can, you scrabble across the floor of the hold and into the darkness of the far corner. The connecting door to the crew compartment is closed, and the hold is wrapped in complete darkness once the hatch shuts tight. You can feel your breath shaking. The silence is terrifying, until the repulsorlifts power up, and *Slave I* lifts from the ground. Slowly, you unwind. Boba Fett will be busy with the flight for a while. Settling into a more comfortable position, you begin your second journey into space.

Go to 337

335

In fact, you don't have to wait too long. While you're sheltering, you hear a voice outside – Fett's. Moments later, he comes onto the ship.

If you have checked either 594 or 598, go to 347

If not, go to 358

336

Fett doesn't waste much time. After a short delay, the repulsorlifts wind up, and the ship sways slightly as it lifts from the landing pad, and heads up through the atmosphere on another mystery journey.

You try to find a comfortable place to sit; after all, you could be in here for quite a while.

Go to 337

337

After a while, *Slave I* prepares for its jump to hyperspace. For you, in the hold, the 'excitement' of the trip is over for a while. Time to think about some of the practicalities. For a start, you have to make sure your hiding place is secure, and that Boba Fett won't find you if he comes into the hold for some reason. You find the best place to hide is in the cell furthest from the interior door. It's well clear of the storage bins which hold repair equipment, and even with the outer hatch open there wouldn't be much light in that area.

You then turn your attention to the cell door. It is designed so that it can be opened from either the control panel by the hatch door, or from the main control deck in the crew compartment. It's not impossible Fett will think to throw the locks – in which case you'd be trapped. While the door is open, you think you can disarm the lock quite easily. On the other hand, any tampering might set off an alarm, and bring Fett to check.

If you have checked 603, read 616

If you try to disable the lock on this cell, look at your Tech Skills score (on your Character Sheet). You may spend Jedi Power Points to increase this temporarily (but not to more than 6!). Add the total to 360 to find the number of the paragraph you must read next. So, if you have a Tech Skills score of 3, and you choose not to spend any JPPs, you would next read 363

If you leave the lock alone, go to 296

338

You slip back into the middle of the shattered bunker. The salvage-hunters – if that's what they are – sit huddled together. They look more frightened of you than they did when they were being threatened by Boba Fett! "It's OK," you tell them. "He's gone!" A middle-aged man with greasy hair steps forward. "Do you know who that was?" he asks. You certainly do! The man grabs your hand. "We owe you our lives! Boba Fett was going to kill us!"

"I don't understand," you tell the man. "What is this information he wanted? Why is he prepared to go to these lengths to get it?" The greasy man looks prepared to tell you, but a woman behind him counsels him to be cautious. "He thinks we know where the new Rebel base is. I tried to tell him that we didn't. We're just scavengers, looking for anything that might have been left behind when he Rebels abandoned Yavin! But Fett insisted that we had to know something. An agent of his had tagged onto our group; told him what we had heard about Han Solo stopping at Marranis for supplies."

Why is Boba Fett so keen to track down the Rebels, or this Solo guy? Al told you the bounty hunter had a "commission" from Jabba the Hutt – how do the Alliance and the galaxy's greatest criminal come together? It's all very odd.

You tell the man about your own run-ins with Boba Fett, and what you did for the rebel cause on Toprawa. The salvage-hunters look at each other. It seems they are coming to believe you. "Our ship is hidden nearby. We're leaving soon." He shakes your hand; you feel him press something into your palm. "You'd better go," he says. "I can't help you in your quest, but if you ever find the Rebels, tell Han Solo that Klopke says hello. I was on the ground crew who patched up the *Millennium Falcon* when she was here. What a wild ship that is!"

You slip the item into your pocket, and offer your thanks and best wishes to Klopke and the others. Checking carefully to make sure Fett isn't waiting for you, you step out of the building. Klopke has helped you make your mind up about what you must do next. You have to do anything you can to stop Fett.

Check 604

If you have checked 590 or 592, go to 328

If you haven't checked either of these, go to 339

339

You realise that you have to stop Fett hunting down the Alliance, no matter what his reasons are. If he manages it, then the Empire will just follow his trail, and the whole Rebellion could come to an end. You have to stop him!

You go back to the bounty hunter's ship. As you get close, you catch sight of Boba Fett, performing preflight checks on *Slave I*. He turns, and climbs up the ramp onto the ship. Seconds later, you arrive at the outer hatch door, and slip aboard. The connecting door to the crew compartment is closed and locked. The freight hold his empty. You hide in one of the cells until the outer hatch closes. The repulsorlift motors start powering up, ready for take off.

Go to 337

340

It's a huge temptation to just blast Boba Fett there and then, but you resist it. He opens the outer hatch, and the hold is filled with harsh artificial light. The bounty hunter steps through.

Curiosity getting the better of you, you venture from your hiding place. You cross to the hatch in time to see Fett striding across the open floor of a docking bay. There's no way of telling what the ship that *Slave I* has docked with is, but it's certainly an Imperial vessel – you can tell that much from the markings and the uniforms worn by the crew. Despite that, you decide you have to take a closer look.

Once you have reached the bottom of *Slave I*'s access ramp, you can see that the ship with which it has docked is a Star Destroyer – one of the most powerful ships in the Imperial armada! You take a cautious look around. There is a ready room to one side of the bay, with a few Imperial naval ratings lounging around, talking. A small galley opens onto the ready room. Further round, there is another door, through which Boba Fett is about to pass. He looks purposeful, determined. You wonder what he is doing here – and realise that the only way to find out is to follow him. Then you catch a whiff of cooked food from the galley, and your stomach growls. It's been a long time since you had a proper meal...

If you visit the galley in search of food, go to 348

If you follow Fett, go to 387

341

Man, do you feel stupid. Not only have you caught your coat in the door, but your brain must have been knocked out of skew when you banged into the hatchway. Suppose Fett had come to check on the door straightaway? At last, you think of going for a weapon – and then you drop the dratted thing on the floor! You really deserve to get caught after this!

But things often work out backwards, don't they? There have been times in the past when you thought you'd done everything perfectly, and then a wall fell on you, or something. This time, when you have been acting like a droid with a memory displacement, fate smiles on you. The hatch opens, only for a second, but long enough for you to whisk your coat through the gap before it slams. Just in case Fett comes to make sure everything is OK, you rush across the hold to find a hiding place. In fact, all remains quiet.

You were lucky. It occurs to you that winning a free trip into the furthest reaches of space with the hired killer of your choice isn't much of a first prize.

Go to 337

342

After you have walked a few metres, you realise where you are being led. "You work for Boba Fett?!" you sigh, unable to believe it. There's no answer, just a shove in the back that hurries you closer to the ship ahead. The ramp is back down, and you are taken to the foot of it.

Boba Fett is inside, with a stun pistol in his fist. He has been fixing the damage caused to *Slave I* when you "escaped". He levels the stunner at your body. "One thing," you interject quickly. "Why go through the charade of having me rescued if your thug here was just going to fetch me straight back. Is this some kind of sick joke?"

"No," replies Fett. "Kelleg wasn't so much letting you go, as letting the others go. I never intended to let you get too far away, and Kelleg has done a good job, don't you think?" Wonderful. Fett flexes his fingers around the butt of the stunner. "Of course," he continues, "I quite like the odd sick joke now and again too." And with that he fires. You just about him hear laughing as the darkness closes in.

Go to 302

343

Slipping your hands into your pockets, you place one palm on the activator panel on Arf's back, instantaneously keying the standby switch. Fett watches you; all he can see is what must seem to be a very casual approach to danger. "I admire your guts," he sneers.

"One day I hope to get a closer look at them." Yuk! Fett chuckles to himself as he pulls out a stun-gun, and you have just enough time to close your eyes before everything goes black.

Check 609

Go to 302

344

Not for the first time, you look at Fett and his helmet visor seems to be wearing a grin. "You really want to know?" he asks. "The only reason you're still alive is that I may need you to help me capture Han Solo." You laugh aloud. "Help *you*? What makes you think I'd do that?" He answers quickly, perhaps a bit insulted by your mockery. "Willingly, perhaps you wouldn't. But I think I know how to get what I want." He doesn't add any more.

If you have checked 593, go to 360

If not, go to 368

345

Boba Fett fights like a demon. He actually seems quite frightened of you, and there is no sign of his legendary efficiency, or the arrogance he normally displays. He's in a real hurry to beat you. Sadly, that's just what happens. Your right arm is hit, and you feel the terrible shock and pain of the laser burn. Your weapon tumbles to the ground, and you follow.

"The stun pistol would have been less painful," sneers Fett. "I'll live," you gasp, defiantly. He laughs. "That's not your decision to make, Storm." He pushes you over onto your back, and you can still hear him laughing as you fade into unconsciousness.

Check 614

Go to 302

346

Outside the ruined bunker, you hesitate for a moment. The wounded guy spoke of a ship. Should you try to find it first, maybe? The doubt lasts for only a few seconds. You know that you have to go and confront Fett. You can make use of the frequency later, after you have defeated him once and for all.

You go back to the bounty hunter's ship. As you get close, you catch sight of Boba Fett, performing preflight checks on *Slave I*. He turns, and climbs up the ramp onto the ship. Seconds later, you arrive at the outer hatch door, and slip aboard. The connecting door to the crew compartment is closed and locked. The freight hold is empty. You hide in one of the cells until the outer hatch closes. The repulsorlift motors start powering up, ready for take off.

Go to 337

347

At the top of the ramp, he pauses, like a wild animal sniffing the air for danger. You suddenly realise that he might see the damage that was done to his ship earlier. You tense, ready to fight, but Fett doesn't draw a weapon or search the hold. Instead, he passes through into the crew compartment. Whew! You were lucky there. For a moment, there, you didn't dare breathe!

You suck in a big lungful of air now, grateful for having escaped. That's when you taste the strange metallic tang in the air. Gas! You try to get up, but it is hopeless. That one gulp has filled you with enough sedative to quiet down a Wookiee with a headache. Slowly, you drift off to sleep, knowing that when you wake up, the nightmare will really begin.

Go to 302

348

The smell of fresh-baked bread and grilled fish is more than you can resist. Taking your chance, when the Imperial personnel in the ready room are distracted by something being shown on the vid-screen at the far end of the room, you slip across the landing bay and into the galley. The droid 'chef' hands over a plate of piping hot breakfast. It looks as if it might protest when you seize a second helping and enough bread to last you a week, but it has no resident security programme, and it doesn't hinder you at all. You slip back the way you came to devour your bounty.

Boba Fett has disappeared from sight, and there's no way you're going to wander round an Imperial battleship to look for him, but – frankly – you don't care what he's doing. Food! It tastes fantastic! You wolf down enough for three people, and carry away enough for another 3. Replenished and resupplied, you make your way back to *Slave I*.

You may recover 2 Jedi Power Points (up to the maximum you are allowed, as shown in the starting box)

Go to 371

349

"All that, just to catch this Han Solo character? You'd betray the Rebellion to the Empire, just to catch up with some guy who owes your boss money?" Fett steps back from the bars, bored with the conversation. You can guess that he doesn't try defending his actions to anyone very often. "Of course! What else? You think I should get involved in some idealistic crusade, like you? Well, let me tell you, I don't do anything without someone paying the price. I have no interest in the outcome of the Rebellion, except for a practical purpose – the Empire pays better. You Rebels seem to think using someone like me is 'dirty'. That's your big mistake. In a war like this, you have to fight as rough as the other side, or you get burned."

He leaves the hold to go back to the flight deck. You are left with a terrible cold feeling in your guts. The Rebellion – your only 'home' for the last two years – is about to be destroyed in order that Boba Fett can find this Han Solo character. Somehow, you have to find a way to stop him! And that means getting out of this cell!!

If you have checked 609, go to 372

If you have checked 615, go to 388

If you have checked neither of these, go to 350

350

You try everything you can think of, but nothing works. Fett has designed the holding cells well; and he has had many other prisoners locked in here, each of them trying to get out. In the end, you have to admit defeat, and settle back to see what lies in store for you next. After three hungry, thirsty days, *Slave I* docks with another ship. Fett comes back through from the crew compartment, and opens the outer hatch. Without a word to you, he descends the ramp onto the floor of the other ship's landing bay. Who knows what is going on?

Check 619

Go to 371

351-355

Close, but not quite. Boba Fett's hand moves quickly, pulling the brutish-looking stun-pistol from his belt, levelling at your onrushing form, and firing in one smooth motion. It feels like you have run headlong into a wall. Blacking out is a merciful release.

Go to 302

356

Boba Fett is quick, but not that quick. He is still pulling the brutish-looking stun-pistol from his belt, when you crash into him, your head driven into his arm, and your weight throwing him back hard against the unyielding flank of his ship. He hits it hard, and the stun-pistol spins away. You kick his legs away from under him, and he topples off the ramp. With a reflex action, he grabs just enough of your collar to pull you off behind him, and you both fall to the earth.

You come up together, coiled like great cats, hands springing towards your weapons...

Read 610, and use the combat rules from the beginning of this book. Record this paragraph number so you can find your way back here.

If you defeat Boba Fett, go to 333

If he defeats you, go to 345

357

"No futile resistance?" Fett asks, drawing a stun gun. "Is there any point?" you ask. He shakes his head. "None at all." And with that, he pulls the trigger, and you have a moment to think about whether you'll ever see the light again before you slip into unconsciousness.

Go to 302

358

Fett passes straight through to the crew compartment, sealing the inner door. Moments later, the outer hatch closes too, and the hold is plunged into blackness. You uncoil your limbs, and stretch out. After a few minutes, the repulsorlift engines stir into life, and the ship shudders as it lifts from the landing field. You try to make yourself a little more comfortable in your hiding place. After all, it might be a long flight.

Go to 337

359

Not for the first time, you look at Fett and his helmet visor seems to be wearing a grin. "So, when Tann got the *Rust Bucket* back…" you begin. Fett completes the sentence. "…it was only because I wanted him to. The only thing I hadn't counted on was that you would escape with them; I had hoped to kill you while we were on Toprawa. But that was easily fixed. I realised you were coming to Yavin, and arranged to get here before you. I made Tann crash, and then found a way to let your colleagues go, while keeping you my prisoner. Right now, they're being led to another ship, equally well-equipped with tracers. With luck, the Rebels who are here on Yavin posing as salvage-hunters will have given them directions, some other means of reaching the Rebels.

"As soon as they leave Yavin, I'll know about it, and I'll follow them wherever they lead. Hopefully, that will be directly to the new Rebel base, and to Han Solo. I get my prisoner, the Empire gets the where-abouts of the Rebel leaders – everyone wins. Except the Rebels. And you. I couldn't let you go, Havet, now could I?"

If you have checked 604, read 617

Go to 349

360

"Why did you take me prisoner on Toprawa?" you ask. "Why not just kill me there and then?" Fett comes even closer to the bars. "I thought of it, don't think that I didn't!" he hisses. "But I had a reason for keeping you alive! Your friend Surna and her stupid brother had a ship. If they could get off Toprawa, where would they go? Straight to the Alliance! So, I arranged for their escape." Huh? Why would he do that? Unless... "That's right. I'd covered the *Rust Bucket* with tracers. If they found the Alliance base, I would have found it too. The only thing I hadn't counted on was that you became involved. As always, Storm, you got in the way."

If you have checked 604, read 617

If you have checked 585, go to 377

If not, go to 390

361-363

It's no good. You just can't disable the door lock. You try to jam it mechanically, and to override the electronics, but neither attempt works. You'll just have to hope that Fett doesn't shut you in.

Go to 296

364-366

There's no way you're going to get trapped in here by accident. You call on all your technical know-how to defeat the lock, jamming the mechanical bolts and cutting the electronic connections. Ha! Let's see Fett try to close the door now.

"Well, well." You whirl round. You tried to be careful, and to keep an eye on the connecting door through to the crew compartment, but you turned your back while you completed a tricky circuit bypass. Fett didn't make a sound as he came in. There's no way you can reach any of your weapons – he has you covered with a heavy duty stun-pistol. Suddenly, being locked in the cell accidentally looks really attractive.

"I didn't know you did repairs in your spare time," Fett smirks. Why is it that this man only has a sense of humour when he has a gun pointed at your head? "I was just passing," you reply, trying to match the high standard of repartee. "Hmmm. Did you manage to jam the lock?" You give it an experimental prod with a probe. "Looks like." Fett gestures towards one of the other cells. "I have plenty of others. Would you like to practice some more on one of those?" The answer you'd like to give is 'no', but Fett pushes you into one of the vacant and undamaged cells. "It really is good to see you again," he remarks as he engages the lock.

Go to 350

367

"Why have you kept me prisoner?" you ask. The bounty hunter finishes the work he was doing, ignoring you. You repeat the question, and he wanders over towards the cell. "Are you in such a hurry to die?" mocks Fett. "No," you reply, "but I thought you were in a hurry to see me dead." Fett laughs, in that dry way that suggests he has never actually found anything very funny. "I can be patient," he says, in a low voice. "Don't kid yourself into dreaming about escape. I have kept you alive because I can kill you any time I want!"

"You could have killed me on Toprawa. You could have let the *Nunchuka* blast Tann's ship when we reached orbit – I take it it was you that stopped them finishing us off. But you didn't. Why?" Fett laughs again – and this time you believe he actually is amused by your naivete. "You're right," he boasts. "I had a reason for keeping you alive! Your friend Surna and her stupid brother had access to a ship. If they could get off Toprawa, where would they go? Straight to the Alliance! So, I arranged for their escape." Huh? Why would he do that? Unless... "That's right. I'd covered the *Rust Bucket* with tracers. If they found the Alliance base, I would have found it too, and when I found the base I would find Han Solo. The only thing I hadn't counted on was that you became involved. As always, Storm, you got in the way. Fortunately, though, I was able to use the *Nunchuka* to separate you from the others." So, he used his influence to get hold of you, and set Surna and the others free... knowing he could track them down at any time!

If you have checked 604, read 617

Go to 349

368

"How did you know I was aboard your ship when you left Toprawa?" you ask. Fett finishes the work he was doing, ignoring you. You repeat the question, and he wanders back towards the cell. "You made it so easy!" he crows. "Blundering around the spaceport like that! Did you really think I didn't have someone watching my ship?" You think about that for a moment, then it occurs to you that he isn't telling the whole truth. "If that was all this was about, you would have killed me there and then; you've tried often enough."

"Don't think I couldn't have killed you any time I wanted!" he shouts. "But you're right! I had a reason for keeping you alive! Your friend Surna and her stupid brother had a ship. If they could get off Toprawa, where would they go? Straight to the Alliance! So, I arranged for their escape." Huh? Why would he do that? Unless… "That's right. I'd covered the *Rust Bucket* with tracers. If they found the Alliance base, I would have found it too, and I would have found Han Solo too. The only thing I hadn't counted on was that you became involved. As always, Storm, you got in the way."

If you have checked 604, read 617

If you have checked 585, go to 377

If not, go to 390

369

You tell Fett about the transmission frequency you were given by the dying man on Yavin Four. It's the only card you have left to play. "Interesting!" remarks the Bounty Hunter. "That could be just what I need…" He pauses to reflect for a moment. "In fact, Havet, you may just have sealed the doom of Han Solo and the entire Rebellion! Congratulations!! Now, I really don't need you any more…" And with that, he squeezes the trigger.

Shame on you, Havet! Giving Fett a secret like that? It would be better to have died – which is what you did anyway. Take yourself back to the beginning of the book, and begin your adventure again.

370

The gun battle in the hallway outside the dining area is ferocious, and you find yourself pressed back by the Imperial soldiers. It's too hot for you here! Surna and the others will just have to find their own way out.

Go to 37

371

After a while, Fett comes back onto the ship, and closes the hatch. The hold is plunged into gloom once more, and you settle back to wait for the undocking procedure to begin. Fett powers up the ship, and you drop away from the bulk of the star destroyer. Within a few minutes, the first hyperspace jump begins. Something in your heart tells you this is the last journey you will make aboard this grim ship. You hope and pray it isn't the last you make, period.

Another few uncomfortable days pass by, as you eke out your supplies. In between long periods of unsettled sleep, punctuated by nightmares, you dream about the first meal you're going to have when you get off this evil vessel. Right now, even the most appalling creation from the kitchens of Al the Alchemist's bar would be a banquet. You're day-dreaming about an ice-cold tube of Star Racer when the ship's motors change note. *Slave I* is landing.

If you have checked 619, go to 399

If not, go to 410

372

Your quick thinking when you were captured has given you a way out of your predicament. When you slipped your hands into your pockets, you switched Arf to standby. Although the droid was removed from your coat when Fett threw you into the cell, if he is in earshot, you should be able to activate him.

If you call Arf, go to 389

If you keep quiet, go to 400

373

You can only watch as Fett opens the outer hatch, and steps onto the other ship. Except for a cursory glance in your direction, he doesn't even acknowledge your existence. Fine by you.

So, just what is this ship Fett has rendezvoused with? Is it connected with his plan to catch up with this Han Solo character? What would you give to be able to follow Fett and find out?

If you have checked 609, but you *haven't* checked 621, go to 380

If you have checked 623, go to 397

If you can't follow either of these choices, go to 350

374

Thrusting your arm through the bars of the cell one more time, you place your palm on the droid's DNA panel, and activate Arf. The dog bursts into life, as cheerful as always, and you have to be quick to shut him up. "No noise, Arf. Never know who might be listening." The droid utters a small whimper to show he understands. "See the controls for the cell doors, Arf? Look there, up on the wall." Arf almost barks to show that he has found them, but he cuts it off at the last second. You bet real heroes like Luke Skywalker never have this much trouble with droids. "Think you can trip the lock mechanism on this door, Arf? Don't open it – it may have an alarm. Just take the lock out."

Arf whirrs, and lifts up on his repulsorlifts. He glides across the hold to a spot just under the control panel, and extends a probe from his nose. For a second, it looks like he can't reach, but the droid beefs up the repulsorlifts under his "paws", and lifts a metre off the ground. You know that hovering like this eats into his power reserves, but you have no choice. It takes Arf a few minutes to throw the right combination through the system, and to trick the lock mechanism into thinking it has been keyed to open. You hear a soft snap as the lock disengages. Arf sinks back to the floor and makes his way sluggishly back to your side.

"Good work, boy!" you praise him, and he manages a half-hearted wag of his tail. "Now go find somewhere to hide. Next time Fett steps off this ship, we're out of here!"

Check 623

Go to 296

375

You step through the open hatch from *Slave I* and walk cautiously across to the landing bay of the other ship. Judging from the markings, it's an Imperial Star Destroyer! What business does Fett have with the Empire? And what business do you have trying to sneak on board one of the Empire's most awesome starships?

Across from where you are, there is a ready room, a waiting area for TIE fighter pilots and other personel. There are a few Imperial navy types in there now, who were probably on duty to check that everything was alright when *Slave I* docked. Right now, they're watching a sportscast on a wide-screen vid. You slip past them, reaching a doorway which opens automatically onto a corridor stretching away from you in both directions. There's no sign of Boba Fett. He could have gone either way, and there are plenty of doors and lift shafts he could have taken. Finding him isn't going to be easy, and you'll run the risk of getting caught, or being left stranded when he takes off.

Maybe you should just forget the idea of finding out what he's up to, and settle for breakfast! Close at hand, there is a small automated galley, which was recently dispensing breakfast to the ratings in the ready room. There is enough left-over food to quell even your hunger pangs. Mmmm! You could really do some damage to those supplies, Havet.

If you keep searching for Boba Fett, go to 401

If you raid the galley, go to 348

376

Maybe Arf's sensitive receptors can pick up some sound through the door? It's worth trying. You pull the droid from your pocket, and tell him to place an audio probe against the door. There's an earphone you can listen through, and you slip that over your lobe. Almost at once, you hear Fett's voice, sounding tinny and distorted, but very recognisable.

"I was hoping to trade for some information," he says, sounding less aggressive than usual, and more creepy. There is a brief pause, and some movement. The voice which replies is too indistinct to recognise, as if he/she/it is whispering. It then becomes more audible. You don't recognise it. It sounds very distorted through the tiny speaker in your ear, as if the guy (yes, it's male) is talking through a comlink already. Why would Fett come on board an Imperial ship to use their communications equipment?

"You want to bargain with me, bounty hunter?" the reply comes. Fett's voice follows, sounding slightly strained, as if he might choke, as if someone had been holding him by the throat... Man, this just gets better and better. "I meant no offence," he replies. "It's just that

I think I have a lead which would be to our mutual profit if I followed it. I wanted to be sure that there was no... misunderstanding!"

"Just what is this 'lead'?" the other asks. His voice sounds really odd. Perhaps it isn't coming through a comlink speaker, perhaps the guy has some kind of voice modulator... "Han Solo," Fett answers. "I think I know where he is." There's a brief pause, as if Fett is hoping that will be enough of an answer, and the other man is waiting for more. Fett cracks first. "An agent of mine says Solo was on Marranis recently." Fett sounds more confident now, his usual arrogance returning. "Interesting to you, perhaps," the other comments, "but not perhaps relevant to our arrangement. I'm only interested in finding where the Rebels are setting up their new base, not in chasing after a lone fugitive. It is my understanding that Solo left the Rebels on Yavin, that he chose to run away because of your pursuit. If he has been seen on Marranis, that merely supports my hypothesis. That is a desert planet – hardly a fit place for the new Rebel base."

"If you are saying you are no longer interested in Han Solo," continues Fett, "that is all I need to know. I thought you wanted Solo to lead you to the Alliance. As you know, I want him to take back to my master, Jabba the Hutt." The other man considers this for a moment (you guess). "Thus far, Solo has been an... irritant. His efforts on behalf of the Alliance have been a grave obstacle to my plans. But if he has left the Alliance, I can ill afford to waste the fleet's time chasing him across the galaxy. However... that does not mean that finding him would not be to my advantage."

Fett's voice becomes a little less distinct for a moment, but you hear very clearly when he says: "Then you have no problem with me continuing to search for Solo on the understanding that if I find Solo before you do, you'll be the first to know? If he is scouting planets for the Alliance, I'll send you that information. All I ask in return, in the name of the illustrious Jabba, is that you release Solo to me if you capture him before I do." The other guy's voice changes slightly. He must be moving around. "We'll see," he says. "But don't fail me, bounty hunter. I have no time for failures."

You hear footsteps approaching the door, and break the link. You know it's important now that you get back aboard *Slave I* before Fett, and there's that long corridor to be followed. Then again, wouldn't you love to know who the other guy was?

If you run back to *Slave I*, go to 402

If you find a hiding place and wait, go to 413

377

"Even so," Fett continues. "Thanks to your normal outrageous good fortune, you helped them escape. They went to Yavin Four first – which made sense, considering what they were looking for. I don't think they found anything. If they had some kind of communications equipment, or they knew the Rebel frequencies and codes, it would be different, but without them they could spend forever trying to make contact with the Alliance. That's why I let you leave this ship on Yavin Four, to see what you knew. It turns out you know very little. However, I'm reluctant to kill you just yet. You and the *Rust Bucket* are the only two leads I have."

Go to 349

378

You get ready to jump the naval guy.

Select your weapon. If you use your lightsabre, read 624; if you use your blaster, read 625; if you don't use a weapon at all, read 626

379

Fett aims the weapon at you for a few seconds, staring into your eyes. Then he lowers the weapon. "You *do* know something, don't you? I can see it in your eyes." He puts the weapon back in its place. "I can see I shall have to delay killing you for a little while longer."

Go to 349

380

Fett disappears down the access ramp. Now's your chance. That moment of inspiration you had when you switched Arf to standby just before you were captured had better pay off! You call out, hoping the little droid is within earshot. "Arf? Arf! Can you hear me?" You catch the sound of a series of muffled barks from across the hold. There is just enough artificial light spilling in through the open hatch to let you see that there is a locker against the wall. "You're in a box!" you call. "Try to get out. See if it's locked."

A few bumps against the lid prove to you and Arf that the locker is, indeed locked. If it's some kind of old-fashioned bolt or key, you've had it. On the other hand... "Arf, check the lock. Is it electronic? Do you think you can trip it?" Arf barks away like a maniac, which is his usual way of signifying confusion. One order at a time, Havet. You're just about to call to the droid again when the lid springs back, and Arf's head appears over the rim of the locker. "Good dog!" you cry. Arf's pretty happy to see you too.

"See the controls for the cell doors? Look there, up on the wall." Arf barks loudly. If Fett had been on board when you tried this, you'd have been caught for sure. "Not so loud! Just open the door, OK?"

Arf whirrs, and lifts up on his repulsorlifts. He glides across the hold to a spot just under the control panel, and extends a probe from his nose. For a second, it looks like he can't reach, but the droid beefs up the repulsorlifts under his "paws", and lifts a metre off the ground. You know that hovering like this eats into his power reserves, but you have no choice.

It takes Arf a few minutes to throw the right combination through the system, and to trick the lock mechanism into thinking it has been keyed to open. You hear a soft snap as the lock disengages, then the door slides back, and you're out! "Good work, Arf!" you praise him, and he manages a half-hearted wag of his tail. You rush across to the locker, where you find the rest of your gear. Armed and ready, you feel 100% better. You slip Arf back on standby and back into your pocket. "OK! Now let's see what's going down out there."

Go to 375

381-382

Ouch! Well, that was a very painful lesson. You're just not fast enough, Havet! The force field gives you a nasty burn on the arm, and you don't get close to grabbing the sacking. You'll just have to find another way out of the cell.

Read 622

Go to 350

383

Ouch! You aren't quite quick enough in retracting your hand, and the force field burns your fingers. At least you have successfully pulled the sacking from Arf's body, and dragged the droid close to the bars of the cell.

Read 622

Go to 374

384-386

Success! You thrust your arm quickly through the bars, and snatch at the sacking which is hiding Arf from view. After a couple of attempts, you have freed him from the cloth, and dragged him closer to the cell bars.

Go to 374

387

Who says you don't have any willpower? Leaving the kitchen behind, you slip quietly through the next door, and into a long corridor. Fett is a short distance away, heading along the passage. He doesn't look back. When he reaches the door at the far end, it opens automatically, and he passes through, bearing to the left. You run up to the door, and look through the viewing panel. There is an open area, with several doors and passages leading off it. Fett has gone to one of the doors, and has pressed the Announce panel. Someone inside must have told him to come in, because the door opens, and Fett steps through.

Checking around, you open the first door yourself, and tiptoe up to the second. There is no viewing panel here, so you can see nothing. Nor can you hear any voices. If you're going to find out what Boba Fett is up to, you're either going to have to go in there, or find some other way to eavesdrop.

If you have Arf with you, and you wish to use him, go to 376

If you reach out with your Jedi senses, go to 398

If you step back from the door, go to 409

388

Call it good planning or instinctive good luck, but when you left Arf hidden out of sight on *Slave I* you did yourself a big favour. He's actually hidden quite close by, under some sacking at arm's length outside the cell. You could grab the sacking, pull Arf close to the bars of the cage, and once you activated him, you might be able to get out of here. After that –

Don't get ahead of yourself, Havet. First, you have to get hold of Arf, and that isn't going to be easy. You have already had a painful lesson about the security of this cell. In addition to the titrox bars themselves, there is a force field which automatically activates if hidden sensors pick up anything being passed between the bars – including hands and arms. It snaps on less than half a second after the sensors see the obstruction. That means you're going to have to be mighty quick. You roll your sleeves up, and get ready to give it a try.

Find your Speed score on your Character Sheet. You may spend Jedi Power Points to increase your score temporarily if you wish (but not to more than 6!). Now take the total, and add it to 380. So, if your Speed is 2 and you spend 1 JPP, you would next read 383.

389

You call Arf. You hear his frantic reply echoing from a locker on the other side of the hold. Fett must have stored him there when he took your gear away. "Hush up!" you call – but too late. The connecting door to the crew quarters opens, and Fett strides through. Without glancing at you, he walks to the locker, and pulls the droid out. Arf utters a few low growls, then whimpers. Fett checks the controls, then finds the off toggle.

"You have a lot of affection for this little toy," Fett says, thinking out loud. "I can't help thinking that's not healthy for a young man of your age. I think this droid should come and ride up front with me." And with that, he leaves the hold once more, and you are trapped in the cell for the rest of the flight.

Check 619 & 621

Go to 296

390

"So," Fett continues. "Thanks to you, I lost my best chance of finding out where the Rebels are hiding. The last option I had was to let you go on Yavin Four, and see if you knew anything. But you don't, do you? You have no idea where the new Alliance base is! In fact, you're worthless to me!" He pulls a weapon from his belt. "I can't think of any reason why you should stay alive for a moment longer!"

If you have checked 604 or 620, and you tell Fett about them, go to 369

If you say nothing, go to 379

391

You reach out with your mind, trying to avoid having a fight with the naval officer. He hesitates, suddenly, as if he has forgotten where he was supposed to be going. Then he looks up. You start to speak, trying to plant the suggestion in his mind, but a rising tide of alarm and panic sweeps through the man, and he fumbles for his blaster pistol.

You must attack him before he can raise the alarm. Go to 378

392-393

You reach out with your mind, trying to avoid having a fight with the naval officer. He hesitates, suddenly, as if he had forgotten where he was supposed to be going. Then he looks up. You send a wave of tranquillity across to him, and speak in a low, calm voice. "It's OK. I'm waiting to meet someone. You can just leave me here." He hesitates again, about to speak. You can sense him trying to come to terms with the fact that a civilian is walking freely around an Imperial Star Destroyer. "I –" he mumbles. "I have to take this message to the captain. I can just leave you here, OK?" You nod, and he walks away. Whew! You'll just have to hope he doesn't remember what happened until you are long gone.

OK. Now you can tackle the remaining door. You're pretty sure Boba Fett is behind it. How can you listen in to see what he is doing?

If you have Arf with you, and you wish to use him, go to 376

If you reach out with your Jedi senses, go to 398

If you step back from the door, go to 409

394-396

You reach out with your mind, trying to control the naval officer. The brief wave of panic that was rising up inside him when he saw you dies down. "It's OK," you tell him. "I'm waiting to meet someone. You can just leave me here." He quickly comes to terms with the fact that a civilian is walking freely around an Imperial Star Destroyer. "I have to take this message to the captain," he mumbles. "I can just leave you here, OK?" You nod, and he walks away. Whew! That was easy! What a dummy he was –

A large hand has descended with crushing weight on your shoulder, forcing you to your knees – the pain is terrible! Your assailant changes his grip, lifting you up, and flinging you back against the wall opposite. You land heavily, and slump to the floor, looking back through a mist of tears to see who has wiped you out so thoroughly. You can see Boba Fett, but it isn't his hand that is crushing you. Fett is standing at the shoulder of a man dressed all in black, his face hidden by a blank mask, that still manages to radiate evil. You know who this has to be. He grips a lightsabre in his left hand. You don't feel any temptation to try going for yours.

"When I felt the disturbance in the Force, I thought – but you're not Luke Skywalker. Who are you?" Fett supplies the answer. "His name is Storm; he's the boy I told you about, Lord Vader."

"The boy who has caused you so much trouble? Small wonder. I had thought there were but three like him in the galaxy. But there can be no doubt. He is a Jedi, and that makes him mine."

And that makes your life expectancy measurable in minutes. When you're ready to start again, go to 1

397

Curiosity getting the better of you, you venture from your hiding place. You cross the hold to the hatch in time to see Fett leaving the landing bay on which *Slave I* stands. There's no way of telling what kind of ship *Slave I* has docked with, but it's certainly an Imperial vessel – you can tell that much from the markings and the uniforms of its crew. You decide to take a closer look.

Slipping down the ramp onto the floor of the gigantic bay, you realise that this must be an Imperial warship. TIE fighters are parked all around. Across from where you are crouching, you can see a ready room in which pilots and other personnel are lounging around, watching a vid-screen and talking. Boba Fett is striding away to your right, heading towards a door. He looks purposeful, determined. You wonder what he is doing here – and realise that the only way is to follow him. Then you catch a whiff of cooked food from a small galley which opens onto the ready room, and your stomach growls. It's been a long time since you had a proper meal...

If you visit the galley in search of food, go to 371

If you follow Fett, go to 387

398

You allow your mind to open, to reach out, trying to feel for the presence of Boba Fett or any other life forms behind the door. Almost at once, you are swamped by an overwhelming sensation of evil – a much greater evil than you have ever sensed before. It's like entering a dimly lit room, and feeling the darkness close around you like a shroud. You break away, stumbling back from the door. As it opens, you realise you have made a terrible mistake.

A man dressed all in black stands in the doorway, impossibly tall, his powerful frame made even broader by the midnight cloak he wears. His face is hidden by a mask that manages to radiate menace as easily as its surface reflects the overhead lights. This can only be one person. He grips a lightsabre in his left hand, while his right hand clenches in a tight fist. "You. Who are you? I felt a disturbance in the Force; I thought – but you're not Luke Skywalker. Tell me your name!" Fett, who is standing behind him, supplies the answer. "His name is Storm; he's the boy I told you about, Lord Vader."

"The boy who has caused you so much trouble? Small wonder. I had thought there were but three like him in the galaxy. But there can be no doubt. He is a Jedi." That particular secret seems to be becoming rather widely known – too widely known for your comfort. Vader leans forward, and fastens a tight grip on your lapels. "You have done well to remain hidden from me up until now," he whispers, his voice distorted, cold. "You would have done even better if you had stayed hidden from me forever."

You have fallen into Darth Vader's clutches. Rather than prolong the agony, perhaps you could start again?

399

Fett comes through into the hold some considerable time later, fully armed. He walks up to the cell in which you are seated. "How are we feeling today, Storm?" he mocks. "Feel up to a little trip outside?" He has to be kidding. Unless there's a restaurant out there. "I'd like you to help me out," he continues. "It seems my contact on Yavin was right – Han Solo is here, on Marranis, right now. Trouble is, he's hiding. From the flight deck, I can see the *Millennium Falcon* – that's his ship, by the way – and no-one has been near it all day. No sign of Solo or his Wookiee friend. Now, I could go out and ask, but I don't think they'd tell a bounty hunter. They might, on the other hand, tell a brave hero of the Rebellion."

"You really think I'd help you hunt a man down, Fett? And betray the Rebellion at the same time? And for what? As soon as my usefulness is over, you'll kill me anyway." Fett shoulders his blaster rifle. "All that is true, Storm," he sighs. "But consider this. I'm not going to feed you any more. That means you'll starve to death in a few days. Out there, I'm sure there are all kinds of places you could find to eat in while you track down Solo. *And*, who knows, you might feel strong enough at the end to try taking me on again. It's not much of a chance, I know. But it's better than nothing."

"You think you have it all worked out, don't you, bounty hunter? Suppose I tell you I'd rather die than give you any help at all?" Fett laughs. "I don't think so, Storm. There are many kinds of hero in the world, but you're not one of the self-sacrificing types. Come on, we've had some great fights already. Wouldn't you like to go around one more time?"

If the alternative is lying here starving to death, sure. You drag yourself to your feet. "What's the deal?" you ask. "Simple," Fett explains. "You go out there, and you find Solo. The minute you do, I kill you. If you manage to find some way out of that – well, you're welcome to try." A small point occurs to you. "I could just go out there and not bother looking," you say. "You could," agrees Fett, "but if I think that's what you're doing, I'll kill you anyway."

It looks like he has thought of everything. All the same, you have to go along with it. As he says, you might get lucky. "OK, helmet-head. Let's do it."

Remove all your blasters from your Equipment except for one BlasTech DL–18 blaster pistol (check 505). This is the only blaster Fett allows you to keep

If you have your lightsabre on your belt (check 503), he removes it. If you have it stored inside Arf (check 504), Fett doesn't find it.

Check 627

Go to 407

400

Something tells you that calling Arf right now would be a bad move. Fett is bound to have the hold wired for sound. If he hears you giving orders to the droid, he'll waltz through and take Arf away. Better to wait for another opportunity, even if it means being cooped up in this grim cell for a few days.

Check 619 (unless you have already done so)

Go to 296

401

Much as you'd like to feed the growling ache in your belly, the call of duty proves stronger. This is a trend you hope isn't going to become a habit.

Your instinct tells you Fett took the right hand corridor when he boarded the Imperial ship. It's just a hunch – but you have to follow it. So, right it is. There are a number of rooms off along the passage, but they all look pretty dull, and quite a few have small view ports in, allowing you to take a sneaky glance at the occupants. There are also two turbolifts, but the cars are several decks away, so you guess Fett didn't climb on one of them. So, finally, you reach the end of the corridor, and a doorway.

It opens automatically into a small chamber with several passages leading into the interior of the ship, and three doors. These look like briefing rooms. None of them has a handy viewport, but one of the doors is actually ajar, making it easy to see that the room is empty. One of the other two, perhaps?

While you're standing there trying to make up your mind, one of the doors opens, and an Imperial communications officer steps out, carrying a datapad. You can see there is another rating in the room, wearing headphones. The guy who has stepped out into the open chamber hasn't looked up and seen you yet. But he's going to, in about another second...

If you wish to use your Jedi Mind-influence power, decide how many Jedi Power Points you will spend (no more than 6!) and remove them from your current total. Now add the number you chose to 390. That is the number of the paragraph you should read next. So, if you spend 3 JPPs, you would go to 393

If you attack the Imperial officer, go to 378

If you ignore him (and hope he ignores you...), go to 403

402

You run back along the corridor at near-light speed, only slowing as you open the door into the landing bay. You risk a look back – Fett hasn't appeared at the other end of the passage yet. The crew members in the ready room are still engrossed in the sportscast, so you slip into the landing bay tube with a grateful sigh of relief, and make your way back to Fett's ship.

You find a hiding place in the hold of *Slave I*, and recover your breath. Now that you know what's at stake, you're more determined than ever to defeat Fett's plans. The sooner the better. One more day aboard this cursed ship is one too many.

Go to 371

403

You ignore the young officer, and – to your amazement – he ignores you! He doesn't so much as look up from his datapad as he trots off along one of the connecting passages. "I wish everything was that easy," you murmur.

OK. That leaves just the one door. Odds are that's where Fett is. Now, how are you going to listen in on his conversation?

If you have Arf with you, and you wish to use him, go to 376

If you reach out with your Jedi senses, go to 398

If you step back from the door, go to 409

404

You whisk out your lightsabre and cut the guy down before he can make a sound. As you drag him quickly down one of the passages, and dump him in an empty room, it occurs to you that your action wasn't exactly heroic. Once again, you are reminded just how easy it is to fall victim to your Jedi curse.

What's done is done. Now what matters is to complete the task you have set yourself – to find out just what it is that Boba Fett is up to.

Reduce your Jedi Power Points maximum score by 1

If you have Arf with you, and you wish to use him, go to 376

If you reach out with your Jedi senses, go to 398

If you step back from the door, go to 409

405

You draw your blaster. The guy from the communications room freezes for a moment, then goes for the weapon on his hip, a purely reflex action. You fire, and he goes down.

The noise that shot made seems to still be echoing round the passages of the ship long after he hits the ground. An alarm sounds, and you hear shouts as the ship's crew starts to react. Worse still, the door nearest you slides open, and a huge man, dressed in black and with his face masked, steps out. With a single gesture, he causes the blaster to fly from your hand. You try to flee, but his fist descends on you like an iron hammer, and you collapse to the ground.

You rise up to see that the dark-garbed giant and Boba Fett are side-by-side looking at you. Fett starts to argue that you should be handed over to him. The other man cuts him short. "Since you brought this assassin aboard my ship, bounty hunter, you should consider yourself lucky I don't have you charged as his accomplice. He is my prisoner."

"Yes, Lord Vader," replies Fett. You can't tell which surprises and horrifies you more – the fact that the bounty hunter can knuckle under so easily, or the fact that you are now in the clutches of Darth Vader!

This isn't good news. This would be a good time to start again. Return to paragraph 1

406

You catch the navy man flush on the jaw with a knock-'em-dead right hand, and he clatters to the ground. Luckily, the noise doesn't attract any attention. Dragging him along one of the side passages, you find an uninhabited room, and dump him behind some storage bins. Not bad, though you say it yourself.

Massaging your hand (the trouble with the Empire is that all its minions have such hard skulls), you return to the small chamber. OK. That leaves just the one door where Fett might be. Just how are you going to check it out?

If you have Arf with you, and you wish to use him, go to 376

If you reach out with your Jedi senses, go to 398

If you step back from the door, go to 409

407

You step down from *Slave I*'s ramp, and set foot on the planet. The air is humid and hot! It takes you about half a second to remember how thirsty you are. Somewhere up ahead, there's a small restaurant. Would Boba Fett object if you were to have a meal? Nah! He's a reasonable guy. Of course, since he just took every last credit you had in the world...

Looking around, you see a Corellian YT-1300 freighter. That must be the *Millennium Falcon*. Are you going to take a look?

If you walk over to the *Falcon*, go to 412

If you aim for the restaurant instead, go to 420

408

"Supposing I wasn't as stupid as Han Solo…" you continue, as if you were thinking out loud. "How would I go about riding out into the desert." The chef picks at the only clean spot on his apron, as if amazed that anything that grey could still be visible. "You could hire a skimmer," he says, smiling. "Less than 200 credits a day." How much less? "I could make you a deal. Say… 150?" The man makes a better thief than he does a chef. "OK, you got it," you reply. "I'll get the money from my boss." The chef nods, and clears away your things. You notice he puts the sandwich back on the rack.

"You report back to Boba Fett, who listens impatiently. "Why would Solo go out joyriding in the desert?" Perhaps he likes building sand-castles? "I don't know!" you reply. "Anyway, it'll cost 250 credits to hire a sand skimmer for the day. You want me to go look for him or what?" Fett hesitates, then pulls a purse from some hidden recess on his armour. "Get a receipt," he orders. You try not to giggle.

Go to 415

409

You don't fancy tackling the door. After all, Boba Fett could walk out at any moment. So, you sneak over to the door marked with the Imperial symbol which shows it is a communications sub-station. A young ensign is inside, sitting with his back to you, headphones on, monitoring engineering reports. Boring work. You tap him over the head so he won't be bored any more.

From your new hiding place, you watch to see if Fett reappears. Time passes slowly. You start to wonder if you missed him some-how, if Fett might not be even now starting up *Slave I*'s engines. You have your hand on the door control as the other door hisses open. The bounty hunter steps into view, then pauses to wait for someone else. Oh man! Fett's companion is a nightmare in black. A huge man, wearing a long cloak, jet armour and a flaring, masked helmet. He sweeps into the chamber, clearly the dominant partner in the conver-sation they have had.

After several seconds, the tall man speaks, his breathing distorted by the mask he wears. "Do not let your obsession with Solo blind you, bounty hunter. Jabba the Hutt's dispute with Solo is merely… finan-cial. I play for higher stakes. It would be a mistake to forget our arrangement." Fett tilts his head back, so that the two are faceplate to faceplate. "I will not forget, Lord Vader," he replies. Vader? Oh, oh! This is getting out of control! "If I find Solo first, I will bring him so that you can discover the whereabouts of the Rebel base. Do not mistake professionalism for obsession. I work for money, my Lord."

"A regrettable lack of moral judgment," comments Vader. "Perhaps," Fett continues, "but we cannot all act with the same certainty as you. Although…" Vader is intrigued. "Yes?"

Go to 418

410

Fett comes through into the hold some considerable time later, fully armed. He makes a few last-minute checks of his equipment, then opens the hatch and steps out. You give him a few moments, then slip out from your hiding place to peer out through the open door. Fett is some distance off, converging on a small spaceport restaurant. You've seen the type before, and you know Fett can't be going there to eat, not unless he has a dying need for food poisoning. So, this has to be something to do with him hunting for Han Solo.

What are you supposed to do now? In fact, you wait, unwilling to step out into the harsh, bright light of the planet's surface in what might be Fett's full view. After a few minutes, you hear the rising whine of a repulsorlift engine, and Fett reappears, mounted on a sand skimmer, slicing out into the desert beyond the port. Has he found a lead? Is Solo out there somewhere?

You drop down from the ramp, and take a look around. There's a YT-1300 transport close by, sitting firmly down in the sand of its landing pit. A small gaggle of buildings lies around the port control tower, and another gaggle about half a kilometre away along a paved highway. Other than that, all this planet can boast is sand, sky and a hot sun. WELCOME TO MARRANIS says a sign on the control tower. And they are. You take another look at the YT-1300. Hmmm. Wonder who owns it. You could go see. Or if you're more desperate than Fett, you could check out the restaurant for some food.

If you check out the ship, go to 412

If you risk your life and enter the restaurant, go to 420

If you head out in pursuit of Boba Fett, go to 423

411

Oh, oh. Foul-up time. You whisk out your lightsabre, but you miss with your first cut, and the guy leaps for an alarm button set in the wall nearby. You drop him, but he falls to the accompaniment of an alarm klaxon. It also crosses your mind that just swatting him aside like this is just the sort of cowardly act you have been told the Jedi were famous for. Looks like you have inherited your grandfather's failings, right enough.

It gets worse. The door nearest you slides open, and a huge man, dressed in black and with his face masked, steps out. He freezes when he catches sight of your lightsabre, but then draws one of his own! A sickly green blade hisses into life, growling angrily. He practices a few cuts at your head, which you evade easily. Of course, he isn't really trying.

"Who are you, boy – and where did you get that weapon?" He steps closer. You can see Boba Fett is standing behind him. "His name is Storm, Lord Vader," the bounty hunter announces. "He has been a thorn in my side for some time now. Let me take him – you can be assured that I will deal with him most severely." Vader cuts him off. "Since you brought this assassin aboard my ship, bounty hunter, you should consider yourself lucky I don't have you charged as his accomplice. He is my prisoner." He hasn't moved his attention from you one fraction. With lightning speed, he sends another high cut at your throat. You parry it with your own blade, and there is a booming crackle of power energy as they strike. "Besides... he is a Jedi. I sense it. And with that name, he can only be the son of Morvet Storm..."

"The grandson, actually," you counter. "Ah, yes," Vader intones. "It has been quite some time. Did you know your grandfather? He was a brave man, an honourable man – and a fool. He stood by while I destroyed the Jedi, and then I killed him. And his son, your father, too, if I remember right. It looks as if I missed you, somehow. I shall have to put that right."

Well, you have discovered the truth at last. Perhaps, armed with this knowledge, you will be able to make a better job of your next attempt... Return to the beginning (you don't really expect to beat Darth Vader in a lightsabre duel, do you?)

412

You move across quietly towards the other vessel on the landing field. As you get close, you see that it is a heavily modified YT-1300, and that the entry ramp is down. Curious. If this ship belongs to Han Solo, then you wouldn't expect it to be unguarded and open. You call a greeting into the hatchway, but no-one answers. You place one foot on the ramp, and then pause to consider the possibility of alarms or booby traps. Perhaps you don't want to go on board after all.

Stepping back, you take a long look round the parched surface of Marranis. If this is Han Solo's ship, he either has to be in the small restaurant, in the town or out there in the desert. What could he be doing on such an inhospitable planet? It doesn't look like a very likely spot for the Rebel base – you might just as well try to build it on some ice-planet…

If you have checked any of these paragraphs – 585, 593, 595 or 600 – go to 418

If you have not checked any of these, go to 421

413

You sneak over to one of the other doors, marked with the Imperial symbol which shows it is a communications sub-station. You open the door. A young ensign is sitting with his back to you, headphones on, monitoring engineering reports. Boring work. You tap him over the head so he won't have to work so hard any more. You slip a small box into the door frame, and activate the door mechanism. It closes, but not all the way. There is a small gap for you to see through.

From your new hiding place, you wait for Fett to reappear. After a few seconds, the other door hisses open. The bounty hunter steps into view, pausing, looking back to wait for someone else. Oh man! Fett's companion is a nightmare in shiny black. A huge man, wearing a long cloak, jet armour and a flaring, masked helmet. He sweeps into the chamber with an air of complete domination; even Fett steps back to let him pass.

After several seconds, he speaks, continuing their conversation. "Do not allow you obsession with Han Solo blind you to everything else, Bounty Hunter. Jabba the Hutt's dispute with Solo is merely… financial. I play for much higher stakes. It would be a mistake to forget our arrangement in your haste to return Solo to Jabba." Fett tilts his head back, so that the two are faceplate to faceplate. "I will not forget, Lord Vader," he replies. Vader? Oh, oh! This is starting to get out of control! "If I find Solo first, I will present him to you so that you can discover the whereabouts of the Rebel base. Do not mistake professionalism for obsession. I work for money, my Lord."

"A regrettable lack of moral judgment," comments Vader. "Perhaps," Fett continues, "but we cannot all act with the same certainty as you. Although…" Vader is intrigued. "Yes?"

Go to 418

414

"I need to find him," you continue. "How do I make a safe journey out into the desert?" The chef picks at a piece of grey cloth between the thick stains. "You could hire a skimmer," he says. "Prospectors use 'em to search for minerals. Used to be a lot of stuff on this planet; jewels, uranium, copper…" You cut him short, not interested in a geological report. "Where do I find one?" He grins, and you notice the terrible state of his teeth. "I could let you borrow mine for – say – 200 credits."

200 credits? He'll be lucky. You have about 10. "I don't have that much," you admit. He looks you over. "Well… maybe we could trade something. You got anything you can offer?" Good question.

The chef will accept a blaster in exchange for the hire of the sand skimmer. Remove the weapon from your Equipment Box if you make the deal, and check 629. Then go to 419

If you refuse to make the deal, go to 423

415

You go back to meet up with your friend the chef. He takes the money gleefully, and leads you out into the yard behind the restaurant. He pulls back a steelweave sheet, to reveal a battered old sand skimmer, partly covered in grey sand. What a wreck! "You want 200 credits to hire that crate?" The chef looks offended. You prod at the vehicle, and your finger goes through the panel. "Are you sure you haven't got another one of these?" The chef points at a shed, and you can see another sand skimmer under a sheet in there. "There's that one, but that's not as fine a vehicle as this. The skis are broken, for one thing."

You think about this for a minute. "So what happens if I need two of these?" you ask. "Well... I might be able to fix the skis in a couple of hours... or you walk into town and see who else has one." He indicates the distant clutch of buildings, partly hidden by the heat haze. When he looks back, he seems quite surprised to see you smiling. "It's a deal," you tell him.

The chef starts the skimmer at the sixth attempt. The engine sounds OK once it's running, and you twist the control to start it coasting away from the building. The chef is surprised that you're so satisfied. You're just looking forward to seeing how Fett is going to follow you into the desert...

Go to 419

416

The communications officer proves to be a greater handful than you expected. Having made a mess of your own attack, you are felled as he pulls his blaster from its holster and fires. You slide to the floor, and feel your strength ebbing away.

Could things get any worse?

Boba Fett has appeared, and is staring down at you from out of a dark shadow. "It's Havet Storm, Lord Vader – the boy I was talking to you about." Who's he talking to? You realise that the shadow is moving, taking the shape of a giant of a man, a nightmare in black. His voice echoes in your mind. "How did he get on board my flagship? Why is he here?" A large black hand reaches out, grasping your neck. You feel your pulse under his fingertips, fading fast. "I... sense something in this boy... something I have felt so rarely in recent times."

His face, like a shining ebony skull, is thrust into yours. "A Jedi...!" he whispers.

You have been defeated. How could you have handled things differently? Perhaps you could start again with a different character. Return to the beginning of the book

417

"Havet!" What the –? That voice came from inside the ship. And surely it was...

"Surna?" You try to see further into the ship's entrance. "Is that you?" The voice doesn't reply for a moment, while you hesitate on the ramp. You're at the point of thinking you imagined it when the same voice hisses again. "Of course it's me you dope! Get on here!" You take a few slow steps up the ramp, stopping once you are at the top of the ramp, standing on some metal grilles on the floor. The circular passage stretches away, all the bulkhead doors closed. So where...? "Down here, you idiot!" You look down, trying to see into the area under the grilles. You can just about make out a pale face and a pair of bright eyes. "Surna – is it really you?! What on earth are you doing hiding down there?"

"Keep your voice down! I saw *Slave I* land. I was left here on guard, and I didn't want to meet up with Boba Fett. I still don't – so just get off this ship and pretend that there's no-one aboard, OK? There's no point me hiding if you're going to shout about it to all and sundry!" If you hadn't believed it before, there's no doubt in your mind now. It's Surna, alright. "I'm pleased to see you too. How did you get here?" She makes a dark face back at you. "Not now! Just shut up and listen, you moron. Is Boba Fett anywhere close by?" You look back, but of course you can't see anything. "I can't be sure," you reply. "Then we'd better make this quick. Do you know what ship you're on? It's Han Solo's *Millennium Falcon*." You knew that... "Is he here?"

"No," she replies, her voice even lower. "He's out in the desert. You have to go and find him." She's not the only one with that idea. "I don't understand..." you say, but Surna cuts you off with a sharp word. "Not now! I'll explain properly later. Just get out of here, and find Solo." You stand still, desperate for answers. "Please, Havet! Go now! Everything depends on you doing this right. Go, stupid!" You nod, and step away from the grille onto the ramp, thinking about everything she's said – and all the things she hasn't. Four words stick firmly in your mind. Dope, idiot, moron and stupid. "It's good to see you again, Surna," you tell her. She growls in frustration. "Get going! Oh – Havet! – don't believe everything you see. I don't want you getting killed for something that isn't real." What does that mean? You stop, as if you were going to carry on the discussion, but Surna urges you to leave yet again. You step down the ramp, and back out into the harsh, bright light of Marranis.

OK. Find Solo. Don't believe everything you see. Don't get killed. Sound advice, all. You walk towards the restaurant while you try to make sense of it all.

Go to 420

418

Fett goes on. "I too have my quest. There is a young man who has thwarted me on many occasions. I must, one day, end his life." Vader scoffs. "One man? The great bounty hunter, frightened of a callow youth?" Hey, not so much of the callow, bucket-head! What does callow mean, anyway? You'll have to check Arf's dictionary when you get a chance. "Not frightened, Lord!" snaps Fett. "But I believe he has special powers, powers which make him as great a danger to you as to me. I believe he is a Jedi!" Vader stiffens, then his hand snakes out to grip Fett by the shoulder. The bounty hunter buckles under the pressure. "A Jedi?!" gasps Vader. "Impossible! I would have known... I would have sensed!... What is his name?"

"Storm..." grunts Fett. "Havet Storm..." Vader ponders. "Storm! There was once a Jedi Knight named Morvet Storm. One of the last of his kind – I killed him, and his crippled son. Could there have been another, a grandson?" He pauses for a moment. "No, it's not possible. If there was another Jedi, I would have sensed it, just as I did at Tatooine two years ago... The Jedi have a code of honour, truth and decency which smells like a rotten plant to anyone trained in the Force. I would have sensed your Havet Storm if he were a Jedi."

"I could be wrong," admits Fett, "Either way, Havet Storm must die." Vader releases his grip on the bounty hunter. "Yes. Make sure that he does. One troublemaker in the galaxy is enough. You deal with Storm; I have Luke Skywalker to contend with."

Vader turns, and leaves along one of the cross-passages. Fett massages his shoulder through his armour, and opens the door. He watches Vader for a few moments, then heads back towards his ship. You follow. For a moment, you are seized with panic, wondering what will happen if Fett reaches *Slave I* ahead of you and closes the outer hatch, but you get lucky. He pauses in the ready room to talk to a crewman, and you manage to slip across the landing bay and onto the ship. Your breath shivers in your chest as you consider what you have been told.

Read 628

Go to 371

The sand skimmer hisses lightly over the desert. It took a few minutes for you to get used to the controls – steering the skimmer across the slopes of the tall dunes is a particularly difficult job – but by the time you got out of sight from the landing field, you started making a reasonable job of it. The skimmer has a low top speed, but you don't need speed. If Solo just wandered out into the wastes, he can't have gone too far. What possessed him to walk, anyway? Couldn't he have just hired one of the skimmers like you have? Surely he's not broke...

You make a few wide half circles, pushing further out into the desert. You wonder about these "wraiths" the chef spoke of. You've never believed in ghosts, but you have seen plenty of strange creatures on alien worlds, so you know better than to take the comment as a joke. You'd prefer not to find out.

The uniform grey sand is occasionally stirred by a slow breeze, but otherwise all you can feel is the fierce heat of the sun. The temperature gauge on the skimmer climbs steadily. Heat haze rises from the flanks of the dunes, rippling the air. What a place! It's almost baking you alive!

It doesn't do the skimmer a lot of good either. With a mechanical sigh, the engine gives out, and the skimmer sinks into the sand. Perfect! Now you're stranded out here! You try to start it a couple of times, but nothing stirs. You step off the back, and aim a kick at the vehicle's flank, but even this applied technique doesn't get it going again. It looks like you'll have to walk, and hope that you meet up with someone soon –

At the moment that you look up, you see movement ahead of you. To one side of a tall, heavy dune, there are two figures walking heavily through the sand, moving obliquely towards you. You can't see them clearly because of the heat haze, but one is a large, hairy individual; the other a human in a white shirt and dark trousers. Solo? Isn't he supposed to have a Wookiee companion? You halt the skimmer, and shield your eyes from the sun as you take a longer look.

Another movement flickers in the corner of your eye. Two shapes have appeared over the crest of a nearer dune, moving almost directly towards you. They are vaguely man-shaped, one taller than the others, but the light is too intense in that direction to make them out. What can they be? A strange kind of "shadow", thrown into the air by the two walking at the foot of the dune? A mirage? Or... ghosts?

If you head towards the two shapes nearest you, go to 422

If you steer towards the two walking at the foot of the dune, go to 427

If you do nothing, go to 432

420

Just like every fast-food franchise at every spaceport in the galaxy, the restaurant here is a dimly-lit (so you can't see the food), noxious (so you can't *smell* the food) slum crewed by hopeless incompetents (so you can't order the food). You feel right at home. The Star Racers have been "chilled" in a cabinet right above the griddle, so you order a malt drink and a sandwich instead. When the food arrives, it keeps its identity pretty secret. Still, it's better than nothing, and since you don't have any money to pay for it…

There are maybe three customers in the place, just counting those who are awake. Someone is lying on the floor, seemingly unconscious. There's another guy dressed in a fur coat and a hat! He can't be a local boy! Several others are sleeping something off – you just hope it isn't food poisoning. The "chef" is writing out a new copy of the menu. Worryingly, he is using the soup as ink.

"Excuse me," you interrupt. "I –" His head snaps upright. You notice the sneaky eyes at once, along with the fact that he has a large open sore on his long snout. You take another hard look at your sandwich, and lose your appetite. "Whaddya want?" he barks. "Can't ya see I'm tryinta write?" Oh, so that's what it is. He wipes his sleeve across his nose – oh, *please!* You push the sandwich even further away.

"I'm looking for Han Solo," you announce. "He's not here," he ripostes. Man, he's way too sharp for you… "You want to tell me where he is?" He squints at you again, hesitating over the spelling of "beef". You smile back at him. "B-A-R-F" you tell him. He writes it down, then looks at the word. He's not stupid, he can see it's wrong. He adds another "f" and then he's happy. "He mightn't wanna be found," he says, standing back to admire his handiwork. "If you was with the Empire…" He manages to say this in a way which could as easily be followed by "…that would be the best news he's had all day" as "…that would be as welcome as fleas at a Wookiee convention."

"Fact is, tho'" your host continues. "He isn't around. He made tha' big mistake of goin' out into tha' desert alone." That's bad news, right? "It's an even split whether tha' wraiths got 'im or he died o' thirst." Wraiths? Is he talking about *ghosts?*

If you decide to check out the desert, and you have checked 627, go to 408

If you go out into the desert and you *haven't* checked 627, go to 414

421

Well, there's no sign of life aboard the ship, and it's unlikely that Han Solo would just be hanging around here. He must have seen *Slave I* land if he were close by, and he would know Fett's ship well. So, Solo is unlikely to be here, which leaves just a few alternatives. He could be in the "town" – the collection of small buildings some distance away – or out in the desert. Either way, it seems that the best place to start your search will be in the restaurant.

Go to 420

422

You head up towards the crest of the nearby dune, where the ghostly shapes are hanging in the air, moving gradually towards you, shadowing the slow progress of the two figures struggling along below them. There's no way you can really hide your progress from them; if they have eyes to see, they will mark your approach easily.

You get closer, and they take on more solid shape. You can hardly believe it – it's Surna's brother, Tann, and Al the Alchemist! Al waves as you clamber up the soft slope. You try to call, but your throat is dry. Finally, you reach the crest of the rise. Al is just twenty paces away from you, large as life and twice as ugly. How did he get here? Before you can voice a question, Al speaks. "Havet! It's good to see you. You're just in time – we've found the Rebel base, and we're on our way there now. Come with us! I think we've finally made it!"

If you go with Tann and Al, go to 433

If you demand an explanation now, go to 429

423

OK, so you'll walk. If you're sensible, how dangerous can it be? Well, within about thirty minutes of leaving the spaceport, you are starting to find out. Do all heroes have this problem? Would Luke Skywalker allow himself to get stuck out on some barren, lifeless landscape? Probably not..

The heat is tremendous. You feel it sapping your strength with every step. Worse, the rising haze distorts your vision, and you quickly lose sight of the spaceport. You climb to the top of another dune, wondering if you shouldn't turn back along the line of your own footsteps straight away, before the slight breeze blows them away, and then you see them. To one side of a tall, heavy dune, there are two figures walking heavily through the sand. You can't see them clearly because of the heat haze, but one is a large, hairy individual; the other a human in a white shirt and dark trousers. Solo? Isn't he supposed to have a Wookiee companion? You halt, and shield your eyes from the sun as you take a longer look.

Read 630

If you steer towards the two walking at the foot of the dune, go to 427

If you do nothing, go to 432

424

Your attempt to defeat these strange apparitions was doomed to failure.

Return to the start of the book, and begin your adventure again.

425

Unable to defeat the strange guards, you fall lifelessly to the sand.

You were so close! Perhaps next time?...

426

It had to come to this, of course. Fett has been your greatest enemy for some time. It's just a pity you couldn't beat him when it counted.

Start from the beginning again. Perhaps you missed a few vital clues along the way?

427

Stumbling through the deep sand, you make your way towards the two figures at the foot of the large dune. You lose sight of them for a moment as they make their way behind another rise in the barren landscape, but you quickly close the gap, and hail them. They stop and look back – and you halt also. The duo are not alone.

Just how you missed the others before is a mystery. There are three tall humanoids in white robes, their faces masked by plain metal plates into which are set narrow lenses. They carry long, barbed lances. They have formed a loose ring around the two figures you were following, and watch closely as you approach warily. The distance narrows, and you come face to face with a weary-looking human, his face showing the strain of walking through the desert, and a tall, powerful Wookiee, his fur matted with sand. Surely it has to be –

"Are you Han Solo?" you ask. The weary human, his hands on his knees as he fights for breath, lifts his head and squints at you. "You... looking for Solo, kid?" You nod, taking another quick glance at the guards, who haven't moved. "Got any water?" asks the man. "If you've got some water to spare, I could tell you where to find Solo." You shake your head. He sighs heavily. "Oh, well. Not that thirsty anyhow. Maybe later."

"But you are Han Solo, right?" He straightens up, staggering a little. The Wookiee utters a faint wailing noise. "For the next half hour or so, maybe," the man replies. "State your business, kid! If you want to hire the *Millennium Falcon*, I'm offering really good rates right now. All you got to do is get me out of this mess, and I'll fly you anywhere you like. Special rates. Hey, I'll cut you an even better deal than the one that got me into this mess in the first place. Remember, Chewie? Hey?! Did Luke ever give us the money for that trip from Tatooine?" The Wookiee growls again. "You're right, it doesn't matter."

"Um," you start, trying to get Solo's attention. "What's going on here?" Solo indicates the guards with a wide sweep of his arm. "Ask these guys. They jumped us out in the desert. Took our weapons. Don't know what it's all about, or where they're taking us... What about you?" This could be interesting. "I came looking for you. Um

– Boba Fett is trying to find you, and I kind of –"

"Fett?" wheezes Solo. "You're working for Fett? I thought you'd come to rescue me, but I'd sooner wander around the desert all day with these three than surrender to that mercenary trash." You know the feeling. You start to offer a fuller explanation, but a lower growl from Chewbacca warns you that the time for talking is over. The guards are closing in.

If you attack the guards, go to 434

If you try to evade their attack, go to 432

428

You wander deeper into the desert.

Read 630

Go to 433

429

"Al – wait!" you call, but the ex-tavern keeper doesn't stop. You chase after him – there are so many questions you need to have answered! "How did you get here? What's going on?" Al moves easily along, and gives you a familiar smile. "You want to see Surna?" he asks. "She's just up ahead." You grab his arm. "Wait! I have to know what's happening! Fett is here somewhere. He's come to find Solo, and the Rebel base. If we don't stop him…"

Al grins. "Don't worry about Fett. If the wraiths don't get him, then we will, right?" Anger rises inside you. Doesn't Al understand what you're saying? "Al – is this real? Is this really happening?" He touches your hand, where it grips his arm. He pulls your fingers loose. "It isn't a mirage, is it?" he asks, mockingly. "Look, just come and meet Surna. She's much better at explaining these things than I am. And the Rebel base isn't far. You worry too much, Havet!"

You can't shake your misgivings. Perhaps – "Al! What's my favourite drink?" He laughs. "Star Racer!" he replies. "You want one? They have a huge stock of the stuff at the base."

If you go with Al and Tann to the rebel base, go to 428

If you try to make them stop, go to 440

430

Solo is impressed with the way you defeated the guards. "Nice trick, kid. Reminds me of someone else... I'll have to tell you about it sometime." You look around, trying to get your bearings. "It's not over yet. We still have Boba Fett on our tail. And we have to get back to the spaceport, if I can just find the way."

But what is the right way? In all the excitement, you're not sure you can even find the trail of your own footprints. You wander off a short distance, trying to find them.

Go to 432

431

The fighting ends suddenly. You collapse to your knees, fighting for breath. What possessed you to attack your friends? A great weight fills your heart, and you find it difficult to stand up. "I'm sorry..." you whisper.

Looking around, you can just about make out the hazy shapes of the other group, the man and the tall, furry humanoid moving away from you in the distance. You run after them, closing the gap rapidly as you tumble down the slope of the dune. Picking yourself up, you prepare to hail them. Then you stop yourself. Should you call? After all, if Fett hears you, and you're right about the man in the white shirt being Han Solo... In fact, should you risk even going over to him, seeing as you might just be bringing Solo's death closer?

If you go over towards the two figures, go to 427

If you stay where you are, go to 432

432

"Storm." The voice comes from somewhere behind you, and even in the fierce heat of the desert it chills you to the depths of your soul. You turn very slowly. Boba Fett has come up on you like a ghost. Behind him, you can see his sand skimmer, idling quietly. You try to surpress a desire to look back over your shoulder. Too late. Fett has already seen the others.

"You've found him, then. I knew you would. Come on, I want to get a little closer."

He pushes you ahead. You walk the last few metres over to where Solo is sitting, nursed by his Wookiee companion, Chewbacca. The Wookiee growls a warning, and starts towards Fett, recognising his friend's worst enemy. Fett cuts him down without another thought. He pushes you to the ground. One one side of you, Solo looks up with tired, dry eyes, his breath short and rasping. On the other, Fett levels his blaster rifle.

"I almost can't believe this is true," says the bounty hunter. His delight is evident. "After all this time, here you are." Solo coughs dryly, and laughs. "Won't Jabba be pleased. Fact is, though, I don't think I'm fit enough to make it back." Fett tilts his head, pondering this. "Playing for sympathy, Solo? Waste of time. It doesn't matter to me if you can't make it – in fact, I prefer it like this. I can tell Jabba where to find the *Falcon*, and I can tell him that you are dead. He ought to be happy enough with that." Fett raises his rifle.

"So long, Solo," he murmurs…

If you attack Fett, go to 437

If you remain still, go to 438

433

You follow your comrades from Toprawa through the desolate wastes. They seem to be moving easily, whereas your strength is fading fast. "Do you have any water?" you ask. "'Fraid not," replies Al. "Still, it's not far now." You go on, another few paces pulled out of the depths of your reserves. "Why did the Rebels pick this place for their base?" Al looks back, his face sharp with impatience. "Don't talk! Walk!"

If you keep going, go to 428

If you stop to demand an explanation, go to 429

434

The desert-dwellers close in, looking menacingly at you. You could flee, but you can't leave Solo in their hands. You make ready to fight.

Read 631 and use the combat rules from the beginning of the book. Record this paragraph number so you can find your way

back here

If you defeat the guards, go to 430

If you lose, go to 425

435

For a long time, you just sit there, trying to think, wondering whether you'll die of thirst before you understand what has happened. There doesn't seem to be a lot of point trying to find your way back to the spaceport. After all the frantic action of the last few minutes, your trail has been completely obscured, and whatever orientation you had is lost.

You hear an engine, and then a skimmer appears over a nearby dune, bearing a small pilot. It draws up nearby. The driver points at the pillion seat, and you clamber on board automatically. If this is a mirage, it at least has a familiar smell of hot metal and lubricant., and its engine noise is reassuringly rough. The skimmer turns back the way it appeared from, and you are whisked back across the desert, away from the scene of your... defeat.

It takes just a few minutes for the spaceport to come into view, appearing out of the haze as if it had been hidden by mirrors. The skimmer roars into the yard behind the restaurant. The pilot kills the engine, and steps from the saddle. You sit still and watch. The pilot lifts small hands to the wide bandage of cloth tied over mouth and nose, gradually unwinding it to reveal... "Surna. Is it really you?" She catches the flatness in your tone. "Hey! Why so sad? I thought you'd be pleased to see me again!" You lift yourself off the skimmer. "I am, believe me, but I don't think you'll be so pleased when you hear what a foul up I made of things." She grins. "Maybe. First things first. You need a long, cold drink, and some explanation."

She leads the way into the restaurant. The chef is there fussing over the tables. Surna leads the way over to a booth, and signals to the chef for some spiced fruit drinks – and lots of ice. He takes about a year and a half to bring the stuff, or at least that's how long your thirst reckons it as. You drink most of the jug before Surna can even sip from her first glass.

"OK," you sigh, sitting back in the chair, and allowing the cool liquid to settle inside you. "What's this all about?" Surna smiles, and plays with the rest of her drink while she collects her thoughts, swilling the ice round in the glass. "Well," she begins. "You remember the last time we saw each other…"

If you have checked 585 or 595, go to 442

If you have checked 593, go to 443

If you have checked 603, go to 444

436

Fett reels away from your attack, tumbling across the sand. He's wounded, but he'll live to fight another day. You wonder for a moment if he'll continue the fight – after all, this is his first chance to get both you and Solo in one battle – but he continues to retreat.

Looking back, you realise why. That first shot Fett fired missed you, but hit Solo. There's not much doubt about it. Solo has been killed by the bounty hunter. Fett calls across the sand. "You were always small fry compared to Solo, Havet Storm. I've gained the victory I wanted. You're too much of a loser to bother with." He disappears into the haze, and you hear him rev up his skimmer and depart.

Read 637

If you have checked any of these paragraphs – 585, 593, 595 or 603 – go to 435

If not, go to 439

437

"No!" you yell, leaping into the space between Fett and Solo. Fett reacts immediately, training his awesome array of weapons at you.

Read 634, and use the combat rules from the beginning of this book. Make a note of this paragraph number so you can find you way back.

If you defeat Boba Fett, go to 436

If he defeats you, go to 426

438

It all seems to happen in a kind of terrible slow motion. Fett levels his weapon at Solo and fires.

If you have checked any of these paragraphs – 585, 593, 595 or 603 – go to 435

If not, go to 439

439

The shock jolts your insides. Looking behind you, you see Solo slumped back against the wall of the dune. Your knees almost buckle under you, as you wait for your turn.

As you return your gaze to Boba Fett, you see that the bounty hunter has shouldered his weapon. He is looking at the body. "You know," he says, "that wasn't as satisfying as I thought it would be. I've dreamed of the day when I would have Solo in my sights…" He shrugs. "Well, I'm not going to suffer two disappointments in one day. I'm going to let you live, Storm." He steps back, watching you carefully in case you make some impulsive attempt to stop him. "All I ask is that you make a better job of dying than he did." And with those mocking words, he turns away, and heads back towards his sand skimmer, leaving you with the bitter taste of failure in your mouth.

You were actually much closer to winning than you might think. Return to the beginning of the book, and give it another go. You'll do a lot better if you handle the first part of the game efficiently. Make sure you do all you can to help the Rebels on Toprawa.

If you really can't face the prospect of playing through the whole book again, read 638

440

"No!" you shout, halting. "This is all wrong. You can't be here! I don't believe it!" You turn, but you freeze before you take a step. Surna is standing there, blaster pistol in her hand. How did *she* get here? "We can't let you leave us, Havet. If you're right about Boba Fett, he could lead the Imperial forces here. You have to come with us."

If you agree to do as she says, go to 433

If you attack them, go to 441

441

Has the heat finally got to you? Your instincts are screaming inside your mind – this isn't what it seems to be! – but surely you can't draw a weapon on Surna and the others…

Read 632 and use the combat rules from the beginning of the book. Record this paragraph number so you can find your way back here

If you defeat your friends, go to 431

If you lose, go to 424

442

"Of course," you reply. "On Toprawa, at the spaceport. You guys escaped on the *Rust Bucket*. I ended up on Boba Fett's ship." Surna nods. "We knew. Tann has the *Bucket* rigged up to listen in on all kinds of Imperial frequencies. They were very excitable about our escape, as you can imagine, and we wanted to monitor what they were telling the fleet. Of course, you had taken care of that, hadn't you?" Naturally. There was little point in taking off from Toprawa if the necessary clearance to pass through the blockade hadn't been obtained. "So, as we escaped, we heard the ground staff on Toprawa say you had been taken aboard *Slave I*. There didn't seem to be anything we could do, so we flew on to Yavin, hoping to make contact with the Alliance.

"Imagine our surprise when Fett turns up while we were in orbit. Tann figured it out straight away – Fett had covered the ship in tracers, so that he could follow us." So, the bounty hunter's plan had got him as far as Yavin, but no further. "We stripped the ship clean while you were on the surface, then did the only thing possible with all the bugs…" Which was? "We put them on Fett's ship, and followed him for a change. We saw you rendezvous with the Imperial ship, and then come here. While *Slave I* was in orbit, checking the place out, we came straight down to the surface and found the *Millenium Falcon* sitting here. No-one aboard. I hid on the *Falcon* hoping you'd

468

come along so I could warn you. Then we just had to hope we could find Han Solo before Fett did, or that you could stop him."

Go to 446

443

"Of course," you reply. "On the *Nunchaka*, that Imperial warship above Toprawa. We were captured. Fett took me off, and told the captain to let you go. Are you trying to tell me that's what happened? That the Empire just let you go?" Surna laughs, and throws her hands wide in a gesture that says she knows it doesn't sound possible. "We left the *Nunchaka*, and set off for Yavin, hoping to pick up some contact with the Alliance. Imagine our surprise when Fett turns up while we're in orbit. Tann figured it out straight away – Fett had covered the ship in tracers, so that he could follow us. He must have planned the whole thing – our escape and everything – while we were still on Toprawa, just so he could follow us and see if we led him to the new Rebel base." Instead, the bounty hunter's plan had got him as far as Yavin, but no further. "We stripped the ship clean while you were on the surface, then did the only thing possible with all the bugs…" Which was? "We put them on Fett's ship, and followed him for a change. We saw you rendezvous with the Imperial ship, and then come here. While *Slave I* was in orbit, checking the place out, we came straight down to the surface and found the Millenium Falcon sitting here. No-one aboard. I hid on the *Falcon* hoping you'd come along so I could warn you. Then we just had to hope we could find Han Solo before Fett did, or that you could stop him."

Go to 446

444

"Of course," you reply. "On Yavin. I went after Fett and we got separated." Surna laughs. "Separated? You jumped back aboard his ship! We had some trouble explaining that, I can tell you." Explaining it to who? "The Rebel Alliance, dummy! Those salvage-hunters on Yavin Four were really Rebel agents, making sure nothing had been left behind. We used that transmission frequency you were given, and called for help. The contact wasn't prepared to believe us at first, and he wasn't happy that you seemed to be hitching a ride with a bounty hunter, but the fact that it was Boba Fett meant that word got passed down the line, and someone contacted Han Solo. Apparently he's real anxious to keep tabs on Fett's whereabouts. So, we were given instructions to come here."

"How did you get off Yavin?!" Surna laughs. "We hitched a ride with the salvage-hunters! We arrived here yesterday, and started cooking up our plan." Which was? Surna grins, leaning right back in her chair. She's enjoying herself. "You're going to love this, Havet."

"Solo is here checking out a possible site for the new Rebel base, right? Only Marranis is wholly unsuitable. It's all rock and sand – any base would be easily visible. And there's the wraiths. They are the local lifeform. They're kind of like energy-based shape-shifters; they read your mind, and show themselves in whatever form their victims are most likely to react to. Then they get you to follow them deeper into the desert, until you die of thirst. They feed off the dead body. Gruesome, right?" Right.

"So, Solo and Chewbacca have been captured by these things. We arrive in the nick of time, and rescue them. We tell Solo our news – about you and Fett and everything. He tells us how he has to get Fett off his back. And so –" And so? "You arrive, and we cook up a plan. The guy who owns this place is a pretty uncooperative character, but Chewbacca makes him see sense." She turns in her seat and calls to the chef. He wanders over. "Show him," says Surna. The guy reaches up behind his head, and tugs at his flesh (YECCH!). It slowly peels back to reveal…

"Al!" The Alchemist looks back at you. "Great disguise, huh? It sure fooled Fett. When I picked off a few bits of flesh, he went right off his food. Couldn't get out into the desert fast enough." Your head is reeling, trying to make sense of all this. "But why? What were you trying to achieve?" Surna continues. "Fett wanted you to find Solo. We had to make sure you went out into the desert believing you would find him." And you did, didn't you? "Don't you get it, Havet? The wraiths read your mind, and took the information that was there. What you saw out in the desert was –"

An illusion! A trick created by the wraiths to lure you out into the desert. And the illusion you saw – "Fett saw the same thing," Surna says, finally helping you see through the deception. "The wraiths got into his mind too. He thinks he killed Han Solo." Then where is the real…? The guy spawled on the floor gets up, and walks over to the table. "Hi. My name's Han Solo. It's good to meet you, Havet."

Go to 445

"So, nothing that happened out there was real," you say as it all sinks in. "Everything was an illusion." Solo grins. He is watching as the man in the hat and the fur 'coat' strides over from the other table. Chewbacca, Solo's Wookiee companion. "You were real, and Boba Fett was real," says Solo. "Nothing else. He thinks he's killed me, so he'll be out of our hair for a while. Sure, he'll find out he's been had sooner or later, but I've bought some time. By the time he does catch up with me, maybe the Alliance will have its new base somewhere."

"Couldn't you have just – you know – taken him out?" you ask. That would have been your preference. "It's better this way. Jabba the Hutt would have just hired someone else, and we would have had the Empire sniffing around as well, wondering what I was doing in this quadrant. And there are a few more worlds I want to check out. The search goes on!"

You have started laughing, and you can't stop. "You have no idea what I felt like!" you shout. The others are all laughing too. "So, kid. What are you going to do? I owe you and your friends a big debt. If Surna hadn't called, I really would have been wandering out in the desert when you and Fett arrived. Anything I can do to help, just ask."

It doesn't take a moment's thought. "We want to help the Rebellion. Can you –?" Solo claps you on the back again – even harder than before. "Consider it done. I'll introduce you to Luke Skywalker. I have a feeling you two have a lot in common." He stands up, hitching his belt. "So – you coming with me?"

"Just try and stop me!" you grin, and you rise up to walk out of the restaurant. The sun is as hot as ever, but who cares? You're finally going to be able to start doing some real damage to the Empire. Maybe you can finally come to terms with your Jedi inheritance, and start using your power constructively.

And you'll finally meet this Skywalker character you've heard so much about. Just the thought of it makes you turn to Solo as you walk across the landing field towards the *Falcon*. "So, what's Skywalker like?" you ask. "Is he as big a hero as they say? Only on Toprawa, I heard…"

That's it! You've done it! Congratulations on finishing *The Bounty Hunter*. Look out for more books in this exciting series.

"Instead of which, we got Solo killed. Seems to me that isn't the best result, Surna. I think Solo is an important part of the Rebellion. Who knows what damage we have done?" Surna waits for a moment, reflecting. "I don't see what else we could have done, Havet. Solo came here to see if Marranis could be used as a Rebel base. No-one here was prepared to help him, so he went out into the desert with Chewbacca unaided. He was already in trouble before we got here. There's a life-form that lives out in the desert – they're called wraiths. They can read minds, and create perfect images out of their own bodies of people you know. You go out into the desert, someone tells you to follow them, and you're never seen again. Spooky stuff. My guess is that they captured Solo, and that we were lucky to find him." Lucky! Out of the frying pan, into the fire more like. You brought Fett right to him.

You sit in the restaurant with Surna for a while longer, wondering about what happened. Then she stands up. "Come on. It's time we were leaving. Let's meet up with Tann and get out of here." After a few more moments, you rise and follow her to the door. "You know, I wonder if any of this was real. Perhaps the wraiths created it all." Surna smiles, and moves on. You look up into the sky. Out there somewhere, the Rebellion goes on, and Fett is gloating over his success. Two good reasons for continuing the fight. The adventures of Havet Storm are not over yet.

Well, you've escaped from Boba Fett's clutches and rejoined your comrades, but that business with Han Solo went badly wrong, didn't it? Feel like trying the game again? If not, you can 'cheat' and find out just what the real solution is by turning to paragraph 444

"I need to find Surna," you tell Al, and you cross the bar, looking for her. You find your comrade in a booth in the far corner, sitting with her brother, Tann. She tilts her head back. "See the guy in the booth behind me?" she asks. You take a squint. "He's Holrga. T'blisk's contact."

If you have checked any of these paragraphs – 553, 559, 561, 563 or 565 – go to 148

If you have checked none of them, go to 449

448

The victory is easily won.

Which weapon did you use? If you used your lightsabre, check 571

Go to 163

449

"The guy you need to see about Tann's ship, right?" you ask. She nods, replying: "not that it makes any difference at the moment, seeing as we don't have the credits to pay off Tann's debt." You ask her if she wants to try getting them – if you could get your hands on Tann's ship, it would be the first step towards getting off Toprawa. "It'd be risky," she says.

If you want to try and earn enough credits to retrieve Tann's ship from T'blisk, go to 98

If you want to try and escape Toprawa without the money, go to 122

DATA BANK

501

One of your most treasured possessions is "Arf", the small K9-series droid your grandfather left for you. "Arf" runs on batteries, and moves smoothly on small repulsorlifts. He's about 40 centimetres long, and has a box-like body. His head is filled with micro-processors allowing him to "think". He is voice-activated, obeying only your commands. He has a sound recorder in his ears, and can playback at your command. He has a short video record function, using his eye-cameras, which you can play-back onto a blank surface (like a wall).

His body is hollow, with a small access hatch hidden cunningly in the belly. A small panel on his back contains a DNA-sample reader, so that if you press your finger to it, the hatch pops open. This is how you first discovered your lightsabre, which grandfather had hidden in the droid's body. The droid's structure is cunningly formulated so that – in place – the lightsabre looks like part of its internal workings, which defeats all sensor scans or inspections.

You carry "Arf" round in the large pocket of your coat. He is light, and you wouldn't go anywhere without him.

Continue with your adventure

502

Arf has been damaged. Until you can make some repairs, he is inoperative.

Continue with your adventure

503

You are carrying your lightsabre, the weapon of a Jedi. Even though you are frightened of your Jedi heritage, and have promised yourself not to use your Jedi powers in case you are uncovered, you cannot bring your-self to get rid of the weapon your grandfather left for you.

In the hands of a properly-trained Jedi, the lightsabre is a powerful weapon. You have had to train yourself, but you think you know how to handle the weapon correctly.

The question is, dare you? Although the Jedi are rumoured to be extinct (something you know isn't quite true), there are plenty of people around with long memories of what they were like, and what the significance of a lightsabre is. On your belt, there is no way you can disguise it, but you can use it immediately if you get into trouble. If the wrong person catches a glimpse of it, however, you could be in serious trouble. You could carry it in Arf's secret belly-hatch instead, where it would be out of sight.

If you wish to change the location of the weapon, remove Check 503 and Check box 504 instead

In Combat, if you use your lightsabre, you must be Up Close. Add the score of one die roll to your Lightsabre skill to see if you hit your target. Normally, you need a score of 7 to hit the target

Add 1 to all attacking dice rolls when you use a lightsabre in Combat

Continue with your adventure.

504

You have stashed your lightsabre in Arf's belly-hatch. No-one will find it there. However, you can't get at it straight-away if there's a fight. On your belt, there is no way you can disguise it, but you can use it immediately if you get into trouble.

If you wish to change the location of the weapon, change the box you have ticked on your Character Sheet, and check box 503

Continue with your adventure

505

You are armed with a BlasTech DL-18 blaster, a civilian side-arm which you keep in a holster under your arm, where it is easy to get hold of. Carrying a weapon on Toprawa has been illegal since the attack on the Imperial Research Station.

In Combat, if you wish to use your blaster, you must be At Range. Add the score of one die roll to your Blaster skill to see if you hit your target. Normally, you need a score of 7 to hit the target

Continue with your adventure

506

You are armed with a Merr-Sonn Quick 6 Sporting Blaster, a lighter version of the standard blaster. It can slip into the pocket of your coat, or into the holster you wear under your arm, where it is easy to get hold of. It isn't going to do much harm to any armoured stormtroopers, but it's perfectly effective normally.

If you use the Quick 6 against an armoured opponent, you must subtract 1 from your die roll

Continue with your adventure

507

You are armed with a SoroSuub Redemptor; strictly Imperial service only, it is a specialist hold-out blaster, small enough to hide in the palm (although it can be equipped with an extending barrel, as this one is). It is almost silent in operation, its energy concentration being so pure.

You took the weapon from Diamond, the Emperor's agent on Toprawa It can be charged for a maximum of six shots, and you have no way of recharging it. Diamond used one shot to assassinate a Rebel spy. Did you or she fire it again? How many shots does the Redemptor have left? Keep a note beside the weapon's name in your Equipment Box.

You slip the weapon behind your belt. It would take a full search to find it there.

The Redemptor's power is so great that you need only score 6 to hit an opponent. With a blaster like this, a near miss is often enough!

Continue with your adventure

508

You are armed with a Merr-Sonn G8 blaster rifle, a popular Rebel weapon. It has more hitting power than your regular blaster. If you come across a circumstance in which you would suffer a penalty in trying to hit something because it is armoured, using the G8 reduces the penalty by one. So, you still need to score 7 to hit an unarmoured security guard, but only 8 (instead of 9) to hit a stormtrooper.

Return to your adventure

509

You have acquired an Imperial blaster rifle. It has more hitting power than your regular blaster. If you come across a circumstance in which you would suffer a penalty in trying to hit something because it is armoured, using the rifle reduces the penalty by one. So, you still need to score 7 to hit an unarmoured security guard, but only 8 (instead of 9) to hit a stormtrooper.

Return to your adventure

510

During the events which led up to you taking part in the assault on the Imperial Research Station, you made an enemy of Boba Fett, the most feared bounty hunter in the galaxy. You can't even remember what the argument was about – but you can bet he does.

Continue with your adventure

511

Last time you met Boba Fett, you wounded him in battle. Although his injuries weren't so severe that he didn't quickly recover, the rumour is that he isn't as good as he used to be.

Continue with your adventure

512

After all the action you have been involved in – not least the attack on the Imperial Research Station – you are a wanted man on Toprawa. The Imperials would dearly like to get you in their hands!

Continue with your adventure

513

Well, that was pretty easy, right? Did you keep a note of where you came from before you read this paragraph? OK, that's where you're going back to now.

Continue with your adventure

514

You have the plans the Rebels drew up to hide their base out in the wild forests of Toprawa. It would be a disaster if they fell into Imperial hands – many Rebel sympathisers have made their way out there already.

Continue with your adventure

515

You had to leave Kalkett behind at the Rebel HQ. By now, he'll either be dead or a prisoner. It's hard to say which is worse. Before you left, he gave you a message to take to his wife, Robinn. You promised to deliver it, no matter what it took.

Continue with your adventure

516

You rescued Kalkett from the attack on the Rebel HQ. Some of your comrades-in-arms took him away from the battleground. By now, he should be safe at home with his wife, Robinn. Perhaps you should check up on them before you leave Toprawa.

Continue with your adventure

517

You are in combat with five Imperial soldiers. The Combat starts At Range. All are armed with blaster rifles. They have Combat Skill 2, and need to score 7 to hit you or your fellow Rebels. When deciding who each soldier shoots at, roll your die. If you score a 1 or 2, you are the target; if you score 3-6, they shoot at one of the Rebels.

Three wounded Rebels are still fighting back. Each has a blaster, and they have Combat Skill 1 (because of their wounds). Like you, they need to score 7 to hit a soldier.

You can retreat from this Combat at any time instead of firing; go to 37

If you have already checked 514, return to your adventure when the combat is over

518

You are in combat with two Imperial soldiers. The Combat starts At Range. Both are armed with blaster rifles. They have Combat Skill 2, and need to score 7 to hit you.

If you defeat them, you can rescue Surna, who had barricaded herself in the Dining Hall. Check 519. Continue with your adventure

519

You have rescued your friend, Surna, from the Imperial forces. Along with some of the other Rebels, she has escaped the battle at the Rebel HQ.

Return to your adventure

520

You have gone into Combat with three Imperial soldiers to rescue Kalkett, the Rebels' Technical Officer. The Combat starts At Range. Kalkett is trapped under a piece of heavy machinery, and can't move. He has a blaster, and can fight back at Combat Skill 3. Like you, he needs to score 7 to hit one of the soldiers.

The Imperial soldiers are armed with blaster rifles. They have Combat Skill 2. Each time it's their turn to fire, roll a die. On a 1-3, they fire at you; on a 4-6, they fire at Kalkett. They need to score 7 to hit you, but, because Kalkett is such a sitting target, they need only 6 to hit him.

Continue with your adventure

521

Two Imperial soldiers are running off with the plans of the new Rebel hideout. You have to catch them!

The Imperial soldiers are armed with blaster rifles, and they have Combat Skill 2. Because they are running away, they can't aim so well, and they need to score 8 to hit you. You can't get Up Close; you just have to fire At Range and hope for the best.

After two rounds, they are joined by two more Imperial soldiers. You have to defeat all the soldiers you encounter to recover the plans.

If you give up the chase (which you can do instead of taking your turn), check 528 and go to 18

Otherwise, return to 5 when the combat is over

522

You have been wounded in the battle at the Rebel HQ. You must immediately spend 3 Jedi Power Points to accelerate the healing process on your wound, or reduce your Strength score by 1 until you can find a doctor who can heal you.

Go to 31

523

You have surprised the Imperial soldiers by attacking them from behind. In any Combats you encounter at the HQ Building, reduce the number of Imperial Soldiers you face by one. So, if the description says here are three soldiers, reduce it to two.

Go to 37

524

You have launched a frontal attack on the jail. The combat starts At Range.

There are three Rebels with you. Each has a blaster rifle,and Combat Skill 2. Because of the protection afforded to the Imperial security guards by the jail's walls, they (and you) need to score 8 to make a hit.

Six security guards are firing back. Each has a blaster rifle and Combat Skill 1. They need a 7 to hit. Use a die to decide who the target is. If you roll 1-2, you are the target; if you roll 3-6, one of the other Rebels is the target.

Fight one round of combat. If you survive, go to 534

If you are hit, go to 44

525

You have attacked the Imperial Officer. The combat can start At Range or Up Close; whichever you choose. You need to score a 7 to hit him.

If you hit him, go to 57

If you miss, go to 535

526

You're just about to leave the room when there is a thunderous explosion. The main doors of the HQ building have been blown in by a heavy blaster, and Imperial soldiers are pouring in! It's an assault – they've found you!

Shocked Rebels are trying to organise a fight-back. The odds are poor. Sooner or later, you're going to have to get out of here.

Return to 37

527

The last Imperial soldier falls. You can hear the sounds of serious fighting elsewhere in the building, but – for now – all is quiet here.

A wounded Rebel calls you over. It's Windward, a member of the General's staff. He hands you a small tube. "The plans... for the new hideaway..." he gasps. You realise he is badly injured. "You have to get... them out of here..." You promise to do all you can, and slip the tube into one of your pockets.

Is there anything you can do for Windward? It doesn't look like it. "Get me a blaster...?" he chokes, his face twisted with pain. "I'll take one more with me... before I go."

You give him the blaster, taken from one of the other fallen Rebels. "Good luck," you whisper. "Mine's all used up..." he says. "Just get those plans out of here." You head for the exit.

Check 514

Go to 37

528

The Empire has captured the plans for the new hideaway. The final collapse of Rebel resistance can't be far away.

Start a new Time Track (clear any ticks you have placed in here already). Tick 3 boxes. Write the number 530 in the last box. If you tick this box, read paragraph 530

Return to your adventure

529

You have programmed Arf for his part in your plan.

Return to your adventure

530

The Rebels on Toprawa have been overrun. The Imperials torture their prisoners to find out where you are, and what your plans might be. There's nowhere left you can hide, Havet.

Sooner or later the Imperial forces will capture you. Why wait? Start your adventure again now, by returning to paragraph 1

531

You are in combat with four Imperial soldiers in the Armoury. The Combat starts At Range. All of them are armed with blaster rifles. They have Combat Skill 2, and need to score 7 to hit you.

In the corner of the Armoury, Majerrit lies slumped over the E-Web. Instead of firing, or moving Up Close, you can use one of your turns to dive over to this weapon. The E-Web allows you to fire three times in a turn, instead of just once.

After two round of Combat, another three Imperial soldiers arrive. After four rounds, a further three arrive.

You can escape at any time instead of taking your normal Turn.

Return to your adventure

532

"I don't ever want to see you again," hisses Boba Fett. As far as you're concerned, it's a deal.

Return to your adventure

533

You are in combat with Boba Fett, in the shadow of his starship. The Combat starts At Range. Fett is armed with a Blaster Rifle, which he uses at Combat Skill 3 (not as sharp as he used to be). If the combat comes Up Close, he switches to his wrist lasers, which he uses at Combat Skill 2. He needs to score 7 to hit you. You don't have to worry about the Imperial guards; they know better than to get in his way.

You can attempt to run away instead of taking your normal move. If you run away, go to 78

Otherwise, return to paragraph 41 when the combat is over

534

You have crossed the open space in front of the jail, and reached the wall of the building. For a brief second, the firing stops. Then the guards counter-attack.

Add another six security guards to the survivors of the first round of Combat. All have Combat Skill 2. They spill out of the jail, so the good news is that you and the surviving Rebels only need a 7 to hit them.

If you feel the odds are too bad, you can use your Turn to run away instead of fighting. The security guards get one last chance to kill you before you escape.

If you run away, go to 11

Otherwise, return to 34

535

You bungled the attack on the Officer, and he has hit the alarm. Several security guards converge on the area while you try to finish off the Officer. They fire wide, trying to encourage you to give up, but not wanting to hit their own man. Several shots hit the side of the ship behind you.

There is a deafening roar of rage. A powerful-looking guy in antique armour is rushing from a ready room towards you.

Have you checked 510? If you have, go to 12

If not, go to 54

536

You can't believe your luck. You arranged to get yourself locked up with the express aim of freeing Surna from the vault, and now the Imperials have spirited her away!

Your plans are not working out too well, eh Havet? Now you have to rescue yourself!

Return to your adventure

537

You are in combat with Boba Fett, in the shadow of his starship. The Combat starts At Range. Fett is armed with a Blaster Rifle, which he uses at Combat Skill 4. If the combat comes Up Close, he switches to his wrist lasers, which he uses at Combat Skill 3. He needs to score 7 to hit you. You don't have to worry about the Imperial guards; they won't get involved.

You can attempt to run away instead of taking your normal move. If you run away, go to 117

Otherwise, return to paragraph 56 when the combat is over

538

You have the access codes from Boba Fett's ship stored in Arf's memory, which should allow you to get into the cells on his ship whenever you want – unless he's there to stop you, of course.

If you tell Surna about Fett's ship, go to 88

Otherwise, return to your adventure

539

Surna tells you that Tann has a gambling problem, and that he plays the tables in Al's cantina, along with some less friendly games in other parts of town.

Return to your adventure

540

You have cleared the departure of Tann's ship with ground control. That's one thing less to worry about. Now all you have to do is find a pilot, fuel and a way past the blockade. This escape isn't going to be easy, Havet.

Return to your adventure

541

You are completely disarmed.

Return to your adventure

542

You get a clear sense that Surna is in the vault somewhere behind the wall at the eastern end of the duct. The western end would be the safest place to set the charge.

Return to 82

543

You failed completely in your rescue bid. Who knows what has happened to Surna as a result of your mistake? As for getting off Toprawa, you can forget about any help from that direction now; you're on your own, Havet.

Return to 82

544

Trapped in your cell after the failure of your plan, you watch helplessly as, in the middle of the night, Surna is taken from her cell along with some of the other prisoners. Over an hour later, the Imperials come back for you.

This could be your only chance to escape. You must fight three security guards; the Combat starts Up Close. They are armed with blasters, and have a Combat Skill of 1. They hit you with a score of 7.

You, of course are unarmed. This means you have a Combat Skill of 1. You can't actually defeat a guard like this, but if you can score 7 (by rolling a six), you can take one of the security guards' blasters, and fight as normal.

If you manage this feat, 8 Rebel prisoners, each with a Combat Skill of 1 (unarmed) join in the fight, as do 3 more Security Troopers. The Rebels have to fight like you do – they must first grab a weapon if they are to actually defeat an enemy soldier. Once armed, each Rebel has a Combat Skill of 2. Roll a die to decide who each Imperial soldier fires at; if you roll a 1, you're the target; if you roll anything else, he fires at one of the other Rebels.

Check 536

If you win the battle and escape, go to 69

If you are hit, go to 93

545

You must fight four security guards; the Combat starts Up Close. They are armed with blasters, and have a Combat Skill of 1. They hit you with a score of 7. To decide who each Imperial fires at, roll a die. If you roll a 1, you're the target; otherwise the Trooper fires at another Rebel.

You have your lightsabre, of course. Six Rebel prisoners, each with a Combat Skill of 1 (unarmed) join in the fight on your side. Each Rebel must first grab a weapon (by rolling a 6) if they are to actually defeat an enemy soldier. Once armed, each Rebel has a Combat Skill of 2.

If you win the battle and you have checked 536, go to 69

If you win the battle but have not checked 536, go to 106

If you are hit, go to 93

546

You are in combat with Boba Fett. Now that you have moved away from his ship, he unleashes the full weight of his advanced weaponry on you. The Combat continues At Range. Fett employs his Concussion Grenade Launcher, which he uses at Combat Skill 3. With this weapon, he only needs to score 5 to hit you, because the grenade's explosion covers such a wide area. If you try to bring the combat Up Close, he uses his Flame Projector in the round in which you miss your Turn. He has Combat Skill 3 with this weapon, but needs only a 4 to hit (in other words, unless you use at least 1 Jedi Power Point, he *has* to hit you).

Only if you bring him Up Close does he switch to his wrist lasers, which he uses at Combat Skill 3. He needs to score 7 to hit you. This combat is bad news!

Return to paragraph 78 when the combat is over

547

You get a clear sense that Surna is in the vault somewhere behind the wall at either the western end or the centre of the duct. The eastern end would be the safest place to set the charge – but who knows what lies behind that?

Return to 83

548

You have been wounded by Boba Fett. You must spend 3 Jedi Power Points to help heal the wounds, or reduce your Speed and Lightsabre Combat scores by 1 until you can find proper medical assistance.

Return to 100

549

If Boba Fett was mad at you before, gunking him with lube like that is going to have made him *really* sore.

But it was worth it!

Go to 55

550

This could be your only chance to escape. You must fight three security guards; the Combat starts Up Close. They are armed with blasters, and have a Combat Skill of 1. They hit you with a score of 7.

You, of course are unarmed. This means you have a Combat Skill of 1. You can't actually defeat a guard like this, but if you can score 7 (by rolling a six), you can take one of the security guards' blasters, and fight as normal.

If you manage this feat, Surna and 6 other Rebel prisoners, each with a Combat Skill of 1 (unarmed) join in the fight, as do 3 more security guards. The Rebels have to fight like you do – they must first grab a weapon before they can actually defeat an enemy soldier. Once armed, each Rebel has a Combat Skill of 2. Roll a die to decide who each Imperial soldier fires at: if you roll a 1, you're the target; if you roll a 2, it's Surna; if you roll anything else, he fires at one of the other Rebels.

If you win the battle and escape, go to 106

If you are hit, go to 93

If Surna is hit, check 543 and go to 69

551

You managed to offend Surna, and to drive her away. She never wants to see you again.

Return to your adventure

552

You get a clear sense that Surna is in the vault somewhere behind the wall at either the western or the eastern end of the duct. The centre would be the safest place to set the charge to avoid Surna – although you can detect the auras of other people there.

Return to 84

553

You have about 2,000 credits of the 65,000 you need to get Tann's ship back from T'blisk.

554

Vain has the two cards he sneaked from his sleeve in his hand.

Return to your adventure

555

Vain has the card he sneaked from his sleeve in his hand. You removed the other one – but was it enough?

Return to your adventure

556

You detect Surna's aura very clearly. She is in the vault directly behind the wall at the western end of the duct. You're not sure what lies behind the other areas of the duct wall, but you know you *mustn't* set the charge off at the western end.

Return to 85

557

So far, so good – you have recovered Tann's ship. Now all you have to do is get into the spaceport, take off from an Imperial fortress, break through the blockade and you're home free.

Return to your adventure

558

The high-stake card game ends in a tragic fight. The combat starts At Range.

Pilliask is armed with a blaster, which he uses at Combat Skill 1.

Vain has a blaster in his pocket. In the first round, he pulls this out, so he can't fire back. He has Combat Skill 2 thereafter.

Groomert has a blaster in a shoulder holster. He too must spend the first round pulling the blaster from its place. He has Combat Skill 3, and wears body armour. This means you, Vain or Pilliask need to score 8 to hit him.

Even if you aren't directly involved, you can join in any combat on either side. You must first spend a round drawing your weapon. You may also use your Jedi Power Points to influence any die roll in this combat, whether you are involved or not.

If one of the other card players has a choice of two targets, use the die to pick one randomly.

Return to your adventure

559

You have nearly 20,000 credits of the 65,000 you need to get Tann's ship back from T'blisk.

Return to your adventure

560

You detect Surna's aura very clearly. She is in the vault directly behind the wall at the western end of the duct. The space behind the eastern end isn't actually part of the vault. So you need to attack the centre of the wall, behind which, if you read it correctly, the Imperials have their guard station.

Return to 86

561

You have 40,000 credits of the 65,000 you need to get Tann's ship back from T'blisk, money that you took from Jabba the Hutt's money-lenders.

Return to your adventure

562

The little guy who pushed past you sure seemed to be in a hurry. Perhaps the food in Al's cantina really has got worse.

563

You have all the money you need for Tann's ship.

Return to your adventure

564

The fight in the gambling den continues At Range.

Vain has a blaster, which he fires at Combat Skill 2.

Groomert also has a blaster, which he fires at Combat Skill 3. He wears body armour. This means you or Vain need to score 8 to hit him.

Even if you aren't directly involved, you can join in the combat on either Vain's or Groomert's side. You may also use your Jedi Power Points to influence any die roll in this combat, whether you are involved or not.

If one of the other card players has a choice of two targets, use the die to pick one randomly.

Return to your adventure

565

You have about 120,000 credits. More than enough for Tann's ship.

Return to your adventure

566

The tragedy in the gambling den has one last act to play. The combat continues At Range.

Vain has a blaster, which he fires at Combat Skill 2.

If you lose, go to 123

If you defeat Vain, go to 127

567

You have attacked the Imperial treasure convoy.

On your team, there is Surna and her brother Tann. Both have blaster rifles. Surna has Combat Skill 3; Tann has Combat Skill 2. They both hit Stormtroopers with a score of 8.

You may also have the aid of four other Rebels, armed with blaster rifles, who hit with a score of 8. If you split up your forces, however, they aren't here.

Your side fires first. Since it would be a disaster if Tann or Surna were killed, you have positioned yourself so that you can leap into combat Up Close straight away, while everyone else is At Range. That means you are the favourite target for the stormtroopers. They have their usual blaster rifles, and hit you with a score of 7. Since they start with Combat Skill 3, that means they have to roll just a 4 to hit! There are only three of them, of course, but even so...

After two rounds of combat, another six stormtroopers arrive in the back-up vehicle. Now, that really would be pushing things a bit.

One last thing. Fight the first round of combat, and then read one of the following:

If your attack takes place on Market Street, read 572

If your attack takes place on the Highway, read 577

If your attack takes place on the Hill Road, read 582

Return to your adventure

568

The patrolman has set off the alarm.

In any future combat against the Imperial forces at the Spaceport, you will face even more defenders than usual

Return to your adventure

569

Man! Even the old guy at the bar seems to know more about what's going on in your life than you do! It really is well past time you were off this planet!

Continue your adventure

570

The guard is armed with a blaster. The combat starts Up Close. He has Combat Skill 1.

If the combat lasts more than two rounds, the guard will hit the alarm anyway. If this happens, check 568

Continue your adventure

571

The guard falls silent. For the moment, you are alone, with no Imperial servants in sight. Taking a quick look around, you catch Surna's nervous chuckle, and Al's relieved sigh. Tann, on the other hand, is looking at you with a new expression of – what? Respect? Admiration? Fear?

"That's a lightsabre!" Oh, oh. "A *Jedi* lightsabre." Surna butts in before you can think of an answer. "You must have seen it before, Tann. Havet's been in more fights on Toprawa than he's had Star Racers." Tann still looks a little shocked. "I heard a few rumours… but…"

"So, what's the big deal?" asks Surna, urgently, convinced this discussion could take place at a better time. "It's a lightsabre – big deal. You found it, right, Havet?" That's the story you allowed to go round the limited circle of Rebels who knew about the weapon. "You don't just find a lightsabre!" shrieks Tann, clearly freaked. "It's a Jedi weapon. There's all kinds of mystic mumbo-jumbo attached to them; you can't just pick one up and wield it! You have to be a Jedi; you have to be *a Jedi!*"

Tann is pretty unsettled. All your life, people have run away when they have discovered that you carried the Jedi heritage; run away or come hunting for you. On Toprawa, the situation was so unsettled anyway that the Rebels ignored the question. Until now. "It isn't what you think," you tell Tann. "I know how evil the Jedi were, but I'm not like that, I just –"

"Evil?" Now Tann looks *really* confused. "You've got it wrong, Havet! The Jedi –" Surna breaks in, impatient to be moving on. "We can't deal with this now!" Or ever, if you have your way.

Continue your adventure

572

After four rounds of combat, a unit patrolling Market Street will arrive. Add another six stormtroopers to the enemy forces if the battle keeps going that long.

Return to 567

573

Greed and arrogance are uppermost in the Twi'lek's shallow mind. You allow your influence to sweep through him. There is no need to twist reality too severely; you can see what he wants to believe, and how easy it would be to convince him he has seen it.

Decide how many Jedi Power Points you will spend. Add this number to 190. This total is the number of the next paragraph you will read. So, if you spend 3 JPPs, you will go now to 193

574

You've made up your mind to leave Toprawa. You've let Al in on your plan – but it seems like the old guy sitting close by has heard most of it too. Why is it such hard work to keep a secret?

Continue your adventure

575

You have run into a little trouble with T'blisk. Although no-one's made a move yet, it's pretty clear he has rumbled the fact that you stole money from one of Jabba's operations to pay back another. Hmmm. Tricky to explain your way out of this.

If you open fire, the Combat begins At Range. Alongside you, Surna has Combat Skill 3; Tann has Combat Skill 2. They both have blasters, and make a hit with a score of 8.

In the room with you, there are five 'people'. T'blisk has a Combat Skill of 1 with a blaster, but uses his knife at Combat Skill 4. Holrga has Combat Skill 1. The three 'goons' on guard duty each have a Combat Skill of 2.

You can choose to go first or second. If you draw your weapon and

open fire immediately, go to 171

If you allow them to make the first move, go to 182

576

By opening fire, you have entered into a battle with T'blisk and his people. Use the information from **575** to fight the combat.

When the combat is over, return to 171

577

After two more rounds of combat, a unit based at a checkpoint on the highway will arrive. Add another six stormtroopers to the enemy forces if the battle is still going.

Return to 567

578

Your sense of guilt about the money grows very deep. You know you have done the wrong thing. Inside you, you feel the bright flame of the Force burn a little dimmer.

Reduce your starting score for Jedi Power Points by 1. Remember, you can never have more JPPs than your starting score. Don't adjust your current score if it is less than your starting score.

579

The old man is not an easy opponent. The Combat begins Up Close. You move first, but you must draw your weapon in the first round. The old man uses his rocket dart launcher at Combat Skill 3.

As an alternative to trying to hit him, you could try grabbing his weapon. Decide how many Jedi Power Points you will spend, and roll the die. If you spent the same number of JPPs as the number on the die, go to 181

If you spent more JPPs than the number on the die, go to 199

If you spent less JPPs than the number on the die, go to 210

If you engage in a normal Combat, complete the fight, and then return to 185

580

Boba Fett leads you up onto the roof. The flat surface is narrow, barely three or four metres across. On either side, there is a sheer drop to the street. He orders you to drop your weapons, and you obey. He removes his pack, and lowers his blaster rifle to the ground. "That pole beside you," he says, gesturing with his head. You bend and pick it up. It's a blunt-headed force pike. The metallic tip is wired to a powerful generator. Just scrape someone with the tip, and they'll feel like they have been standing in front of the exhaust valve on a TIE fighter.

You must fight Boba Fett using the force pike. One hit, and it's a long way down to the street. The combat begins Up Close, and Fett moves first. You have only Combat Skill 1 with the unfamiliar weapon; you need to score 7. Fett has Combat Skill 3.

Check 557

If he hits you, go to 216

If you hit him, go to 205

581

There are four crew members in the gun tower whom you must overcome. The combat starts At Range. The Officer has a blaster in a holster on his belt; he has Combat Skill 2. He must draw the weapon in the first round of the battle.

The other three Imperial soldiers have blaster rifles stacked against the wall. It takes them one round to run across the gun compartment to their weapons; they have Combat Skill 2 with them.

If you attempt to stop them getting their Blaster Rifles, you must miss either your first or second rounds, and read 586

Otherwise, complete the combat here, and then return to 187

582

No reinforcements can reach the remote Hill Road in time to affect this battle.

Return to 567

583

You have disabled the twin heavy blasters menacing Tann's ship.

Continue with your adventure

584

Having wrested the rocket dart launcher from the old man, you can now use it. The Combat continues Up Close; you may use the dart launcher at whatever your Blaster Combat Skill level is. The old man now has no weapon, but will reach into his cloak on the first round to pull out a standard blaster, which he uses at Combat Skill 3.

Return to paragraph 181

585

Tann, Surna and Al have escaped from Toprawa on the *Rust Bucket*. The relief is like a refreshing blast of cool air.

Add 2 Jedi Power Points to your current total

Return to your adventure

586

You run across the gun compartment to keep the three soldiers from getting to their weapons. The Combat is now Up Close, and they can't use their blaster rifles even if they can grab them. The soldiers have Combat Skill 1 without their weapons. Even if one of them hits you, they don't do any real damage, but they will knock you away from the blaster rifles, allowing them to grab them and start firing back.

Return to 581

587

You left all your weapons on the roof when you faced Boba Fett – so now you are completely disarmed! Al the Alchemist finds a BlasTech DL-18, but that's all you are now equipped with.

Remove all your weapons from the Equipment Box. You may keep/add the BlasTech DL-18 (check 505)

588

Losing your other weapons is bad enough, but you also left your lightsabre on the roof! Al sends someone to go and look for it, but it has gone, along with Fett and all your other gear.

Remove your lightsabre from the Equipment Box

589

You must fight the security guards in the control tower. In the first moments of the battle, there are three guards, each armed with a blaster, which they use at Combat Skill 1.

The combat begins At Range, and you may fire first.

If, after three rounds of combat, you are still uninjured, read 595

Otherwise, return to 219

590

Your only chance to escape now is to use the access codes you stole, steal aboard *Slave I* and stowaway in the slave pens. Surna and the others aren't happy, but what choice do you have?

Continue your adventure

591

You have been injured by your fall.

You must spend 3 Jedi Power Points at once, to limit the damage done to your leg, or reduce your Speed score by 2 (don't reduce it to less than 1)

Return to your adventure

592

You are a prisoner on *Slave I*, along with Surna, Tann and Al.

Return to your adventure

593

Separated from all the people you have known for the last two years, and now a prisoner of Boba Fett. This isn't proving to be a good day…

Your prospects look grim. You could always restart your adventure from paragraph 1, you know. But, if you're determined to press on, return to your adventure

594

You have been rescued from Boba Fett's ship by the strange man with the scraggly beard. While you ponder what to do, he is disappearing down the ramp. He stops and looks back. "He might have heard the shot! Follow me!" Then he disappears.

If you follow your rescuer immediately, go to 279

Otherwise, continue your adventure

595

Over the sounds of the fight, you hear Tann lift the *Rust Bucket* from the ground. You have done enough here now; if you wait any longer, reinforcements may arrive, and you'll be overwhelmed.

If you retreat, go to 260

Otherwise, complete the battle and return to 219

596

You have met up with Kelleg, who was with the Rebel forces who fought at the battle of Yavin.

Continue with your adventure

597

You have recovered all your gear and weapons. Remove the note you made earlier.

Continue with your adventure

598

Thinking about it, using your lightsabre wasn't the most subtle way to get into the crew compartment. After all, Boba Fett can hardly miss a gaping hole where the door used to be.

Continue with your adventure

599

You haven't had a chance to make sure it is working, but it feels good to have your lightsabre once again!

Continue with your adventure

600

Boba Fett's cunning trap has ensured that you are his prisoner. At least Surna and the others are safe!

Continue with your adventure

601

If you have checked 511, go to 602

You open fire on Boba Fett. The Combat Starts At Range. Fett is armed with a blaster rifle, which he uses at Combat Skill 4. If the combat comes Up Close, he switches to his wrist lasers, which he uses at Combat Skill 3. He needs to score 7 to hit you. You need to score a 9 to hit him, because of his armour.

If you score a 7 or 8 when trying to hit Boba Fett, go to 295

Otherwise, return to paragraph 289 when the combat is over

602

Because you have wounded him before, Boba Fett isn't the man he used to be. The Combat still starts At Range. Fett uses his blaster rifle at Combat Skill 3. If the combat comes Up Close, he switches to his wrist lasers, which he uses at Combat Skill 2. He needs to score 7 to hit you. You need to score a 9 to hit him, because of his armour.

If you score a 7 when trying to hit Boba Fett, go to 295

Otherwise, return to paragraph 289 when the combat is over

603

You are on board Fett's ship. You were separated from Surna and the others on Yavin. You are truly on your own now, Havet!

Continue your adventure

604

Klopke has given you a strange furry animal; it looks like a Wookiee, but it's just a lifeless toy. What can it mean? Then, looking at the back of toy, you see a number – it looks like a space communications frequency. Is this some way of getting in touch with the Rebels?

Continue your adventure

605

You feel a wave of nausea sweep through you. Your hand rests heavily on the weapon at your side. How can you let Boba Fett get away with these foul deeds?

Reduce your Starting Jedi Power Point score by 1 (but not to less than 1). This affects the maximum number of JPPs you can ever have, even after resting

606

You feel a momentary blast of anger rise up, but you quell it, directing the Force to keep your mind calm and clear. Your heart tells you that these people must be avenged, that Boba Fett cannot be allowed to continue his wave of terror, but you control that certainty inside you. Nothing is gained from rash anger.

Add 2 Jedi Power Points to your current total

607

You have lost Arf – for good this time!

Remove the droid from your Equipment Box. There's no way you can replace Arf during this adventure.

Also, if you have checked 504, read 608

Otherwise, continue your adventure

608

Have you just realised exactly how bad the situation is? When you cut Arf loose, you also lost your lightsabre, which was tucked in the hatch in the droid's belly!

Remove the lightsabre from your Equipment Box. There's no way you can replace it either

Continue your adventure

609

Arf is on standby.

Continue your adventure

610

If you have checked 511, go to 611

You must deal with Boba Fett. The Combat Starts Up Close. Fett is using his wrist lasers at Combat Skill 3. He needs to score 7 to hit you. You need to score a 9 to hit him, because of his armour.

Return to paragraph 356

611

Because you have wounded him before, Boba Fett isn't the man he used to be. The Combat starts Up Close. Fett uses his wrist lasers at Combat Skill 2. He needs to score 7 to hit you. You need to score a 9 to hit him, because of his armour.

Return to paragraph 356 when the combat is over

612

You have injured Boba Fett in combat.

If you have checked 511 already, check 613

If you hadn't checked 511 before, check it now

613

The blow you dealt Boba Fett must have been a very serious one. Can the bounty hunter even survive his injuries?

Return to paragraph 333

614

You have suffered a severe injury to your arm. You must spend 3 Jedi Power Points immediately, or lower your starting JPP score by 1 (but not to less than 1). If you can't do either of these (or don't choose to), you must reduce your Strength by 1 point (but not to less than 1!), and your Lightsabre Combat skill to 1. These can only be repaired by proper medical attention – which you won't find until after this adventure is over.

Return to your adventure

615

You have placed Arf out of sight on *Slave I*.

Continue your adventure

616

One of the things you had better consider right away is food! You're starving! Well, at least you have one good thing going for you. Al left some of the supplies he brought in the hold. You find a few days worth of emergency rations, and three tubes of Star Racer! All right!

Restore your Jedi Power Points to their maximum score (the starting score you have recorded in the box). Return to paragraph 337

617

You have a sudden moment of panic! The toy Wookiee Klopke gave you – it has the transmission frequency on it! Did Fett take it from you when he captured you? You move your hand to your pocket, and feel the toy still nestled in your pocket. What a relief!

Return to 332

618

If you get out of this alive, you are never, *ever* going to complain about being stuck on a planet again, right?

Return to your adventure

619

Even though you have been told some of Fett's plans, there's nothing you can do about them while you are stuck in this cell!

Return to your adventure

620

The dying man has given you a precious piece of information – the transmission frequencies for the Rebel Alliance. Be careful what you do with that information, Havet!

Return to your adventure

621

Fett has taken Arf from you. How are you going to escape now?

Return to your adventure

622

You have received a nasty burn from the force field in Boba Fett's slave-ship. You must spend 2 Jedi Power Points at once, or reduce your Lightsabre Combat score by 1.

Return to your adventure

623

Good old Arf – he's saved your neck again! You've escaped from the cell on Fett's prison-ship.

Return to your adventure .

624

You attack the Imperial navy man with your lightsabre. You move first and the combat starts Up Close. He will draw a blaster with his first move, which he can then use at Combat Skill 1.

If you defeat the navy man in the first turn, go to 404

If you defeat him after the first turn, go to 411

If he defeats you, go to 416

625

You attack the Imperial navy man with your blaster. You move first and the combat starts At Range. He will draw a blaster with his first move, which he can then use at Combat Skill 1.

If you defeat the navy man, go to 405

If he defeats you, go to 416

626

You close in on the Imperial navy man, aiming a blow at his head. You are both Combat Skill 1 at fist-fighting.

If you defeat the navy man, go to 406

If he defeats you, go to 416

627

The end of your adventure is in sight. Fett will keep you in his sights every second, but you know you have to step out onto the planet and try to find Solo.

Return to your adventure

628

So, you have discovered the truth at last. All your life you have believed that the Jedi were criminals, but now you know the truth. They were decent, good men and women. And Vader hunted them down – he killed your father and grandfather. That fact will remain with you for the rest of your life.

Now, more than ever, you know what you must do. The Empire must fall, and you must throw all your talents into the service of the Rebellion.

But, what of revenge? How can Vader be made to pay? You realise that will have to wait for another time, another place. And for Book 3 in the Lost Jedi series...

Add 1 to your maximum Jedi Power Point score. You may also add 2 JPPs to your current total

Return to your adventure

629

The chef takes you out the back of the restaurant, and shows you a decrepit old sand skimmer. "That costs 200?!" you howl. The chef looks offended, and wipes a layer of sand from the upper surface. He pops a key into the lock, and the skimmer starts at the sixth time of asking. "There you go," he grins. "It's a fine vehicle. You'll be able to go anywhere you want on that!" Yes, but will you ever get back? "Which way did Solo go?" The chef points vaguely out into the desert. Great...

Return to your adventure

630

The desert heat is sapping your Strength. You must either spend 2 Jedi Power Points, or reduce all your Attribute scores by 1.

Return to your adventure

631

The strange desert dwellers guarding Han Solo are closing in. The combat starts Up Close, and you may move first. They fight with Combat Skill 2, using their long-bladed weapons.

If you have checked 640, you may read 641

Otherwise, select your weapon. If you use a blaster, read 633

If you use your lightsabre, read 639

If you have no weapon, you fight at Combat Skill 1

When the combat is over, return to the adventure at 434

632

You have attacked your friends. The combat starts Up Close, and you may move first. Your comrades each fight at Combat Skill 2.

Select your weapon. If you use a blaster, read 633

If you use your lightsabre, read 639

If you have no weapon, you fight at Combat Skill 1

When the combat is over, return to your adventure

633

The heat seems to be affecting your aim. You can't see properly!

Your Blaster Combat Skill is 0 during this combat

634

You are facing your final confrontation with Boba Fett.

If you have checked 511, go to 635

If you have checked 613, go to 636

Fett moves first, and the Combat starts At Range. He will use his blaster rifle at Combat Skill 4. If the Combat comes Up Close, he switches to his wrist lasers at Combat Skill 3. As ever, you need to score 9 to hit him, because of his armour.

Return to your adventure at 437

635

Because you have injured him before, Fett isn't as powerful as he used to be. His Combat Skill scores in this combat are 3 for his blaster rifle or 2 for his wrist lasers.

Return to 634

636

Seriously injured in your last fight, Fett seems very sluggish in this contact. His Combat Skill scores in this combat are 3 for his blaster rifle or 2 for his wrist lasers. Also, you only need to score an 8 to hit him, since he is moving so slowly.

Return to 634

637

The defeat you have just inflicted on Boba Fett will have weakened him severely. In fact, it's doubtful if the bounty hunter will ever fully recover. The next time he ends up in a major fight – he could face quite a handicap.

So, next time you watch the third of the *Star Wars* films, you can remember that although Luke and his friends actually have the pleasure of defeating Boba Fett, it was your work that made it possible...

638

Where you went wrong was in failing to help Surna, Tann and Al escape from Toprawa at the same time as you did.

If you want to start the game again, return to the beginning of the book

If you want to find out what Surna and the others could have told you if you had been successful, read 444

639

Your opponents seem to be terrified of the lightsabre. They fall back, scarcely able to defend themselves.

Subtract 1 from their Combat Skills. Continue with the combat

640

No bodies. Having defeated your comrades, or what you thought were your comrades, you look around, but there are no bodies. Which means that… they were never really there. A mirage? You shake your head, trying to clear the fog from your tired mind. Something put the image of Al and the others into your mind. Now that you have seen through one "mirage", perhaps the Force will help you defeat any others.

Return to your adventure

641

You have already discovered that not everything on this planet is what it seems. Closing your eyes and reaching deep inside yourself, you draw on the Force, allowing it to look out from your heart in a way that your eyes cannot. When you open your eyes once more, the guards have gone.

Go to 430

642

The idea suddenly pops into your brain – how come Fett has made no attempt to find you? He must know you escaped from the ship. Does that mean he has more important business, or was Kelleg's rescue some kind of trick?

Return to your adventure

Havet Storm

Strength ☐

Speed ☐

Blaster ☐

Lightsabre ☐

Tech Skills ☐

Jedi Power Points _____

Don't spend more than 6 points on any Attribute or increase any Attribute past 6 when using JPPs

Equipment

Arf [528]

Lightsabre [belt] [508]

DL-18 Blaster [holster] [507]

ID [520]

[Arf] [529]

[bag] [532]

_____ ☐	_____ ☐
_____ ☐	_____ ☐
_____ ☐	_____ ☐
_____ ☐	_____ ☐

Data Bank

503	504	509	510	511	513	514	515	516	517	518
521	525	526	527	530	533	541	542	544	550	551
552	553	554	555	556	557	560	562	563	565	568
569	572	574	580	584	586	589	590	599	603	604
605	606	608	614	618						

Time track ☐ ☐ ☐ ☐ ☐ [Read 595] ☐ ☐ [Read 56]

Havet Storm

Strength ☐

Speed ☐

Blaster ☐

Lightsabre ☐

Tech Skills ☐

Jepi Power Points _____

Don't spend more than 6 points on any Attribute or increase any Attribute past 6 when using JPPs

Equipment

Arf [528]

Lightsabre [belt] [508]

DL-18 Blaster [holster] [507]

ID [520]

[Arf] [529]

[bag] [532]

_____ ☐ _____ ☐

_____ ☐ _____ ☐

_____ ☐ _____ ☐

_____ ☐ _____ ☐

Data Bank

503	504	509	510	511	513	514	515	516	517	518
521	525	526	527	530	533	541	542	544	550	551
552	553	554	555	556	557	560	562	563	565	568
569	572	574	580	584	586	589	590	599	603	604
605	606	608	614	618	☐	☐	☐	☐	☐	☐

Time track ☐ ☐ ☐ ☐ ☐ [Read 595] ☐ ☐ [Read 56]